Practice of Medicine

ELEVENTH EDITION REVISED

GIVING THE SYNONYMS, DEFINITIONS, CAUSES, SYMPTOMS, PATHOLOGY, DIAGNOSIS, PROGNOSIS, AND TREATMENT OF EACH DISEASE.

By DANIEL E. HUGHES, M.D., Late Chief Resident Physician, Philadelphia Hospital; formerly Demonstrator of Clinical Medicine, Jefferson Medical College. Edited by R. J. E. SCOTT, M.A.,B.C.L., M.D., Formerly Attending Physician to the Demilt Dispensary, New York; Editor of Gould and Pyle's Cyclopedia of Medicine and Surgery, etc.

63 Illustrations. 12mo. xix + 785 Pages. Cloth, $4.25 postpaid.

The Treatment is specially full. 406 valuable prescriptions have been included.

"This popularity is due to the fact that the book gives practical discussions of diseases as briefly as is consistent with the subject, theories being eliminated."—*Journal American Medical Association.*

"This book is intended as a working manual in which the physician may find that which he needs for a rapid restudy of any disease without having to go over the controversial matter usually found in treatises on practice. * * * For case reference and rapid study, there is no better book."—*Medical Council.*

"The work is thoroughly modern and is particularly valuable for its discussion of diagnosis and treatment, an immense number of excellent prescriptions being incorporated under the latter head. It is, we believe, unique in including sections on mental diseases and diseases of the skin."—*New York Medical Journal.*

COMPEND

OF

HUMAN ANATOMY

BLAKISTON'S COMPENDS

The Best Series of Manuals for the Use of Students

Price of each, Cloth, $2.00 net

☞These Compends are based on the most popular text-books and the lectures of prominent professors, and are kept constantly revised, so that they may thoroughly represent the present state of the subjects upon which they treat.

☞The authors have had large experience as Quiz-Masters and attachés of colleges, and are well acquainted with the wants of students.

☞They are arranged in the most approved form, thorough and concise, containing over 900 fine illustrations, inserted wherever they could be used to advantage.

☞Can be used by students of *any* college.

☞They contain information nowhere else collected in such a condensed, practical shape.

Illustrated Circular Free

POTTER'S ANATOMY. Eighth Revised and Enlarged Edition. Including Visceral Anatomy. Can be used with either Morris' or Gray's Anatomy. 139 Illustrations and 16 Plates of Nerves and Arteries, with Explanatory Tables, etc.

BRUBAKER. PHYSIOLOGY. Fifteenth Edition, with 26 Illustrations. Enlarged and Revised.

LANDIS. OBSTETRICS. Ninth Edition. Revised and Edited by Wm. H. Wells, M. D., Associate Professor of Obstetrics, Jefferson Medical College, Philadelphia. 80 Illustrations.

POTTER. MATERIA MEDICA, THERAPEUTICS AND PRESCRIPTION WRITING. Eighth Revised Edition.

WELLS. GYNECOLOGY. Fourth Edition. With 153 Illustrations.

GOULD and PYLE. DISEASES OF THE EYE AND REFRACTION. Including Treatment and Operations and a Section on Local Therapeutics. With Formulæ and 109 Illustrations, several of which are in colors. **Fourth** Edition.

LIPSHUTZ. COMPEND OF SURGERY. 185 Illustrations.
This volume replaces the Compend of Surgery formerly written by the late Orville Horwitz, M. D.

LEFFMANN. CHEMISTRY, Inorganic and Organic. Sixth Edition. Including Urinalysis, Animal Chemistry, Chemistry of Milk, Blood, Tissues, the Secretions, etc.

STEWART. PHARMACY. Ninth Edition. Based upon Prof. Remington's Text-book of Pharmacy.

ST. CLAIR. MEDICAL LATIN. Second Edition.

SCHAMBERG. DISEASES OF THE SKIN. Sixth Edition. Revised and Enlarged. 119 Illustrations.

PITFIELD. BACTERIOLOGY. Third Edition. 86 Illustrations.

HIRSCH. GENITO-URINARY AND VENEREAL DISEASES, AND SYPHILIS. Third Edition. With 59 Illustrations.

POTTER'S
COMPEND
OF
HUMAN ANATOMY

REVISED BY

D. GREGG METHENY

M.D., L.R.C.P. AND S. (EDIN.), L.F.P.S. (GLASGOW)

ASSOCIATE IN ANATOMY, JEFFERSON MEDICAL COLLEGE, PHILADELPHIA

EIGHTH EDITION

WITH 139 ILLUSTRATIONS; ALSO NUMEROUS TABLES AND
16 PLATES OF THE ARTERIES AND NERVES

PHILADELPHIA
P. BLAKISTON'S SON & CO.
1012 WALNUT STREET

THE MAPLE PRESS YORK PA

PREFACE TO THE EIGHTH EDITION

After many years of wandering in the embryological minutiæ of "transcendental anatomy," it has at last become apparent to most teachers and examiners in anatomy that the only kind of anatomy that could be of any practical value to a physician or surgeon, as such, is the anatomy that can be actually seen and handled. Consequently in this text, details of embryology, histology, and physiology have been largely left to the textbooks dealing with those subjects, in order that gross human anatomy might be the more thoroughly explained.

While all of the "recognized authorities" and the publications of the various anatomical associations have been freely consulted, these descriptions have been based entirely on the actual facts to be found *in the human body* and are not dominated by any one single authority. The many new discoveries and the changes in teaching methods that have been made in recent years, have made it necessary to make so many additions and changes in the text that the entire work had to be rewritten. Parts of the nomenclature of the German Anatomical Society are now being used so universally, that it became necessary to include it, in its entirety, in the Latin form. However, since comparative anatomy has been almost entirely ignored in the B.N.A., and as so many of its terms are not only inconsistent but also evidence personality rather than broad anatomical principles, it seems certain that it still requires much revision if it is to endure; therefore while the B.N.A. terms are given in the Latin form, only such of them as seem entitled to survival are given in the English form in preference to the older regular terms.

It is confidently hoped that the student will find these descriptions not only accurate and up-to-date, but intelligible as well.

D. GREGG METHENY.

4609 SPRUCE ST., PHILADELPHIA.

v

PREFACE TO THE SEVENTH EDITION

The twenty years which have elapsed since this compend was first issued have brought many changes of nomenclature and description into the teaching of Anatomy. The present edition has been entirely re-written and brought into harmony with the latest text-books on this subject. The text has been expanded wherever greater detail seemed desirable, but in so doing the condensed form of statement heretofore adopted has been carefully followed. The total number of illustrations has been increased from 117 to 138, and many of the cuts used in former editions have been replaced by newer ones. The Tables and Plates, heretofore published in an appendix, have been thoroughly revised, and are now placed in their natural positions in the text. These changes have increased the size of the volume by 82 pages, and have made it practically a new book, which the author hopes will receive a continuance of the favor heretofore extended to the previous editions.

Originally designed for the use of the medical student in preparing for the exercises of the quiz-room and for his examinations, the text is confined to the essentials of each structure treated of, which are arranged in such a manner as to facilitate their rapid acquirement. All superfluities of description have been studiously avoided, and only such matter inserted as should be thoroughly known in order to pass a rigid examination on any organ or structure of the human body. The descriptions will be found to closely follow Gray, though Morris, Quain, and other recognized authorities have been freely consulted during the preparation of the text. For many of the special arrangements the author is indebted to the lectures of Professor W. H. Pancoast, formerly of Jefferson Medical

College, and to the quizzes of Dr. Henry Morris, at one time assistant
to the chair of Anatomy in the same school.

While striving to carry out the object of this series in furnishing the
medical student with a condensed manual of Anatomy, the author has
endeavored, from a strong appreciation of the importance of the subject,
to make this volume deserving of first rank among its kind; and believing
that a judicious condensation, which does not slight the essential features
of the subjects treated, cannot fail to be of benefit in any department
of science, he again commits this compend to the teachers and students
of Anatomy, in the hope that it may continue to be found worthy of a
place alongside the more exhaustive and exhausting text-books.

SAM'L O. L. POTTER.

CONTENTS

ABBREVIATIONS

Anas.	Anastomoses.	Inf. . . .	Inferior.
Ant.	Anterior.	Int. . . .	Internal.
Art. or A. . .	Artery.	L.	Left.
Asc.	Ascending.	M.	Middle.
Br.	Branch.	N.	Nerve.
Cerv.	Cervical.	Pl.	Plexus.
Com.	Common.	Post. . . .	Posterior.
Commun. . .	Communicating.	R.	Right.
Desc.	Descending.	Sup. . . .	Superior.
Ext.	External.	Superf. . .	Superficial.
	Trans.	Transverse.	

EXPLANATION

Figures or letters in parentheses, thus—(14), (*a*), refer to the same figures or letters on the adjoining illustration; except in the Tables of Arteries, in which figures in parentheses serve as cross-references to other divisions of the tables.

A COMPEND OF
HUMAN ANATOMY

The term Anatomy is derived from the Greek ἀνα, *through*, and τὲμνειν, *to cut*, it strictly means *dissection*, but is technically applied to that science which treats of the structure of organized bodies.

The divisions of Descriptive Human Anatomy are,—*Osteology*, the anatomy of the bones; *Syndesmology*, of the joints; *Myology*, of the muscles; *Angiology*, of the vessels; *Neurology*, of the nerves; *Splanchnology*, of the internal viscera; *Adenology*, of the glands; *Dermatology*, of the skin; *Genesiology*, of the generative organs.

OSTEOLOGY

The number of Bones in the Adult Human Skeleton is variously stated by different anatomists. Excluding the teeth (which belong to the tegumentary system), the Wormian and the sesamoid bones, the number is 206. Excluding also the 6 ossicles of the middle ear the whole number would be 200. Leaving out also the 2 patellæ and the hyoid bone, the number in the skeleton proper would be 197 bones. Of these, the vertebral column contains 26, the cranium 8, the face 14, the walls of the thorax (sternum and ribs) 25, the upper extremities 64, and the lower extremities 60. They are divisible into four classes,—the long and short medullated, and the flat and irregular cancellous bones.

Long Bones number 90, act as supports, or levers, and are known by having a medullary canal in the centre of each, a shaft (*diaphysis*), and two extremities. They are developed by osseous deposit in cartilage, and include the clavicle, humerus, radius, ulna, femur, tibia, fibula, metacarpal and metatarsal bones, and the phalanges.

Short Bones number 30, and are found where strength is required, but limited motion. They are also developed by osseous deposit in cartilage and include the bones of the carpus and tarsus, the former having 16 and the latter 14.

Flat Bones number 38, protect the viscera by forming walls around them, and afford extensive attachment for muscles. They are developed by osseous deposit in membranes, and consist of 2 dense layers, separated by a cellular or cancellous osseous tissue, the *diploë*. They include the occipital (os occipitale), parietal (os parietale), and frontal (os frontale) (bones of the cranium); the nasal (os nasale), lacrimal (os lacrimale), and vomer (bones of the face); the scapula, os innominatum (os coxæ), sternum and ribs (costæ).

Irregular Bones are 39 in number, and include the vertebræ, sacrum, coccyx (coccygis), the temporal, ethmoid, and sphenoid bones, and the bones of the face, except the *nasal* (os nasale), *lacrimal* (os lacrimale), and *vomer*.

Bones of the Head number 22, and comprise the—

Cranial Bones 8,—the frontal, 2 parietal (ossa parietalia), occipital (os occipitale), 2 temporal (ossa temporalia), the sphenoid and the ethmoid (os ethmoidale).

Facial Bones 14,—2 maxillary (maxillæ), 2 malar (ossa zygomatica), 2 nasal (ossa nasalia), 2 lacrimal (ossa lacrimalia), 2 palate (ossa palatina), 2 inferior turbinal (conchæ nasales inferiores), vomer and mandible.

Bones of the Trunk number 53, as follows, viz.—

Vertebræ 24,—7 cervical, 12 thoracic, and 5 lumbar vertebræ.

Thorax 25,—7 pairs of true ribs, 3 pairs of false ribs, 2 pairs of floating ribs (articulating with the bodies of the thoracic vertebræ), and the sternum.

Pelvis 4,—the sacrum, the coccyx (os coccygis), and 2 ossa innominata (ossa coxæ) each os innominatum consisting of 3,—the ilium (coxæ), ischium, and pubis.

Bones of each Upper Extremity number 32, as follows:—

Shoulder 2,—the clavicle (clavicula) and scapula.

Arm 1,—the humerus.

Forearm 2,—the radius and ulna.

Hand 27,—8 carpal bones,—the scaphoid (os naviculare), semilunar (os triquetrum), cuneiform, pisiform (os pisiforme), trapezium (os multangulum majus), trapezoid (os multangulum minus), os magnum (os capitatum), and unciform (os hamatum),—5 metacarpal, and 14 phalanges.

Bones of each Lower Extremity number 29, viz.—

Thigh 1,—the femur.

Leg 2,—the tibia and fibula.

Foot 26,—7 tarsal bones,—the astragalus (talus), os calcis (calcaneus), scaphoid, (naviculare pedis), cuboid (os cuboideum), external, (tertium) middle (secundum), and internal cuneiform (primum),—5 metatarsal, 14 phalanges.

Unclassified Bones are the—

Patellæ 2, which are sesamoid bones, each developed in the tendon of the quadriceps extensor femoris muscle.

Hyoid Bone (os hyoideum) 1,—the tongue-bone, not articulated to the skeleton.

Malleus, Incus, Stapes (3 pairs),—the bones of the middle ear (ossicula auditis).

Sesamoid Bones, of variable number, situated in the tendons of the gastrocnemius and peroneus longus muscles, and in the flexor tendons of the great toe and the thumb.

Wormian Bones (ossa Suturarum), sometimes found in the cranial sutures, are not constant in number or size.

Principal Eminences on Bones. *Heads* are convex and smooth, for articulation in movable joints. *Condyles* are irregularly shaped heads. *Trochanters,* when for turning the bone. *Tuberosities* are broad, uneven prominences. *Tubercles* are small tuberosities. *Spines,* or *Spinous processes,* when sharp and slender. *Apophysis* (an excrescence), is a process or marked bony prominence which has never been separate from the bone. *Epiphysis* (an accretion), is a process which was developed separately and afterward became united to the bone by ossification of the intermediate tissue.

Other Names given to Bony Prominences. There are several adjectives applied to them from their fancied resemblances, such as—*Azygos,* without a fellow; *Clinoid,* like a bed; *Coracoid,* like a crow's beak; *Coronoid,* hooked like a cow's horn; *Hamular,* hook-like; *Malleolar,* like a mallet; *Mastoid,* like a nipple; *Odontoid,* tooth-like; *Pterygoid,* wing-like; *Rostrum,* a beak; *Spinous,* thorn-like; *Styloid,* pen-like; *Squamous,* scaly; *Vaginal,* ensheathing, etc.

Cavities of Bones. Articular cavities are called *Cotyloid,* cup-like; *Glenoid,* shallow; *Trochlear,* pulley-like; *Facet,* if smooth; *Alveolar* or *Alveoli,* when socket-like. Non-articular cavities are named fossæ, sinuses, aqueducts, foramina, canals, fissures, notches, cells, grooves, depressions, etc.

Composition of Bone. *Organic* or animal matter, about $\frac{1}{3}$, consisting of gelatin, vessels and fat. *Inorganic,* or mineral, about $\frac{2}{3}$, consisting of phosphate and carbonate of calcium ($62\frac{1}{3}$ per cent.), with fluoride of calcium, phosphates of magnesium, sodium, and chloride of sodium ($4\frac{1}{3}$ per cent.). *Heat* will remove the organic matter and leave the inorganic; dilute *Nitric* or *Hydrochloric acid* will remove the inorganic, and leave the organic. In old age the inorganic constituents predominate, and the bones are brittle; in youth the organic predominate, and epiphyseal dislocation is more common than fracture, especially in the long bones of the extremities.

Structure of Bone. Bone is composed of an outer compact layer, and an inner cellular or spongy structure. It is surrounded, except at the articular cartilages, by a vascular fibrous membrane, *the Periosteum*, which receives the insertions of all tendons, ligaments, etc.; and the central cavity of long bones is lined by a similar structure, the *Endosteum*. The transverse section of the bone, examined microscopically, shows—

Haversian Canals,—diameter $\frac{1}{500}$ inch, for the passage of vessels.

Canaliculi,—diameter $\frac{1}{16000}$ inch, radiating from the canals, and connecting them with the lacunæ.

Lacunæ,—arranged circularly around the canals, and contain the bone-cells, appearing as irregular dark spaces.

Haversian Spaces,—connect the canals with the medullary spaces, and divide one Haversian system from another. An *Haversian System* comprises an Haversian canal with its lamellæ, lacunæ, and canaliculi.

Concentric Lamellæ,—of bone tissue, around the canals.

Circumferential Lamellæ,—are bone layers binding the canals together.

Interstitial Lamellæ,—woven in between the concentric lamellæ.

The Marrow of Bone. In young bones it is a tenacious, transparent fluid, free from fat. In adult bones it is of a yellow color, and consists of fat in varying proportion and extractive matters. It is found in the medullary canal, the cancellous texture, and the large Haversian spaces.

Vessels found in Bones. Arteries, veins, and some say lymphatics. *The Arteries* are,—the nutrient, entering at the nutrient foramen; the articular, nourishing the cancellous structure; and the periosteal, which supply the periosteum and the compact structure. *The Veins* emerge from the ends, the shaft, and from the nutrient foramen.

The process of Ossification. The site of bone is first occupied by a mucoid substance, which becomes temporary cartilage (*blastema*) in the second month of fœtal life. The young bone-cells (*osteo-blasts*) are then deposited in the cartilage at certain points, and their deposition and subsequent pressure cause the absorption of the cartilage. In most of the bones of the head and face, ossification is intra-membranous instead of intra-cartilaginous. *The first bones* in which ossification appears are the clavicle and inferior maxillary (5th to 7th fœtal week); the *last* is the pisiform bone (12th year). *Epiphyses* ossify after birth and begin uniting to the bone from the age of puberty, and in the inverse order to that in which their ossification began, except the lower end of the fibula, which ossifies and is joined to the shaft earlier than its upper end.

THE BONES OF THE TRUNK

THE VERTEBRAL COLUMN

Characteristics common to the Vertebræ. Each of the 24 spinal vertebræ consists of a body and an arch, the latter being formed by 2 radix arcus vertebræ (pedicles) and 2 laminæ, which support 7 processes. The—

Body (corpus vertebræ) is thick and spongy, convex in front (1) from side to side, concave vertically, and on the upper and lower surfaces, which are surrounded by a bony rim. Anteriorly are small *foramina* for nutrient vessels, posteriorly a large *foramen* for the exit of the venæ basis vertebrarum.

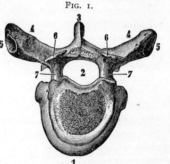

FIG. 1.

Pedicles (radix arcus vertebræ) (7),—project backward from the body, inclining outwardly. They are notched above and below (incisura vertebralis superior et inferior), thus forming, with the adjacent notches, the *Intervertebral Foramina* (Foramina Intervertebralia) for the entrance of vessels and the exit of the spinal nerves.

Laminæ,—are 2 broad plates, meeting in the spinous process behind, and rough on their upper and lower borders for the attachment of the ligamentum subflava.

Transverse Processes (4),—one on each side projecting outward; those of the first ten thoracic vertebræ have articular facets (5) for the tubercles of the ribs.

Articular Processes (Zygapophyses) (6),—two on each side, superior (6) and inferior, project from the junction of the laminæ and pedicles, and articulate above and below with the articular processes of the adjacent vertebræ. Their upper facets look backwards and upwards in the cervical region, backwards and outwards in the thoracic, and backwards and inwards in the lumbar.

Spinous Process (3),—projects backward from the junction of the laminæ with each other, sometimes very obliquely.

Spinal Foramen (foramen vertebrale) (2),—is the space enclosed by the body, pedicles and laminæ, and which, when the vertebræ are articulated, forms part of the spinal or neural canal.

The Spinal Vertebræ are distinguished as cervical 7, thoracic 12, and lumbar 5. Each of these divisions has several peculiar features, but their especial characteristics are as follows:—

Cervical Vertebræ,—are pierced at the bases of their transverse processes by the costo-transverse foramina, which transmit the vertebral artery, vein, and plexus. The anterior boundary of a costo-transverse foramen is called the Costal process, it is a true cervical rib. Its termination is called anterior tubercle of the transverse process. The posterior tubercle is the tip of the true transverse process. The superior articular facets look backwards and upwards.

Thoracic Vertebræ,—have facets and demifacets on their bodies, for articulation with the heads of the ribs, these facets are called the foveæ costales. The superior articular facets look backwards and outwards.

Lumbar Vertebræ,—are marked by the absence of the foramina and facets which distinguish the other two classes. The superior articular facets look backwards and inwards.

Peculiar Vertebræ are 9 in number,—the Atlas or 1st cervical, the Axis or 2d cervical (epistropheus), the Vertebra Prominens, or 7th cervical (the 1st thoracic is nearly always more prominent), the 1st, 9th, 10th, 11th, and 12th thoracic, and the 5th lumbar. The—

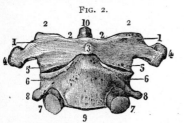

FIG. 2.

Atlas (3),—is a bony ring supporting the head. A bony arch takes the place of a body, and its spinous process is a mere tubercle. Its *Lateral Masses* (1) form its chief bulk, supporting large *Articular Processes* (foveæ articulares), which look inwards, the superior (2) articulating with the condyles of the occipital bone.

Axis (9),—is marked by its *Odontoid Process* (dens) (10) projecting upward from the body into the anterior part of the spinal foramen of
the atlas, where it articulates with the anterior arch (3), and receives
the occipito-axoid (ligamentum apicis dentis) and the check ligaments (ligamenta alaria). Its transverse processes (8) are very small
and are not bifid. Its inferior articular surfaces (7) have the same
direction as those of the other cervical vertebræ.

Vertebra Prominens,—has a long and prominent spinous process which
ends in a tubercle for the ligamentum nuchæ.

Thoracic. Vertebræ. The 1st has one facet and a demifacet for the 1st
and 2d ribs. The 9th has a demifacet only. The 10th has but one
facet on the body and one on the transverse process. The 11th and
12th have each but one facet on the body, and none on the transverse
processes. The 12th resembles a lumbar vertebra in size and shape.

5th Lumbar Vertebra,—is much deeper in front than behind; its spinous
process is small, but its transverse processes are large and thick, and
point slightly upward.

Important Relations of Certain Vertebræ.

3d Cervical corresponds in situation to—the bifurcation of the common
carotid artery, and the superior cervical ganglion.

5th Cervical, to—the junctions of the larynx with the trachea and the
pharynx with the œsophagus, and the middle cervical ganglion of the
sympathetic.

2d Lumbar, to—the junction of the duodenum with the jejunum, the commencement of the thoracic duct and the portal vein, the origin of the
superior mesenteric artery, the lower margin of the pancreas, the opening
of the ductus communis choledochus, the lower end of the spinal cord,
and the crura of the diaphragm.

[The sacral and coccygeal vertebræ are described as bones of the pelvis.]

THE THORAX

The Thorax is an osseo-cartilaginous cage formed by the bodies of the
dorsal vertebræ posteriorly, the ribs and costal cartilages laterally, and
the sternum in front. Its shape is conical, the axis inclined forward, the
base below and closed by the diaphragm.

Structures passing through its Apex, are—the trachea, œsophagus,
large vessels of the neck, pneumogastric (vagus), phrenic, and sympathetic
nerves, thoracic duct, and in inspiration the apex of the lung.

Structures contained in its Cavity, are—the trachea, bronchi and lungs, the heart and great vessels, internal mammary arteries, azygos and bronchial veins, pneumogastric, phrenic, and splanchnic nerves, œsophagus, thoracic duct, lymphatic vessels and glands.

The Sternum, or breast-bone, consists of 3 parts—the manubrium (1), or handle; the gladiolus (2), or sword; and the ensiform or *xiphoid* appendix (3). It presents the—

Interclavicular Notch,—on its superior border.

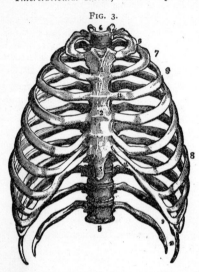

FIG. 3.

Manubrium (1),—articulates with the clavicle, 1st costal cartilage, and a part of the 2d.

Gladiolus (2),—articulates with the costal cartilages from the 3d to the 6th inclusive, and partly with the 2d and 7th.

Ensiform Appendix (3),—articulates with the cartilage of the false ribs, and in part with the 7th costal cartilage. It is cartilaginous in youth.

Development and Muscles. The sternum is *developed* by 6 centres, 1 each for the manubrium and ensiform appendix and 4 for the gladiolus. The *muscles* attached to it are 9 pairs and one single muscle,—the sterno-cleido-mastoid, sterno-hyoid and sterno-thyroid, 3, to its upper part;—the rectus abdominis, external and internal oblique, transversalis and the diaphragm, 5, to its lower part;—the pectoralis major, 1, anteriorly;—and the triangularis sterni, 1, posteriorly.

The Ribs are 12 in number on each side, 7 of which are *true ribs*, being each connected to the sternum by a separate cartilage;—and 5 are *false ribs*. Three of the latter are connected by their cartilages to the cartilage of the 7th rib (11), while two are called *floating ribs* (10), having each one extremity free.

Characteristics Common to most of the Ribs. Each rib consists of a head, neck and shaft, and presents the following points, viz.—

Head,—is divided by a ridge into 2 facets, which articulate with the facets on the bodies of the dorsal vertebræ, the lowermost facet is always slightly the larger; the ridge giving attachment to the inter-articular ligament.

Neck about an inch long, presents on its upper border a *crest* which affords attachment to the ligamentum costo-transversarium anterius (superior costo-transverse), to its posterior surface the middle costo-transverse ligament (l. colli costæ), its anterior surface is smooth.

Tuberosity,—at the junction of the neck with the shaft, has a facet for articulation with the transverse process of the next lower vertebra, and a rough surface for the posterior costo-transverse ligament (l. tuberculi costæ).

Shaft,—twisted on itself, is concave internally, convex externally, its upper border round and smooth, its lower border grooved for the intercostal vessels and nerves. At its external extremity is an oval depression for the insertion of the costal cartilage.

Angle,—just in front of the tuberosity, is marked by a rough line, to which are attached the muscles of the deep layer of the back.

Development. Each rib has 3 centres, one each for the head, shaft, and tuberosity. The last 2 ribs, having no tuberosity, are developed each by 2 centres.

Peculiar Ribs, are the 1st, 2d, 10th, 11th, and 12th. They respectively present the following peculiarities—

1st Rib,—is broad, short, not twisted, has no angle, only one facet on the head; but on its upper surface are seen *two grooves* for the subclavian artery and vein, and between them a *tubercle* for the scalenus anticus muscle.

2d Rib,—is not twisted, its tuberosity and angle are very close together, and its upper surface presents rough surfaces for the serratus magnus and scalenus posticus muscles.

10th Rib,—has but one facet on its head.

11th Rib,—has no neck, no tuberosity, and but one facet on its head.

12th Rib,—has neither neck, angle, tuberosity nor groove, and but one facet on its head.

THE PELVIS

The Pelvis is formed by the sacrum, os coccygis (coccyx), and two ossa innominata (coxæ) and is divided into,—the pelvis major (*false pelvis*), comprising the upper and expanded portion,—and the pelvis minor (*true pelvis*), below the ilio-pectineal line (linea arcuata). The false pelvis corresponds to the iliac fossæ (1), and is marked by its walls being deficient anteriorly between the iliac borders, and posteriorly between the sacrum and the posterior iliac spines. The true pelvis has a—

Brim, or inlet (apertura pelvis minor superior),—bounded in front by the crest and spine of the pubes (7), behind by the promontory of the sacrum (15), laterally by the ilio-pectineal line (linea arcuata). Its axis corresponds to a line intersecting the umbilicus and the middle of the coccyx (os coccygis). Its average diameters in the female are,—4 inches antero-posteriorly, over 5 inches transversely, under 5 inches obliquely. In the male each of these measurements is about ½ an inch less.

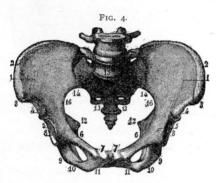

FIG. 4.

Cavity,—is a short curved canal, connecting the brim with the outlet. In front its depth is about 1¾ inches, posteriorly 4 to 4½ inches in the female, 4½ to 5½ inches in the male. Its diameter is about 4¾ inches in the female, 4½ inches in the male, all around.

Outlet (apertura pelvis minor inferior),—is bounded by the pubic arch above (11), the tip of the coccyx (os coccygis) behind, and the tuberosities of the ischia (9) laterally. Its axis, if prolonged, would touch the promontory of the sacrum. Its diameters in the female are each about 4¼ inches, in the male about 3½ inches.

Chief Differences between the male and female pelves. The *male pelvis* is marked by strength of the bones, prominence of the muscular impressions, a deep and narrow cavity, and large obturator foramina. The *female pelvis* has lighter bones, broader iliac fossæ, the spines being further apart, greater diameters at every point, the sacrum less curved, and the pubic arch wider.

The Sacrum, or sacred bone, is triangular, curved, with its convexity backward, and is situated, base upwards, between the ossa innominata (coxæ) forming with the coccyx the posterior wall of the pelvis. The bone consists of a central portion (4) which consists of the coalesced bodies of five vertebræ, and on each side a pars lateralis (lateral mass) or ala (wing) which is made by the fusion of the transverse processes and what might be called "pelvic ribs." Therefore the pars lateralis presents a transverse portion and a costal or alar portion. The sacrum presents the following points, viz.—

Ridges (cristæ sacrales articulares) (4),—four transversely across both surfaces, mark the union of its original segments.

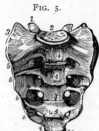

FIG. 5.

Anterior Sacral Foramina,—eight for the anterior sacral nerves.

Grooves (5),—eight shallow and broad, for the aforesaid nerves.

Promontory,—at its junction with the last lumbar vertebræ.

Posterior Sacral Foramina,—eight for the posterior sacral nerves.

Tubercles,—representing the spinous processes of the segments.

Groove,—posteriorly, on each side of the spinous tubercles.

Cornua,—two at the posterior inferior portion of the bone.

Articular Surface (3),—on each side, articulates with the ilium.

Notch,—laterally and inferiorly, for the 5th sacral nerve.

Base (2),—has all the characteristics of the lumbar vertebræ, with the last of which it articulates.

Apex (16),—has an oval surface for articulation with the coccyx.

Sacral Canal,—the continuation of the spinal canal, is incomplete posteriorly at its lower end. It transmits the *Cauda Equina;* into it open the sacral foramina laterally.

The Coccyx consists of 4 (or 5) rudimentary caudal vertebræ coalesced into a triangular bone, the base (1) of which articulates with the apex of the sacrum. Its posterior surface is rough for muscles and ligaments, its anterior surface is smooth and marked by ridges at the junction of its constituent vertebræ. It presents the following points:—

FIG. 6.

Cornua (2),—two superiorly, articulating with the sacral cornua to form foramina for the 5th sacral nerves.

Apex,—is sometimes bifid and turned to one side.

The Ossa Innominata (coxæ), are placed one on each side of the osseous pelvis, and are each formed by the union, about puberty, of 3 bones,—the ilium, ischium, and pubes. The innominate (os coxæ) as a whole presents the following points, viz.—

It is a large flat bone, constricted in the middle, and twisted upon its long axis, so that the expanded portion (iliac) above the constriction is in a plane almost at right angles to that of the expanded portion (ischio-pubic) below. It presents an outer surface, an inner surface, and a continuous border which is circumferential. Beginning at its upper part the border of the os coxæ (innominate or hip bone), it presents a crest (1), and, continuing forwards and around, the anterior superior spine (2), a shallow notch, the anterior inferior spine (4), a smaller notch, the ilio-pectineal eminence (5), superior (ascending) ramus or body of the ossis pubis, pubic tubercle (spine) and crest of pubis (9), the symphysis ossis pubis, the ischio-pubic ramus (9), constituted in front by the inferior (horizontal or descending) ramus of the pubis and behind by the ramus of the ischium, the tuber ischiadicum (tuberosity of the ischium) 12, the lesser sciatic (sacro-sciatic) notch (13), the ischial spine 14, the greater sciatic (sacro-iliac) notch (16), the posterior inferior spine of the ilium (17), and lastly the posterior superior spine of the ilium. The inner surface is divided by the ilio-pectineal line into an upper portion and a lower portion. The upper portion (false pelvis) presents in front the iliac fossa, and behind, the articular (auricular) surface and a rough surface for the posterior sacro-iliac ligament. The lower part of the inner surface (true pelvis) presents the obturator groove and the obturator foramen (8). In addition to what is described with the ilium, ischium and pubes, the outer surface presents:—

Acetabulum, or cotyloid cavity,—receives the head of the femur. It is situated at the junction of the 3 bones externally, the ilium and ischium each forming about two-fifths, and the pubic bone one-fifth of it. A depression in its centre lodges a mass of fat containing vessels for the nourishment of the synovial membrane. The Cotyloid Notch (Incisura Acetabuli) is a deficiency in its lower margin, transmitting nutrient vessels to the joint; to the edges of the notch is attached the ligamentum teres, and it is bridged over by the transverse ligament, a continuation of the cotyloid ligament (labrum glenoidale) which surmounts the brim of the acetabulum. Crossing the ischium horizontally, immediately below the acetabulum, is a deep groove for the obturator externus tendon.

Obturator or Thyroid Foramen (8),—on the anterior surface between the pubes and ischium, large and oval in the male, small and triangular in the female; is closed by the obturator membrane, except above at the obturator canal or groove where the obturator nerves and vessels pass through.

The Ilium is the superior part of the innominate bone, its outer surface presents the following points, viz.—

Crest (1),—along its upper border, having an outer and inner lip for muscular attachment, and ending in the superior spines.

Anterior Superior Spine (2),—to which are attached the sartorius and tensor fasciæ (vaginæ) femoris muscles and the inguinal (Poupart's) ligament.

Anterior Inferior Spine (4),—for the straight tendon of the rectus femoris.

Notch, between the above-named spines, transmitting the external (lateral) cutaneous nerve, and lodging some fibres of the sartorius.

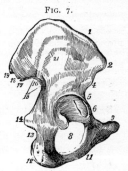

FIG. 7.

Posterior Superior Spine (19),—for the attachment of the erector spinæ muscle, and the oblique part of the sacro-iliac ligament.

Posterior Inferior Spine (17),—for the sacrotuberous (great sacro-sciatic) ligament.

Great Sciatic (Sacro-iliac) Notch (16),—below the last-named spine, transmits the great sciatic, superior gluteal, and pudic (pudendal) nerves, the pyriformis muscle, and the sciatic, pudic (pudendal) and gluteal vessels, also a nerve supplying the obturator externus muscle.

Gluteal ridges (Curved Lines) (21) posterior, anterior, and inferior, on the outer surface of the bone, from the spaces between which arise the glutei muscles.

Groove,—above the acetabulum, for the reflected tendon of the rectus femoris muscle.

The Ischium is the lowermost portion of the os coxæ (innominate bone), and presents the following points, viz.—

Body (superior ramus),—forms two-fifths of the acetabulum, and the external margin of the obturator foramen; on it is a broad groove for the tendon of the obturator externus muscle. Its posterior margin assists in forming the great sciatic (sacro-sciatic) notch.

Spine (14),—for the gemellus superior, coccygeus, and levator ani muscles, and the lesser sacro-sciatic ligament.

Lesser Sciatic (Sacro-sciatic) Notch (13)—below the spine, transmits the obturator muscle, its nerve, and the pudic vessels and nerve as they re-enter the pelvis, having crossed the spine of the ischium. The sacro-sciatic notches are converted into foramina by the sacro-sciatic ligaments; the greater notch by the lesser ligament (sacro-spinous), the lesser notch by the greater ligament (sacro-tuberous).

Tuberosity (12),—the lowest and most prominent part, gives attachment to the greater sacro-sciatic (sacro-tuberous) ligament, and to several muscles. On it one rests when sitting.

Horizontal Ramus (inferior ramus),—bounds the obturator foramen inferiorly, articulates with the (descending) (inferior) ramus of the pubes, and gives attachment to the obturator membrane and several muscles.

The Pubes. The pubic or pectineal bone forms the anterior portion of the innominate. It presents the following points, viz.—

Body,—with its fellow forms the *Symphysis*, giving origin to several muscles and ligaments.

Crest (9),—on the upper part of the body, terminates externally in the spine.

Spine,—affords attachment to one end of inguinal (Poupart's) ligament.

(Linea Ilio-pectinea), (pecten ossis pubis) in part,—gives attachment to the conjoined tendon, Gimbernat's (lacunar) ligament, and the triangular ligament.

Horizontal Ramus,—forms part of the margin of the obturator foramen, and of the acetabulum.

Pectineal Eminence (5),—gives attachment to the psoas parvus muscle.

Muscles attached to the hip bone number 36, comprising those of the abdomen, thigh, perineum, floor of the pelvis, and rotators of the hip-joint.

THE BONES OF THE HEAD

THE FRONTAL BONES (OS FRONTALE), (1, Fig. 8)

Points on its Frontal (Vertical) Portion, are as follows:—
Externally,—An upper angle (6),—Lateral angles (12),—

Frontal Eminences (tuberosities),—one on each side of the median line.

Depression,—marking the site of the frontal (metopic) suture before obliteration.

Superciliary Arches (Ridges),—behind which are the frontal sinuses.

Supraorbital Notches or Foramina,—in the supraorbital arches, at about their inner third, for the supraorbital vessels and nerves.

Nasal Eminence (24),—at lower end of the frontal depression.

External Angular, (Lateral or Zygomatic) Processes (13),—articulate with the malar (zygomatic) bones and form the anterior part of the temporal ridges.

Internal (Medial) Angular Processes,—articulate with the lacrimal bones.

Nasal (Frontal) Spine and Notch,—between the internal angular processes.

Internally,—

Sagittal Sulcus or *Groove,*—for superior longitudinal sinus and the falx cerebri.

Frontal Crest,—for attachment of the falx cerebri.

Foramen Cæcum,—for a small vein to the longitudinal sinus.

Fig. 8.

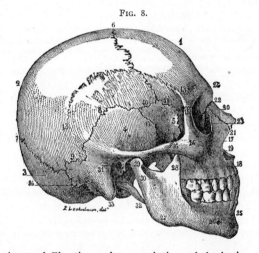

Depressions and Elevations,—for convolutions of the brain.

Between the two tables of the vertical portion in the adult are the—

Frontal Sinuses,—two spaces at the anterior inferior part of the bone, which are lined with mucous membrane, and open into the middle meatus of the nose.

The Orbital Plates (Pars Orbitalis). Each plate presents the following points,—

Fossa,—for the lacrimal gland, near the external angular process.

Fovea Trochlearis,—a depression at the nasal margin for the pulley of the superior oblique muscle.

Ethmoidal Notch,—having the following foramina on its margin.

Anterior Ethmoidal Foramen,—for the anterior ethmoidal vessels and the naso-ciliary branch of the ophthalmic nerve.

Posterior Ethmoidal Foramen,—for posterior ethmoidal vessels.

Grooves,—on the cranial surface, for branches of the anterior and middle meningeal arteries.

Articulations, Development, and Muscles. Each half of the frontal bone *articulates* from its upper angle to its lateral angle, with the parietal,—from lateral angle to zygomatic process, with the front part of the apex of the Great Wing of the sphenoid,—zygomatic process, with the malar,—posterior border of orbital plate, with Lesser Wing of the sphenoid, margins of ethmoidal notch with the ethmoid,—medial border of the orbital plate from behind forwards, with orbital plate of ethmoid,—lacrimal, nasal process of maxilla,—frontal spine, with the nasal. It is *developed* by 2 centres in membrane, 1 for each lateral half. The *muscles* attached to it are 3 pairs,—the temporal, corrugator supercilii, and orbicularis palpebrarum.

THE PARIETAL BONES, (2, Fig. 8)

General Characteristics. They are 2 quadrilateral bones situated at the superior and lateral regions of the cranium. Each has a frontal (anterior superior) angle (6), anterior border, sphenoidal (anterior inferior) angle (10), a lower border, a truncated mastoid (posterior inferior) angle (9), a posterior border, an occipital (posterior superior) angle (7), and an upper border. The articulations are,—the superior border of each joins the other by the *Sagittal Suture;* the anterior border joins the frontal bone forming the *Coronal Suture* (6); the posterior border articulates with the occipital, forming the *Lambdoid Suture* (7); the inferior border from before backwards with the great wing of the sphenoid (5), squamous and mastoid portions of the temporal (4). Forming the lateral walls of the skull they are named parietal, from *paries,* a wall.

Points on each Parietal Bone. Externally the bone is convex and presents for examination,—

Temporal Ridge (13),—continuous with the same on the frontal bone, bounded above by the superior temporal line, and below by the inferior temporal line.

Parietal Eminence (tuberosity),—the point where ossification commenced.

Parietal Foramen,—close to the upper border, transmits an emissary vein to the superior longitudinal (sagittal) sinus. Is not constant. Internally, the bone is concave, and marked by—

Depressions,—for the Arachnoideal Granulations (Pacchionian bodies), and for the cerebral convolutions.

Furrows,—for branches of the middle meningeal artery.

Groove,—for the lateral (transverse) sinus, at the posterior inferior angle.

Half-groove,—along the upper border, for the superior longitudinal (sagittal) sinus of the dura mater.

Development. Each parietal bone is *developed* from 1 centre in membrane. The *only muscle* attached to it is the temporal.

THE OS OCCIPITALE, (3, Fig. 8)

is a symmetrical bone. Its border presents an upper angle, and on each side, lateral angle, jugular process, jugular notch, petrosal process along the edge of the basilar process, and the apex of the basilar process.

General Features and Surfaces. It is trapezoidal in form, curved upon itself, and placed at the posterior and inferior region of the cranium. Externally its surface is convex and presents for examination the following, viz.—

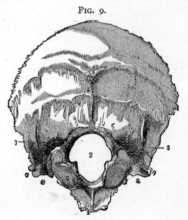

FIG. 9.

External Occipital Protuberance (5), *and Crest* (4), for the attachment of the ligamentum nuchæ.

Superior and Inferior Nuchal (Curved) Lines,—extending outward on each side of the external occipital crest; in one skull in every six there is to be seen a supreme nuchal line above the others.

Foramen Magnum (2),—transmitting the medulla oblongata and its membranes, the vertebral arteries, and the recurrent portions of the spinal accessory nerves.

Condyles (6),—two in number, for articulation with the atlas.

Tubercles,—1 on each condyle, for the check ligaments.

2

Anterior Condylar Foramina (canalis hypoglossi),—two for the hypoglossal nerves.

Posterior Condylar Foramina (canalis condyloideus posterior) (3),—two (often absent) for emissary veins.

Jugular Processes (7),—two, each partly bounding the foramen lacerum posterius basis cranii.

Jugular Fossæ (8),—each forming part of the foramen lacerum posterius basis cranii.

Internally, the surface is concave, showing—

Fossæ,—four for the cerebellar and posterior cerebral lobes.

Internal Occipital Protuberance,—where 6 cranial sinuses meet to form the torcular (wine-press) Herophili.

Crucial Ridge,—the vertical portion for the falx cerebri and falx cerebelli; the transverse portion for the tentorium cerebelli, having also a groove for the lateral (transverse) sinus.

Groove,—for the lateral (transverse) sinus, and the inferior petrosal sinus, along the postero-lateral border.

Internal Openings,—of the foramina described above.

Basilar Process (1) **of the Occipital** lies in front of the foramen magnum (2), articulates with the body of the sphenoid bone, smooth and grooved in the mid-line for the medulla oblongata and pons varolii, which lie upon it, grooved laterally by the inferior petrosal sinuses; rough inferiorly for the attachment of muscles, and presenting the—

Pharyngeal Tubercle or Spine,—for the attachment of the superior constrictor muscle of the pharynx and its tendinous raphé.

Articulations and Development. The occipital *articulates* as follows.— The condyles articulate with atlas, apex of the basilar process with body of sphenoid, side of basilar process and apex of jugular process with petrous portion of temporal, from jugular to lateral angle with mastoid portion of temporal, from lateral angle to upper angle with parietal. It is *developed* by 4 centres, 1 each for the posterior part, the basilar process, and the 2 condyles; its ossification being completed about the 6th year of age.

Muscles attached to the Occipital Bone. There are 12 muscles attached on each side to the following portions, viz.—

Superior Nuchal Line 3,—the occipito-frontalis, trapezius, and sterno-cleido-mastoid muscles.

Space between the nuchal lines 2,—the complexus and splenius.

Space below the inferior nuchal line 3,—the obliquus capitis superior, rectus capitis posticus major and rectus capitis posticus minor.

Basilar Process 3,—the superior constrictor of the pharynx, rectus capitis anticus major and rectus capitis anticus minor.

Jugular Process 1,—the rectus capitis lateralis.

THE TEMPORAL BONES (OSSA TEMPORALIA), (4, Fig. 8)

Situation and Divisions. They are situated at the inferior lateral portions of the skull, and contain the organs of hearing. Each bone is formed by the union of three parts, namely, the *Squamous*, *Petro-mastoid*, and *Tympanic*.

The Squamous Portion is a semicircular plate, smooth externally, and grooved internally for the middle meningeal artery, with depressions for the cerebral convolutions. Externally are seen the—

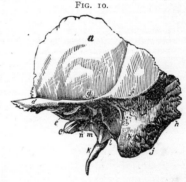

FIG. 10.

Zygomatic Process (d), or Zygoma,—arising by 3 roots, and extending forward to articulate with the malar bone.

Zygomatic Tubercle (e), at the base of the process, for the external lateral ligament of the lower jaw.

Anterior Articular Ridge (eminentia articularis),—formed by the anterior root of the zygoma.

Mandibular (Glenoid) Fossa (g),—between the anterior and posterior articular ridge, (middle root of the zygoma) for articulation with the condyle of the lower jaw, and is covered with cartilage.

Glaserian Fissure,—divides the squamous from the tympanic; it transmits the laxator tympani muscle, the tympanic artery, and lodges the processus gracilis of the malleus and the inferior process of the petrous.

Opening of the Canal of Hugier,—lies in the angle between the squamous and petrous portions of the bone; and transmits the chorda tympani nerve.

Temporal Ridge (f),—in part, here known as the suprameatal ridge.

THE PETRO-MASTOID,—is usually described as consisting of a mastoid portion and a petrous portion.

The Mastoid Portion. Its cerebellar surface is grooved for the lateral sinus (9); externally it presents the following,—

Mastoid Foramen (h),—the largest of several foramina, for a vein.

Mastoid Process,—at the tip, for the sterno-cleido-mastoid, splenius, and trachelo-mastoid muscles.

Digastric Fossa (j),—for the posterior belly of the digastric muscle.

Occipital Groove (8),—for the occipital artery.

The Mastoid Cells,—in the interior of the mastoid process, open on the posterior wall of the middle ear, and are lined with mucous membrane.

The Petrous Portion is very hard, pyramidal in form, contains the internal ear, projects inward and forward, and presents a base, an apex, a cerebral surface, cerebellar surface, tympanic surface, and basilar surface;

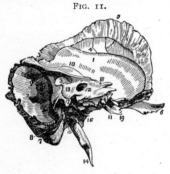

FIG. 11.

upper border, anterior border, posterior border; the tympanic bone is blended with the inferior border and conceals it.

On the Base are seen, the—

Meatus Auditorius Externus (i),— the external opening of the ear.

Auditory Process of the Tympanic,— a bony ring for the external cartilage of the ear.

Apex lies internally, at the base of the skull, forming the outer boundary of the foramen lacerum medium, and contains the internal carotid canal.

CEREBRAL (Anterior) Surface, presents from within outward—

Inner Opening of the Carotid Canal (11),—for the internal carotid artery and plexus.

Depression,—for the Gasserian ganglion of the 5th pair of cranial nerves.

Hiatus Canalis Facialis or Hiatus Fallopii,—for the great petrosal nerve, branch of the middle meningeal artery.

Foramen,—for the small petrosal nerve.

Eminence,—over the superior semicircular canal of the ear.

Depression,—over the tympanum.

Cerebellar (Posterior) Surface presents,—

Meatus Auditorius Internus (12),—transmits the 7th and 8th pairs of cranial nerves and the auditory artery, and lodges a process of dura mater.

Opening of the Aquæductus Vestibuli (13),—transmits to the vestibule a small artery and vein, and lodges a process of dura mater.

Basilar (Inferior) surface, presents from within outward—

Rough Quadrilateral Surface (19),—for the origin of the tensor tympani and levator palati muscles.

Opening of the Carotid Canal,—transmitting the internal carotid artery, and the carotid plexus of the sympathetic nerve.

Aquæductus Cochleæ,—transmitting an artery and vein to the cochlea.

Jugular Fossa,—a depression for the sinus of the internal jugular vein, forming with the occipital bone the foramen lacerum posterius, which transmits that vein and the 8th pair of cranial nerves, etc.

Foramen for Jacobson's Nerve (tympanic branch of the glossopharyngeal),—in the ridge between the jugular fossa and the carotid canal.

Foramen for Arnold's Nerve (auricular branch of the pneumogastric),—in the outer wall of the jugular fossa.

Jugular Surface,—for articulation with the jugular process of the occipital bone. The Tympanic Surface can be seen by looking in the external auditory canal, forms most of the osseous wall of the middle ear or tympanum. It presents the *Promontory* of the *Cochlea,* *Fenestra Vestibuli,* and *Fenestra Cochleæ.*

The Tympanic Bone forms most of the external auditory canal. Its under surface is slightly concave, forming a fossa for part of the parotid gland. It presents a sharp ridge which projects downwards, and forms the,—

Vaginal Process (*l*),—ensheathing the root of the styloid process.

Styloid Process (14),—a long projection for the stylo-pharyngeus, stylo-hyoid, and stylo-glossus muscles; and the stylo-hyoid and stylo-mandibular ligaments, which are attached thereto.

Stylo-mastoid Foramen (15),—between the styloid and mastoid processes, for the exit of the facial nerve, and the entrance of the stylo-mastoid artery.

Auricular Fissure,—for the exit of the auricular branch of the vagus (Arnold's nerve).

In the angle between the petrous and squamous portions, are seen the—

Septum Tubæ,—a lamina separating the following canals. Its inner end projects into the tympanum, and is called the *Processus cochleariformis.*

Opening,—of the canal for the tensor tympani muscle.

Osseous Opening,—of the Eustachian tube (*n*) inferiorly.

The Anterior Border articulates partly with the alar spine of the sphenoid bone.

The Posterior Border assists in forming the jugular foramen, and is grooved for the inferior petrosal sinus.

The Superior Border separates the anterior fossa of the skull from the middle fossa; to it is attached the tentorium cerebelli, and it is grooved for the superior petrosal sinus (10), and in infants it presents a *floccular fossa*.

Articulations and Development.   The temporal *articulates* as follows,— Anterior border of the petrous and squamous with the great wing of the sphenoid,—upper border of the squamous and mastoid with the parietal,— posterior border of the petro-mastoid with the occipital,—apex of zygomatic process with malar, and indirectly the glenoid fossa with the mandible.   It is *developed* by 4 principal centres, one each for the squamous portion, styloid process, and tympanic, and one for the petro-mastoid portions.   Its ossification is completed about the 2d or 3d year.

Muscles attached to it.   There are 14 muscles attached to the following-named portions.   To the—

Squamous Portion 2,—the temporal and masseter.

Mastoid Portion 6,—the occipito-frontalis, sterno-cleido-mastoid, splenius capitis, trachelo-mastoid, digastric, and retrahens aurem.

Petrous Portion 3,—the tensor tympani, levator veli palatini (levator palati) and stapedius.

Styloid Process 3,—the stylo-glossus, stylo-hyoid, and stylo-pharyngeus.

THE SPHENOID BONE, (5, Fig. 8)

Position and Form.   Wedged in between the bones of the skull anteriorly, it resembles a bat with out-stretched wings.   It is named from the Greek word σφήν, a wedge, enters into the formation of 5 cavities, 4 fossæ, 3 fissures, and presents for description—

Body of the Sphenoid Bone.   Placed in the median line, cuboid in shape, it presents on its UPPER SURFACE from before backward, the following points,—

Sphenoidal or *Ethmoidal Spine* (3),—articulating with the ethmoid bone.

Smooth Surface,—grooved for the olfactory nerves.

Sulcus Chiasmatis or *Optic Groove*,—supporting the commissure of the optic nerves.

Tuberculum Sellæ or *Olivary Process*,—an olive-shaped eminence behind the optic groove.

Middle Clinoid Processes,—bounding the Sella Turcica in front.

Fossa Hypophyseos or *Sella Turcica* (16) (Turkish saddle), lodges the hypophysis (pituitary body) and the circular sinus of the brain.

Dorsum Sellæ (cantle of the saddle) (16),—grooved for the 6th nerves.

Posterior Clinoid Processes (6),—for attachment of the tentorium cerebelli, grooved by the optic tracts.

FIG. 12.

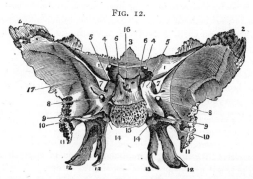

Grooves,—laterally, for the cavernous sinus and internal carotid artery.

POSTERIOR SURFACE is rough and quadrilateral (15): it articulates with the basilar process of the occipital bone, ossification being completed from the 18th to the 20th year of age.

FIG. 13.

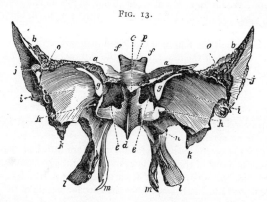

ANTERIOR SURFACE is nearly vertical, and presents the—

Sphenoidal crest,—in the median line, articulating with the perpendicular plate of the ethmoid bone, and forming part of the nasal septum

Openings of the Sphenoidal Sinuses (e),—cavities in the body of the bone which exist in adults, not in children.

Sphenoidal Conchæ or *Sphenoidal Turbinal Bones,*—which partially close the sinuses, and articulate with the ethmoid and orbital processes of the palate bones.

INFERIOR SURFACE helps to form the nasal fossæ, and presents the—

Rostrum (*d*),—which articulates with a groove on the vomer.

Alar Grooves,—on each side of the rostrum, for articulation with the wings of the vomer.

Vaginal Processes,—1 on each side of the rostrum.

Pterygo-palatine Grooves,—which, with the sphenoidal processes of the palate bones, form the pterygo-palatine canals, for the transmission of the pterygo-palatine arteries and nerves.

Greater Wings of the Sphenoid. Each wing presents on its CEREBRAL SURFACE the following points,—

Foramen Rotundum (8),—for the maxillary division of the 5th nerve.

Foramen Ovale (9),—for the mandibular division of the 5th nerve, the small petrosal nerve, and small meningeal artery.

Foramen Vesalii,—transmitting a small vein; often absent.

Foramen Spinosum (10),—transmitting the middle meningeal artery and veins, also sympathetic filaments from the cavernous plexus.

THE ORBITAL or ANTERIOR SURFACE assists in forming the external wall of the orbit, the inferior orbital (spheno-maxillary) and superior orbital (sphenoidal) fissures. It articulates with the frontal and malar bones, and presents a—

Notch,—transmitting a branch of the ophthalmic artery.

Spine,—for part of the lower head of the external rectus muscle.

External Orbital Foramina,—transmitting nutrient arterial branches.

EXTERNAL SURFACE consists of an upper portion, the temporal, separated by a ridge, the infra-temporal crest, from a lower portion, the spheno-maxillary surface. It presents the following points,—

Infra-temporal or *Pterygoid Ridge,*—dividing the temporal fossa from the spheno-maxillary.

Alar Spine of the Sphenoid (11),—to which are attached the internal lateral ligament of the lower jaw, and the laxator tympani muscle.

CIRCUMFERENCE is partly serrated for articulation with the temporal and frontal bones, and partly smooth for the anterior margin of the foramen lacerum medium and the inferior margin of the superior orbital (sphenoidal) fissure, which margins it assists in forming.

Lesser Wings (1) **of the Sphenoid,** or the Processes of Ingrassias (*a*),—terminate internally in the *Anterior Clinoid Processes* (5); their anterior borders articulate with the orbital plate of the frontal bone, the posterior are free, dividing the anterior cerebral fossa from the middle ones. Connected intimately with each of these wings are the—

    Optic Foramen (4),—formed by the separation of its roots, and transmitting the optic nerve and the ophthalmic artery.

    Superior Orbital or *Sphenoidal Fissure* (7), or Foramen Lacerum Anterius (*g*),—is bounded above by the lesser wing, below by the greater wing, and transmits the 3d, 4th, ophthalmic division of the 5th, and the 6th nerves, the ophthalmic vein, branches of the lacrimal and middle meningeal arteries, some filaments of the sympathetic and a process of the dura mater.

Medial (Internal) and Lateral (External) Pterygoid Processes of the Sphenoid. These wing-like processes descend, 1 on each side of the body, and divide each into 2 thin, bony plates (*lm*), connected together anteriorly, and presenting the—

    Pterygoid Fossa,—between the plates posteriorly, the origin of the internal pterygoid muscle.

    Scaphoid Fossa,—at the base of the internal plate, serves as the origin of the tensor veli palatini (tensor palati) muscle.

    Hamular Process,—a hook-like projection at the apex of the internal plate, around which plays the tendon of the tensor palati muscle.

    Canalis Pterygoideus or *Vidian Canal* (14),—at the root of the process, for the Vidian nerve and vessels.

    Triangular Notch,—at the end of the process, articulates with the tuberosity of the palate bone.

Development of the Sphenoid. By 14 or 16 centres, as follows,—2 for the greater wings, 2 for the lesser wings, 2 for the anterior part of the body, 2 for the posterior part of the body, 2 for the medial (internal) pterygoid processes, and 2 for the sphenoidal conchæ (turbinal processes), 2 for the lingulæ and 2 for the epipteric bones which usually join the tips of the great wings. Ossification begins in the 2d fœtal month, and is completed about the 11th year, by the union of the turbinal processes with the body.

Muscles attached to the Sphenoid.—12 pairs of muscles are attached to the sphenoid bone, as follows:—

    Orbital muscles, 6—all except the inferior oblique of the eye.

    Muscles of Mastication, 3—the temporal, external and internal pterygoids.

    Also the superior constrictor, tensor palati, and laxator tympani, 3.

THE ETHMOID BONE

General Characteristics. It is a spongy, light bone, depending from the ethmoidal notch of the frontal, and from between its orbital plates. It consists of a body and 2 lateral masses, and is named from the Greek word ἠθμός, a sieve.

Points on its Body. The body (*b*) consists of a horizontal or cribriform plate and presents the—

FIG. 14.

Crista Galli (*c*),—or cock's comb, projecting upward, for the attachment of the anterior end of the falx cerebri.

Cribriform Plate (*d*),—on each side of the crista galli. It is concave for the olfactory bulbs (*i*), and perforated for the transmission of the olfactory nerves, the nasal branch of the ophthalmic nerve. and numerous small vessels.

Perpendicular Plate (*a*),—assists to form the nasal septum, is usually inclined to one side, grooved for filaments of the olfactory nerves, and has attached to it the cartilage of the nose.

Lateral Masses. They consist of a number of cellular cavities, and each one presents the following points,—

Ethmoid Cells,—the anterior opening by the *infundibulum* into the middle meatus of the nose, the posterior into the superior meatus.

Orbital Plate (lamina papyracea, os planum) (*h*),—helps to form the inner wall of the orbit and is notched superiorly to form with the frontal bone the two ethmoidal foramina, or grooves.

Uncinate, or *Unciform Process*,—descends to articulate with the inferior concha, or turbinal, and forms part of the inner wall of the antrum.

Superior Concha, or *Turbinal Process* (*f*),—is a subdivision of the posterior part of the middle turbinal process.

Middle Concha, or *Turbinal Process* (*g*),—is larger and more curved than the superior. These processes bound the superior meatus of the nose.

Articulations, Development, and Muscles. The ethmoid *articulates* with 15 bones, viz.—all those of the face except the malar, and the frontal and sphenoid of the cranium. It is *developed* by 3 centres, 1 for each lateral mass, and 1 for the body, ossification being completed about the 6th year. There are *no muscles* attached to it.

OSSA NASALIA OR NASAL BONES, (20, Fig. 8)

The Nasal are 2 small bones forming the bridge of the nose by articulation with each other in the median line (4). From side to side they are convex externally and concave internally, where they are grooved longitudinally for the external branch of the naso-ciliary, or nasal nerve and some small arteries. They are perforated about the centre by a foramen (1), for a small tributary to the facial vein. The *superior border* (2) articulates with the nasal notch of the frontal bone; the *inferior border* (3) serves for the attachment of the lateral cartilage of the nose. The *external border* (5) articulates with the nasal process of the maxilla; the *internal border* (4) with its fellow, with the nasal spine of the frontal above and with the ethmoid bone below. They are each *developed* by one centre of ossification, and have *no muscles* attached to them except a few fibres of the occipito-frontalis.

FIG. 15.

THE MAXILLÆ, (18, Fig. 8)

The Maxillæ are 2 hollow bones, together forming the upper jaw. Each bone consists of 4 processes, and a body which possesses interiorly a large cavity, the sinus maxillaris, or *antrum of Highmore.*

Antrum of Highmore is a tetrahedral cavity in the body of the bone, which opens into the middle meatus of the nose by an aperture which is very small in the recent subject, admitting only a small probe. Its walls are very thin, and are covered internally by mucous membrane. It presents the—

Aperture,—partly closed by the articulation of the uncinate, or unciform process of the ethmoid with the ethmoidal process of the inferior turbinal, and that of the maxillary process of the palate with a fissure in the maxilla; also by the maxillary process of the inferior turbinal which hooks over the lower edge of the orifice.

Posterior Dental Canals,—on the posterior wall of the cavity.

Processes,—in its floor, formed by the alveoli of the 1st and 2d molar teeth, the roots of which occasionally perforate it.

Other Points presented by the body. The body has 4 surfaces, the facial externally, the zygomatic posteriorly, the orbital superiorly, and an internal surface forming part of the outer wall of the nose and the cavity of the mouth. The anterior or facial surface presents the—

Incisive Fossa (2),—on the facial surface, above the incisor sockets, for the origin of the depressor alæ nasi muscle.

Canine Fossa (1),—more externally, for the levator anguli oris muscle.

Infraorbital Foramen (3),—above the canine fossa, transmitting the infraorbital vessels and nerve, from the *infraorbital canal* in the orbital surface of the bone.

Maxillary Tuberosity (7),—articulates with the tuberosity of the palate bone. The nasal surface presents—

FIG. 16.

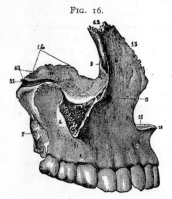

Conchal or *Turbinal Crests*,—inferior and superior, for articulation with inferior and middle conchæ, bounding horizontal grooves which correspond to the meati of the nose.

Vertical Grooves,—on the inner surface, one, the lacrimal, assisting to form the nasal duct, the other, pterygo-palatine, to form the pterygo-palatine, or posterior palatine canal.

Rough Surface,—for articulation with the palate bone.

Orbital Surface,—articulating with the lacrimal, ethmoid, and palate bones interiorly, partly bounding the spheno-maxillary fissure exteriorly, and forming the lower margin of the orbit anteriorly.

Infraorbital Groove (11),—along the orbital surface, ending in the infraorbital canal and foramen. (See above.)

Depression,—for the origin of the inferior oblique muscle of the eye.

Processes of the maxilla are 4 in number, as follows:—

MALAR or ZYGOMATIC PROCESS (4, 5),—is triangular, looks outward from the body, and is rough for articulation with the malar bone.

NASAL or FRONTAL PROCESS (8),—is thin anteriorly and serrated superiorly (12) for articulation with the nasal bone; posteriorly it is smooth and articulates with the lacrimal. It presents the—

Conchal or *Turbinal Crests*,—superior and inferior, the former articulating with the middle concha or turbinal process of the ethmoid bone.

Outer Surface,—gives origin to the orbicularis palpebrarum and levator labii superioris alæque nasi muscles, and the tendo oculi.

Lacrimal Groove,—on the posterior border (9), helping to form the nasal canal.

ALVEOLAR PROCESS (6),—forms the curved line of the teeth, and presents —*Alevoli,*—or sockets, for 8 teeth in the adult, 5 in the child.

PALATINE PROCESS,—forms part of the floor of the nasal cavity, and the roof of the mouth. It articulates with the vomer, the palate bone, and with its fellow process, and presents the—

Incisive Foramen, or Foramen of Stenson,—leading into the anterior palatine canal, for the terminal branches of the posterior palatine arteries.

Foramina of Scarpa, 2,—transmitting the naso-palatine nerves.

Groove,—on the under surface, for the protection of the vessels and nerves.

Orifice,—of the posterior palatine canal, at the posterior end.

Nasal Crest,—at the articulation of the two processes with the vomer.

Anterior Nasal Spine (10),—the anterior extremity of the nasal crest.

Articulations and Development. The maxilla *articulates* with 9 bones,—the frontal (12), ethmoid (14), vomer (13), nasal (15), lacrimal, malar, palate, inferior turbinal, and opposite maxilla. It is *developed* probably by 4 centres,—1 for the facial and nasal parts, another for the orbital and malar, a 3d for the incisive, and a 4th for the palate portion.

Muscles attached to it, are 11, viz.—the orbicularis palpebrarum, and levator anguli oris alæque nasi, 2, to the *nasal process;*—the levator labii superioris, levator anguli oris, compressor naris, depressor alæ nasi, orbicularis oris, and inferior oblique of the eye, 6, *to the body;*—the buccinator, 1, to the *alveolar process;*—the masseter, 1, to the *malar process;*—and the external pterygoid, 1, to the *tuberosity.*

FIG. 17.

THE OSSA LACRIMALIA OR LACRIMAL BONES

The Lacrimal are 2 small quadrilateral bones, situated in the anterior part of the inner wall of the orbit. Each bone presents a—

Groove (3),—on the external surface, forming part of the nasal canal.

Ridge (1),—also externally, for attachment of the tensor tarsi muscle.

Furrow,—internally, corresponding to the ridge on the external surface.

Hamular Process (2),—projecting forwards around the nasal canal.

Superior Border (8),—articulates with the internal angular process of the frontal bone.

Inferior Border (9),—articulates anteriorly with the lacrimal process of the inferior turbinal bone.

Anterior Border (6),—articulates with the nasal process of the maxilla.

Posterior Border (7),—articulates with the orbital plate of the ethmoid bone.

Internal Surface,—closes the anterior ethmoidal cells.

Articulations, Development, and Muscles. The lacrimal *articulates* with 4 bones,—the frontal, ethmoid, maxilla, and inferior turbinal. It is *developed* from 1 centre, and has but 1 *muscle* attached to it, the tensor tarsi or Horner's muscle.

THE OSSA ZYGOMATICA, OR MALAR BONES, (14, Fig. 8)

The Malar or cheek bones are situated at the outer and upper part of the face, aiding to form the cavities of the orbits and the temporal and zygomatic fossæ. Each bone presents 3 surfaces, 3 processes and 3 borders.

The Orbital surface (*c*) forming the lateral and front part of the orbit, is concave laterally; it is bounded in front by the margin of the orbit (*b*)

FIG. 18.

and behind by the rough orbital border. About the middle of this surface is seen the orbital ends of the Zygomatico-facial, or malar, canals. The Zygomatic, or infratemporal surface forms the front end of the zygomatic arch. The facial surface is subcutaneous and is also known as the malar surface or malar tuberosity; it presents the outer ends of the two small malar canals. Orbital, or fronto-sphenoidal process (*a*) in man, and those animals having a closed orbit, articulates with the great wing of the sphenoid and the orbital process of the frontal bone. It forms the upper end of the temporal border (*h*) which forms the anterior boundary of the temporal fossa and is continuous with the temporal ridge of the skull. This border terminates below and behind in the zygomatic or temporal process (*f*), which is rough for articulation with the zygomatic process of the temporal bone. The lower or masseteric border (*g*) is rough for attachment of the masseter and zygomatic muscles. It terminates medially in the long slender maxillary process (*d*) which is very rough for articulation with the maxilla and forms most of the lower margin of the orbit (*b*).

Articulations, Development, and Muscles. The malar *articulates* with 4 bones,—the frontal, sphenoid, temporal, and maxilla. It is *developed* by one centre of ossification, and has 4 *muscles* attached to it,—the levator labii superioris, zygomaticus major and minor, and the masseter.

THE PALATE BONES

The Palate Bones are 2 L-shaped bones, situated posteriorly in the nares. Each bone assists in forming the floor and outer wall of the nose, the roof of the mouth, the floor of the orbit, the inner wall of the antrum, the zygomatic, spheno-palatine, and pterygoid fossæ, and presents the following points:—

HORIZONTAL PLATE (*a*), completes the nasal floor and hard palate; has a—

Ridge,—on the inferior surface, for the tensor palati aponeurosis.

Groove,—assisting to form the posterior palatine canal.

Foramina,—transmitting the anterior and posterior palatine nerves.

FIG. 19.

Anterior Border,—is serrated, for articulation with the maxilla.

Posterior Border,—is free and concave, for the attachment of the soft palate.

Inner Border (*d*),—is thick, and articulates with its fellow, forming a groove for the reception of the vomer. Its posterior extremity is the—

Posterior Nasal Spine,—for the origin of the azygo uvulæ muscle.

VERTICAL PLATE (*b*), a broad and thick lamella, presents the following:—

Ridge for Middle Concha,—on the inner surface. Below it is the—

Ridge for Inferior Concha (*g*),—dividing the middle meatus of the nose from the inferior, and articulating with the inferior concha or turbinal bone.

Posterior Border,—articulates with the pterygoid process of the sphenoid.

Groove,—on the external surface, helping to form the posterior palatine, or pterygo-palatine canal.

Two Smooth Surfaces,—externally, one forming the inner wall of the spheno-palatine or pterygo-palatine fossa; the other, part of the inner wall of the maxillary antrum.

Two Rough Surfaces,—also externally, one for articulation with the maxilla; the other with the pterygoid process of the sphenoid.

Deep Notch,—which by articulation with the sphenoid bone, forms the *spheno-palatine foramen* (*h*),—for the spheno-palatine vessels and the superior nasal and palatine nerves.

TUBEROSITY OR PYRAMIDAL PROCESS (*c*), is wedged into the notch between the plates of the pterygoid process of the sphenoid, with which it articulates laterally. In it are the—

Palatine Foramina,—for the anterior, middle and posterior palatine nerves.

Posterior Surface,—aids in forming the pterygoid fossa.

ORBITAL PROCESS (*i*),—triangular in shape, large and hollow. It has—

Three Articular Surfaces,—for the maxilla, sphenoid, and ethmoid.

Two Free Surfaces,—the orbital forming part of the floor of the orbit, the external aiding to form the spheno-palatine fossa.

Rounded Border,—forms a part of the spheno-maxillary fissure.

SPHENOIDAL PROCESS (*j*), projects backward, articulates superiorly with the body of the sphenoid, and externally with the pterygoid process of the sphenoid. On its upper surface is a—

Groove,—which assists in forming the spheno-palatine or pharyngeal canal.

Inner Surface,—forms part of the outer wall of the nasal fossa.

Articulations, Development, and Muscles. The palate *articulates* with 6 bones,—the sphenoid, ethmoid, vomer, maxilla, inferior turbinal, and its fellow palate bone. It is *developed* by one centre at the junction of the two plates. There are 4 *muscles* attached to it,—the azygos uvulæ, internal pterygoid, superior constrictor and tensor palati.

THE CONCHÆ NASALES INFERIORES OR THE INFERIOR TURBINAL BONES

The Inferior Turbinal Bones are 2 thin, curved osseous plates situated in the nasal fossæ, their convex surfaces presenting inwardly. Each bone is

FIG. 20.

attached above to the inferior turbinal crests of the maxillary and palate bones, and presents the following, viz.—

Lacrimal Process (3),—aiding to form the nasal duct, by articulation with the lacrimal and maxilla.

Ethmoidal Process (1),—articulating with the unciform process of the ethmoid, thus helping to partially close the aperture of the antrum.

Maxillary Process (4),—also helps to partially close the aperture of the maxillary antrum, by hooking (7) over the lower edge of that orifice.

Free Border (5),—below, coming to about ½ inch above the floor of the nose.

Articulations, Development and Muscles. The inferior turbinal *articulates* with 4 bones, the ethmoid, lacrimal, palate, and maxilla. It is *developed* by one centre, and has *no muscles* attached to it.

THE VOMER

The **Vomer** (plough-share) forms the postero-inferior part of the nasal septum, but is usually bent to one side. Its—

Superior Border (1, 2),—has a groove and two alæ or wings, for articulation with the rostrum and vaginal processes of the sphenoid bone.

Anterior Border (3),—is grooved for the ethmoidal plate and the nasal cartilage.

Inferior Border (4),—the longest, articulates with the nasal crest of the maxillary and palate bones.

FIG. 21.

Posterior Border,—is free and presents toward the pharynx.

Naso-palatine Grooves,—laterally, for the naso-palatine nerves.

Furrows,—on the lateral surfaces (6), for vessels and nerve-filaments.

Articulations, Development and Muscles. The vomer *articulates* with 6 bones,—the sphenoid, ethmoid, 2 maxillary, and 2 palate bones. It is *developed* by one centre, which appears about the 6th fœtal week in cartilage between two laminæ which coalesce after puberty. It has *no muscles* attached to it.

THE MANDIBLE, (25, Fig. 8)

General Characteristics. The Mandible is the lower jaw, receives the inferior teeth, and is the second bone of the body in which ossification appears, the clavicle being the first. It consists of a body and two rami.

The **Body** (1) is shaped somewhat like a horseshoe, and presents for examination the following:—

Alveolar Portion (15),—above the oblique line, containing on its upper border *alveoli* for 16 teeth in the adult, for 10 in the child (*i, b, c, m*).

Symphysis (3),—a vertical ridge on the median line, marking the junction of the two symmetrical portions of which the bone originally consisted.

Mental Process,—a prominent triangular eminence, characteristic of man, forming the chin.

Externally on each side from the symphysis backward, are the—

Incisive Fossa (4),—above the chin, for the origin of the levator menti.

Meatal Foramen (5),—below the 2d bicuspid alveolus, transmitting the mental artery and nerve.

External Oblique Line (1),—for the origins of the depressor labii inferioris and depressor anguli oris muscles from its anterior half.

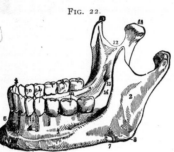

Fig. 22.

Groove (7),—near the angle, for the facial artery.

Internally, on each side from the median depression backward, are the—

Mental Spines, or *Genial Tubercles,*—the superior for the genio-hyoglossus muscle; the inferior for the genio-hyoid.

Mylo-hyoid Ridge,—obliquely backward, for the mylo-hyoid muscle.

Sublingual Fossa,—near the genial tubercles, for the sublingual gland.

Fossa,—below the sublingual, for the anterior belly of the digastric muscle.

Submandibular Fossa,—below the ridge, for the submandibular gland.

The Rami of the Mandible, the ascending portions of the bone, are 2 in number, and each presents the—

Coronoid Process (10),—anteriorly, for the insertion of the temporal muscle.

Condylar Process (11),—posteriorly. Its condyle articulates with the glenoid fossa of the temporal bone, its *neck* receives the insertion of the external pterygoid muscle, its *tubercle* has attached to it the external lateral ligament of the lower jaw.

Sigmoid Notch (12),—a deep depression separating the above-named processes from each other, and crossed by the masseteric vessels and nerve.

Groove,—on the coronoid process internally, and prolonged downward upon the body, for the attachment of the buccinator muscle.

Ridges,—on the external surface, for the insertion of the masseter.

Lingula or Spix's Spine,—a projection on the margin of mandibular foramen, for the attachment of the spheno-mandibular ligament.

Mandibular Foramen, or Canal (13),—opening behind the spine, lies within the ramus and body of the bone for the inferior dental vessels and nerve. It communicates with each alveolus and with the mental foramen.

Mylo-hyoid Groove (14),—below the spine, for the mylo-hyoid vessels and nerve.

Rough Surface,—behind the groove, for the internal pterygoid muscle.

Angle of the Jaw (8),—at the junction of the posterior border of the ramus with the inferior border of the body, for the insertion of the masseter and internal pterygoid muscles, and the stylo-mandibular ligament.

Articulations and Development. It *articulates* with one pair of bones, —the temporal. It is the earliest formed bone in the body except the clavicle, and is probably *developed* by 2 centres, one for each lateral half, the two halves coalescing at the symphysis about the 1st year of age. In *adult life* the ramus arises almost vertically from the body, and the dental canal lies about the middle of the body. In *old age* the ramus seems to extend obliquely backward, the angle becoming very obtuse; and the alveolar portion being absorbed, the dental canal is near the superior border.

Muscles attached to the Mandible,—number 15 pairs,—the masseter, internal and external pterygoids and temporal, 4, to *the ramus;*—the genio-hyo-glossus, genio-hyoid, mylo-hyoid, digastric, and superior constrictor, 5, to the internal surface of *the body;*—the depressor labii inferioris, depressor anguli oris, levator menti, orbicularis oris, platysma myoides, and buccinator, 6, to the external surface of *the body.*

THE ORBITS

The Orbits are 2 conoidal cavities, situated between the forehead and the face, their bases outward, their apices pointing backward, the lines of axial prolongation meeting at the sella turcica of the sphenoid bone. They contain the organs of vision with their appendages, and are each formed by 7 bones,—the frontal (1), ethmoid (2), sphenoid (3, 4, 5), lacrimal (6), maxilla (7), palate (8), and malar (9), of which the first three are common to both orbits. Each orbit communicates with 1 cavity and 4 fossæ, as follows, viz.—

Cavity of the cranium,—by the optic foramen (11) and superior orbital or sphenoidal fissure (10).

Fossæ (4),—the nasal, temporal, zygomatic, and spheno-palatine or spheno-maxillary,—by the nasal duct (12) and the inferior orbital or spheno-maxillary fissure (13).

Foramina communicating with each orbit are 9 in number,—the optic foramen (11), superior orbital or sphenoidal fissure (10), anterior (21) and posterior (22) ethmoidal foramina, supraorbital (14), infraorbital (15), and zygomatico-facial and temporal or malar foramina (16), the nasal or lacrimal canal (12), and the inferior orbital or spheno-maxillary fissure (13).

Roof of the Orbit is formed by the orbital plate of the frontal bone anteriorly (1), and the lesser wing of the sphenoid (4) posteriorly. It is concave, and presents the—

Lacrimal Fossa (17),—at its outer angle, for the lacrimal gland.

Fovea Trochlearis (18),—at the inner angle, for the pulley of the superior oblique.

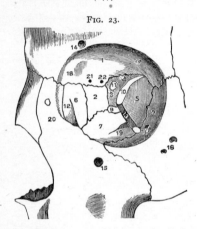

FIG. 23.

Floor of the Orbit is formed by the orbital surface of the maxilla (7), and the orbital process of the malar (9) and palate bones (8).

It is nearly flat and presents the—

Palato-maxillary Suture,—posteriorly.

Infraorbital Canal,—anteriorly.

Infraorbital Groove (9),—posteriorly.

Medial or Inner Wall of the Orbit is formed by the nasal process of the maxilla (20), the lacrimal (6), the orbital plate or lamina papyracea of the ethmoid (2), and the body of the sphenoid (3). It presents—

A Groove,—for the lacrimal sac, and the *Lacrimal Crest,* anteriorly.

2 Sutures,—the ethmo-lacrimal, and the ethmo-sphenoidal.

Lateral or Outer Wall of the Orbit is formed by the orbital process of the malar bone (9), and the greater wing of the sphenoid (5). It presents the *Orifices* (16) of the zygomatico-facial and zygomatico-temporal or malar canals, and the *Spheno-malar Suture.*

Angles of the Orbit present the following points:—

IN THE SUPERIOR EXTERNAL ANGLE:—

Superior Orbital or Sphenoidal Fissure (10), or Foramen Lacerum Anterius,—transmits the 3d, 4th, ophthalmic division of the 5th, and the 6th nerves, the ophthalmic vein, branches of the lacrimal and middle meningeal arteries, filaments of the sympathetic nerve, and a process of the dura mater.

Articulations,—the fronto-malar, and fronto-sphenoidal.

IN THE SUPERIOR INTERNAL ANGLE:—

Suture,—the lachrymo-ethmo-frontal, in which are the following foramina:

Anterior Ethmoidal Foramen (21),—transmitting the anterior ethmoidal artery and the nasal nerve.

Posterior Ethmoidal Foramen (22),—transmitting the posterior ethmoidal artery and vein.

IN THE INFERIOR EXTERNAL ANGLE:—

Inferior Orbital or Spheno-maxillary Fissure (13)—(described under the Zygomatic Fossa).

IN THE INFERIOR INTERNAL ANGLE:—

A Suture,—the ethmo-maxillo-palato-lacrimal.

Other Points connected with the Orbit are two, the supraorbital notch and the optic foramen, as follows:—

Supraorbital Notch or Foramen (14),—at the junction of the inner and middle thirds of the upper circumference, transmitting the supraorbital artery, veins, and nerve. A line prolonged from this notch through the interval between the bicuspid teeth of either jaw, will cross both the infraorbital and mental foramina, and the canine fossa of the maxilla.

Optic Foramen (11),—at the apex, is formed by the 2 roots of the lesser wing of the sphenoid, and transmits the optic nerve and the ophthalmic artery. From around its margin arises a tendinous ring, the common origin of the 4 recti muscles of the eye.

Muscles arising within the Orbit are the 4 recti and 2 oblique of the eye, the levator palpebræ, and the tensor tarsi (8 in all).

THE FOSSÆ

The Nasal Fossæ together form the cavity of the nose, being separated from each other by the *Septum Nasi* (11). They open in front by the anterior nares, behind by the posterior nares; and extend from the palate processes of the maxilla and palate bones (17), upward to the base of the cranium. They are formed by 14 bones,—the ethmoid, sphenoid, frontal, vomer, 2 nasal, 2 maxillæ, 2 lacrimal, 2 palate and 2 inferior conchæ or turbinal.

The Septum Nasi (11) forms the inner wall of each nasal fossa, and is formed chiefly by the perpendicular plate of the ethmoid bone, the vomer,

and the triangular cartilage of the septum; to a less extent by 5 other bones,
—the rostrum of the sphenoid, the nasal spine of the frontal, and the crests
of the nasal, palate, and maxillary bones.

Points presented by each Nasal Fossa are as follows:—

ON THE ROOF:—

Openings,—posteriorly, into the sphenoidal sinuses.

Olfactory Foramina,—and the *Nasal Slit*, in the cribriform plate of the
ethmoid bone.

ON THE FLOOR:—

Orifice,—of the anterior palatine canal.

Suture,—between the bones forming the hard palate.

Nasal Spine,—anterior and posterior, and the *Ridge* connecting them.

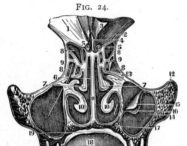

FIG. 24.

ON THE LATERAL OR OUTER WALL,
from above downward:—

*Superior Concha or Turbinal
Process*,—of the ethmoid.

Superior Meatus of the nose—
into which open 3 orifices,—
those of the posterior ethmoidal and the sphenoidal
sinuses, and the sphenopala-
tine foramen.

*Middle Concha or Turbinal
Process* (7),—of the ethmoid.

Middle Meatus of the nose,—
into which open 2 orifices,
those of the antrum (14) and

infundibulum, the latter draining the anterior ethmoidal cells (8),
and the frontal sinus.

Inferior Concha or Turbinal Bone (10),—below which is the—

Inferior Meatus—of the nose, the largest; into it open 2 orifices, those
of the lacrimal and anterior palatine canals. To these may be
added the apertura pyraformis (anterior) and posterior nares.

The Temporal Fossa. Situated on each side of the cranium, it is shallow
above and behind, but deep in front and below, and is formed by parts
of 5 bones,—the frontal, sphenoid, temporal, parietal, and malar. It is
bounded above and behind by the temporal ridge, in front by the malar,
frontal, and sphenoid bones, and below by the zygoma and the pterygoid
bounded above and behind by the temporal ridge, in front by the malar,
frontal, and sphenoid bones, and below by the zygoma and the pterygoid

ridge on the greater wing of the sphenoid.   It is traversed by 6 sutures,—
the spheno-malar, spheno-frontal, spheno-parietal, spheno-temporal,
frontal-parietal, and temporo-parietal.   It opens below into the zygomatic
fossa; and lodges the temporal muscle, and the deep temporal vessels.

The Zygomatic Fossa extends downward from the temporal fossa, and
is bounded—

In front,—by the tuberosity of the maxilla.

Laterally or *Externally,*—by the zygoma, and the ramus of the mandible.

Medially or *Internally,*—by the lateral or external plate of the pterygoid
process.

Above,—by the temporal fossa, the squamous portion of the temporal
bone and the greater wing of the sphenoid.

Below,—by the alveolar border of the mandible bone.

Fissures opening into the Zygomatic Fossa are two, the—

Inferior Orbital or *Spheno-maxillary Fissure,*—between the greater wing
of the sphenoid externally, and the maxilla and palate bones medially
or internally.   It connects the orbit with the zygomatic, temporal, and
spheno-palatine fossæ; and transmits the infraorbital artery, the maxillary nerve and its orbital branches, and the ascending branches of
Meckel's ganglion.

Pterygo-maxillary Fissure,—between the tuberosity of the maxilla and
the pterygoid process of the sphenoid.   It transmits branches of
the internal maxillary artery, and connects the zygomatic fossa with
the spheno-palatine.

The Spheno-palatine Fossa is a triangular cavity between the pterygoid
process of the sphenoid bone and the tuberosity of the maxilla, and is
situated at the junction of the spheno-maxillary, pterygo-maxillary, and
sphenoidal fissures.   Into it open—

  3 *Fossæ,*—the orbital, zygomatic, and nasal.

  2 *Cavities,*—the cranial, and buccal.

  5 *Foramina,*—the Vidian and spheno-palatine or pharyngeal canals and
    the foramen rotundum, posteriorly; the spheno-palatine foramen on
    the inner wall; and the posterior palatine canal inferiorly, occasion-
    ally also the accessory palatine canals.

THE SUTURES AND FONTANELLES

The Sutures of the Skull are 13 in number, as follows:—
At the vertex of the skull are 3, the—

Sagittal or Interparietal,—formed by the junction of the two parietal bones.

Metopic, between the halves of the Frontal, may persist until late in life.

Coronal or Fronto-parietal,—extends transversely across the vertex of the skull anteriorly.

Lambdoid or Occipito-parietal,—extends transversely across the vertex of the skull posteriorly.

At the sides of the skull are 5, the—

Fronto-malar and Fronto-sphenoidal,—anteriorly.

Spheno-parietal, *Squamo-parietal* and *Masto-parietal*,—posteriorly.

At the base of the skull are 5, the—

Basilar,—in the central line of the base.

Petro-occipital, *Masto-occipital*, *Petro-sphenoidal* and *Squamo-sphenoidal* —on each side.

The Facial Sutures are very numerous, the most important being the following:—

Zygomatic Suture,—at the temporo-malar articulation.

Transverse Suture,—extending from one external angular process of the frontal bone across to the other, and connecting that bone with the malar, sphenoid, ethmoid, lacrimal, maxillary, and nasal bones.

Symphysis of the Chin,—the site of a fœtal suture.

The Sutures are formed by dentations of the external tables interdigitating with each other, the adjacent edges of the internal tables lying in unjoined proximity. The sutures are not formed until a long time after the formation of the skull, probably to permit of the marginal growth of the bones.

The Fontanelles are 6 membranous intervals in the infant's skull, corresponding in situation with the angles of the two parietal bones. They are as follows:—

Anterior,—at the junction of the sagittal and coronal intervals.

Posterior,—at the junction of the sagittal and lambdoid intervals.

Lateral Fontanelles, 4,—two at the anterior inferior angles, and two at the posterior inferior angles of the parietal bones.

The Ossa Suturarum (Wormian Bones) are supernumerary small pieces of bone, irregularly shaped, and developed by special centres in unclosed portions of the cranial sutures and fontanelles, being most frequent in the lambdoid suture.

The Hyoid Bone is shaped like a horse-shoe and has no articulation with the skeleton, but supports the tongue. It consists of a *Body*, two greater and two lesser *Cornua* or horns. On the body is a *Crucial Ridge*, with a *Tubercle* at the centre. It is *developed* by 5 centres,—one for the body and one for each horn. Attached to it are 10 muscles, 3 ligaments and 1 membrane, as follows:—

To the Body or *Basi-hyal,*—the genio-, mylo-, stylo-, sterno-, thyro-, omo-hyoid, the genio-hyo-glossus, and the hyo-glossus muscles; also the pulley of the digastric, the hyo-epiglottic ligament, and the thyro-hyoid membrane.

To the Greater Cornu, or *thyro-hyal,*—the hyo-glossus, middle constrictor muscles, and part of the thyro-hyoid; also the thyro-hyoid ligament.

To the Lesser Cornu, or *cerato-hyal,*—the stylo-hyoid ligament.

FORAMINA AT THE BASE OF THE SKULL

with the various structures transmitted by each foramen

Internally, the Anterior Fossa has 1 single and 4 pairs, viz.—

Foramen Cæcum,—lodges a fold of dura mater, and transmits a vein to the longitudinal sinus.

Ethmoidal Fissure,—the nasal branch of the 5th nerve.

Olfactory,—olfactory nerves, and nasal branches of the ethmoidal arteries.

Anterior Ethmoidal,—ant. ethmoidal artery and the nasal br. of the 5th nerve.

Posterior Ethmoidal,—posterior ethmoidal artery and vein.

Middle Fossæ contain 10 foramina in each fossa, viz.—

Optic Foramen,—optic nerve and ophthalmic artery.

Foramen Lacerum Anterius, Superior Orbital or *Sphenoidal Fissure,*—the 3d, 4th, ophthalmic division of the 5th, and the 6th cranial nerves and filaments of the sympathetic; ophthalmic vein, a branch of the lacrimal artery, orbital branches of the middle meningeal artery, and a process of dura mater.

Foramen Rotundum,—maxillary division of the 5th nerve.

Foramen Vesalii,—a small vein. This foramen is often absent.

Foramen Ovale,—mandibular division of the 5th nerve, lesser petrosal nerve, and the small meningeal branch of the internal maxillary artery.

Foramen Spinosum,—middle meningeal artery, meningeal veins, and sympathetic filaments from the cavernous plexus.

Foramen Lacerum Medium, is not a true foramen in that it is completely blocked by fibro-cartilage, the cerebral surface of this cartilage is deeply grooved or may even be tunneled from behind forwards by—internal carotid artery, carotid plexus, Vidian nerve, and artery.

Small Foramina,—for the small and external superf. petrosal nerves.

Hiatus Canalis facialis Fallopii,—large petrosal nerve, and a branch of middle meningeal artery.

Posterior Fossa contains 6 pairs and 1 single foramen, viz.—

Meatus Acusticus or Auditorius Internus,—facial and auditory nerves, auditory artery.

Aquæductus Vestibuli,—small artery and vein, process of dura mater.

Foramen Lacerum Posterius (Jugular Foramen),—the glosso-pharyngeal, pneumo-gastric, and spinal accessory nerves, internal jugular vein, meningeal branches of the ascending pharyngeal and occipital arteries.

Mastoid Foramen (often absent),—a small vein, also occasionally the mastoid artery.

Anterior Condylar or Hypoglossal Foramen,—hypoglossal nerve, meningeal branch from the ascending pharyngeal artery.

Posterior Condylar Foramen (often absent),—posterior condylar vein.

Foramen Magnum, medulla oblongata and its membranes, the vertebral arteries, and the spinal accessory (n. accessorius) nerves.

Externally, at the base of the skull, from the front backward, are 22 foramina on each side, and 1 single, the foramen magnum, as follows:—

Foramina of Scarpa (2) (*Anterior Palatine*), 2 in the median line,—for the naso-palatine nerves.

Foramina of Stenson (2) (*Incisive*), laterally,—terminal branches of the posterior palatine arteries.

Posterior Palatine (3),—posterior palatine vessels, anterior palatine nerve.

Accessory Palatine Foramina (1 or 2 on each side),—the middle and posterior (small) palatine nerves.

Orifice of the Posterior Naris,—air to the lungs.

Pterygo-palatine Foramen,—pterygo-palatine vessels.

Foramen Ovale (10),—mandibular nerve.

Orifice of the Vidian or *Pterygoid Canal,*—the Vidian nerve and vessels.

Foramen Spinosum (11),—middle meningeal artery.

Foramen Lacerum Medium (12),—see under Middle Fossæ.

Opening for the Eustachian Tube,—air to the middle ear.

Opening of Tensor Tympani Canal,—the tensor tympani muscle.

Glaserian Fissure,—laxator tympani muscle, tympanic artery; lodges the processus gracilis of the malleus.

Carotid Foramen (19),—internal carotid artery, nerves from the superior cervical ganglion to the carotid plexus.

Anterior Condylar or Hypoglossal Foramen,—Hypoglossal nerve.

Foramen Lacerum Posterius (20),—see under Posterior Fossa.

FIG. 25.

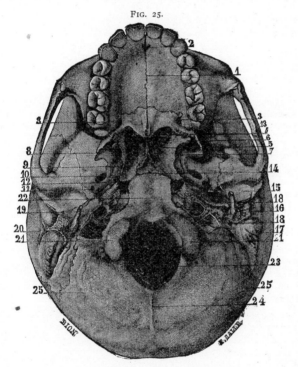

Foramen for Jacobson's Nerve,—tympanic branch of the glosso-pharyngeal.

Foramen for Arnold's Nerve,—auricular branch of the pneumogastric.

Opening of the Aquæductus Cochleæ,—artery and vein to the cochlea.

Stylo-mastoid Foramen (18),—facial nerve, stylo-mastoid artery.

Auricular Fissure,—exit of Arnold's nerve, auricular branch of the vagus.

Posterior Condylar Foramen,—see under Posterior Fossa.
Foramen Magnum (23),—see under Posterior Fossa.

Face presents 4 pairs, viz.—

Supraorbital Foramen or Notch,—supraorbital artery, vein, and nerve.
Infraorbital Foramen,—infraorbital artery, vein and nerve.
Orifice of the Anterior Naris or *Apertura pyraformis,*—air to the lungs.
Mental Foramen, mental nerve and artery.

POINTS AT THE BASE OF THE SKULL

illustrated and numbered on fig. 25

Median Suture (1),—of the palatine vault, crucial in form posteriorly.
Posterior Nasal Spine (4),—the posterior border of the palatine vault.
Vomer (5),—or nasal septum, its posterior border.
Hamular Process (6),—of the pterygoid process of the sphenoid bone.
Internal Plate (7),—of the pterygoid process of the sphenoid bone.
External Plate (8),—of the pterygoid process of the sphenoid bone.
Scaphoid Fossa (9),—on the internal plate (7) of the pterygoid process.
Zygoma (13),—or zygomatic process of the temporal bone.
Basilar Suture (14),—between the occipital and sphenoid bones.
Basilar Process (22),—of the occipital bone.
Articular or *Glenoid Fossa* (15),—for the mandible.
Glaserian Fissure,—squamo-tympanic.
External Auditory Meatus (16),—opening of the ext. auditory canal.
Mastoid Process (17),—of the temporal bone.
Styloid Process (18),—of the temporal bone.
Occipital Condyles (21),—articulate with the atlas.
External Occipital or *Nuchal Crest* (24),—terminating at the protuberance.
Inferior Nuchal or *Curved Lines* (25),—of the occipital bone.

BONES OF THE EXTREMITIES

THE SHOULDER

Bones forming the Shoulder are the clavicle and scapula connecting the arm with the trunk, and in this respect homologous to the innominate bone in the lower part of the body, being sometimes called the *shoulder girdle,* as the innominate bones are called the *pelvic girdle.*

The Clavicle, collar- or key-bone, is a short bone by structure, having no medullary canal. It is curved like the letter *f*, its inner two-thirds being prismatic and convex anteriorly; its outer third flattened, and concave anteriorly. It is placed horizontally between the sternum and the scapula and is the most elastic bone in the body. It presents, from within outward, the following points, viz.—

FIG. 26.

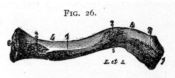

Facets (6),—for articulation with the sternum and the cartilage of the 1st rib, at its sternal end.

Upper border extending the length of the medial two-thirds, rough at its sternal end for attachment of the sterno-cleido-mastoid. Laterally it becomes lost on the smooth flat upper surface of the acromial third.

UNDER SURFACE PRESENTS:—

Impression (2),—for the rhomboid, or costo-clavicular ligament.

Groove (1),—on the lower surface, for the subclavius muscle.

Tubercle,—for the conoid part of the costo-clavicular ligament.

Oblique Line,—for the trapezoid part of the same ligament.

Facet (7),—on the acromial end, for articulation with the scapula.

Nutrient Foramen,—in the subclavian groove or in posterior surface, and runs towards the shoulder.

Anterior Border (5),—Medial two-thirds convex forwards and rough for attachment of pectoralis major. Lateral third is concave forwards, presents deltoid tubercle and is rough for attachment of deltoid.

Posterior Border (4),—medial two-thirds concave and not well-defined, acromial third is convex backwards and rough for attachment of the trapezius. Medial two-thirds ossify from cartilage, lateral third from membrane.

The Scapula, or shoulder-blade, is a large, flat, and triangular bone, situated on the posterior and lateral portion of the thorax, from the 2d rib to the 7th, inclusive. Its—

VENTER, or anterior surface, presents from within outward,—

Ridges,—giving attachment to the subscapularis muscle.

Marginal Surface,—along the inner border for the attachment of the serratus magnus muscle.

Subscapular Fossa and Angle,—for the subscapularis muscle.

DORSUM, or posterior surface, presents the following, viz.—

Spine (10),—a bony ridge, which affords attachment to the trapezius and deltoid muscles, and ends in the acromion process.

Supraspinous Fossa (1),—above the spine, for the supraspinatus muscle.

Infraspinous Fossa (2),—below the spine, larger than the supraspinous, convex at its centre, lodges the infraspinatus muscles, and the nutrient foramen.

Marginal Surface,—along the external border, to which are attached the teres minor muscle above, the teres major below, and sometimes a few fibres of the latissimus dorsi at the lower angle.

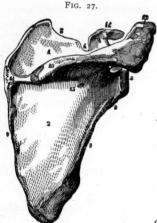

FIG. 27.

Groove,—crossing the margin, for the dorsalis scapulæ vessels.

Smooth Surface (11),—behind the root of the spine, over which the trapezius muscle glides.

ACROMION PROCESS (12), or summit of the shoulder, extends from the spine, and projects over the glenoid cavity, articulating with the clavicle by an oval facet. It affords attachment to the deltoid and trapezius muscles, and by its apex to the coraco-acromial ligament.

CORACOID PROCESS (14), or crow's beak, projects from the upper border and neck of the bone over the inner and upper part of the glenoid cavity. Into it is inserted 1 muscle, the pectoralis minor; the coraco-brachialis and the short head of the biceps arise from it by a common tendon, and 3 ligaments are attached to it,—the conoid, trapezoid, and coraco-acromial.

SUPERIOR BORDER (3) presents the—

Suprascapular Notch (4),—converted into a foramen for the suprascapular nerve by the transverse ligament, over which passes the suprascapular, or transverse scapular artery. The omo-hyoid muscle is attached to the border just internal to this notch.

AXILLARY BORDER (5) is the thickest, and presents a—

Rough Surface (8),—for the long head of the triceps muscle just below the glenoid cavity.

Notch,—for circumflex scapular artery.

Groove,—the origin of a part of the subscapularis muscle.

VERTEBRAL BORDER (9) is the longest, and presents an—

Anterior Lip,—for the attachment of the serratus magnus.

Posterior Lip,—for the supra- and infraspinatus muscles.

Interspace,—between the lips, for the levator anguli scapulæ, the rhomboideus minor, and the fibrous arch of the rhomboideus major muscles.

OTHER POINTS of interest on the bone are the—

Medial, or *Superior Angle,*—affords attachment to part of the serratus magnus, levator anguli scapulæ, and supraspinatus muscles.

Inferior Angle (7),—affords attachment to part of the serratus magnus and teres major muscles, and to a few fibres of the latissimus dorsi.

Glenoid Cavity (6),—at the external angle or head of the bone, a shallow cavity for the reception of the head of the humerus. It is deepened by the glenoid ligament which is attached around its margin; and gives origin to the long head of the biceps flexor cubiti muscle.

Neck,—is the contracted part of the bone behind the glenoid cavity; from it arises the anterior root of the coracoid process.

THE ARM

The Humerus is the only bone in the arm, and articulates with the scapula above, and with the ulna and radius below. It presents for examination a shaft and two extremities, on which are the following points, viz.—

Head (*b*),—is nearly hemispherical, and smooth for articulation with the glenoid cavity of the scapula.

Anatomical Neck (*c*),—is a constriction in the bone, just below the head, for the attachment of the capsular ligament.

Greater Tuberosity, or *Tubercle* (*d*),—has 3 small facets for the insertions of the supraspinatus, infraspinatus, and teres minor muscles.

Lesser Tuberosity, or *Tubercle* (*e*),—on the inner side of the bone, gives insertion to the subscapularis muscle.

Bicipital, or *Intertubercular Groove* (*f*),—lies vertically between the tuberosities for the upper third of the bone and lodges the tendon of the long head of the biceps flexor cubiti. Into its inner or medial lip (*h*) are inserted the teres major and latissimus dorsi muscles, while its outer or lateral lip (*g*) receives the insertion of the tendon of the pectoralis major, which covers the groove.

Surgical Neck,—is situated immediately below the tuberosities, and is a slight constriction in the upper part of the shaft.

Shaft (*a*),—is cylindrical above, prismatic and flattened below.

Rough Surface (*i*),—for the insertion of the deltoid muscle, about the middle of the external surface of the shaft.

Musculo-spiral Groove, or *Sulcus n. Radialis* (*a*),—lodging the musculo-spiral, or radial, nerve and the superior profunda artery, is situated

on the posterior surface of the shaft, separating the origins of the
outer and inner heads of the triceps muscle.

FIG. 28.

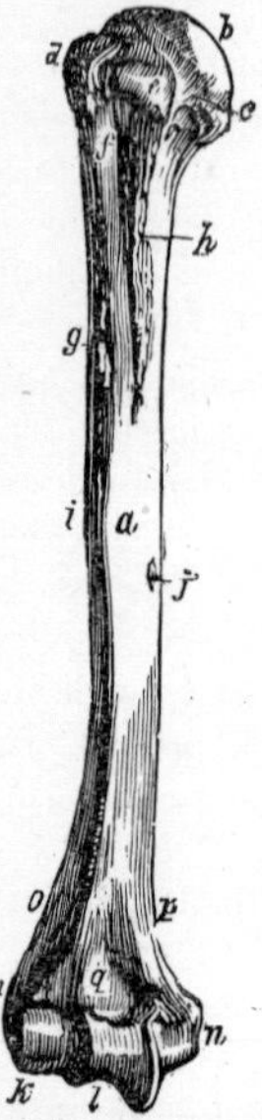

Orifice (j),—of the nutrient canal, about the middle of
the shaft, on its internal border.

Condylar Ridges,—internal or medial (*p*) and external
or lateral (*o*), arising from the respective condyles,
extending upward along the shaft.

Lateral or *External Condyle (m),*—gives attachment to
the external lateral ligament and the extensor and
supinator group of muscles.

Medial or *Internal Condyle (n),*—lower and more prominent than the other, gives attachment to the internal
lateral ligament and the flexor and pronator group of
muscles of the forearm.

Capitellum (k),—forms the outer or lateral part of the
inferior articular surface; for articulation with the
radius, it is on the front of the lateral condyle, above it
is the radial fossa.

Trochlear Surface (l),—articulates with the greater
sigmoid cavity (incisura semilunaris) of the ulna; is a
deep depression between two borders and extends
from the anterior to the posterior surface of the bone.

Coronoid Fossa,—above the front of the trochlear surface, receives the coronoid process of the ulna when
the forearm is flexed.

Olecranon Fossa (q),—above the back part of the trochlea, receives the
tip of the olecranon process, when the forearm is extended.

THE FOREARM

The skeleton of the forearm is composed of 2 bones.

The Ulna, or elbow-bone, is the principal bone of the forearm. It is
larger and longer than the radius, forming the greater portion of the
articulation with the humerus. It does not enter into the formation of the
wrist-joint, being excluded therefrom by an interarticular fibro-cartilage.
It presents for examination a shaft and two extremities, on which are
the following points:—

Olecranon Process (4),—at the upper extremity, forming the elbow. It
is curved forward, its apex being received into the olecranon fossa of
the humerus when the forearm is extended. Its posterior surface
gives insertion to the tendon of the triceps. In its function and
structure it resembles the patella.

Coronoid Process (5),—below the olecranon projects forward forming the Tuberosity (3), its apex being received into the coronoid fossa of the humerus when the forearm is flexed. Its upper surface is concave for articulation with the humerus, its lower surface rough for the insertion of the brachialis anticus muscle. Its inner surface has a margin for the internal lateral ligament, a tubercle for the flexor sublimis digitorum, and a ridge for the pronator radii teres.

Greater Sigmoid Cavity, or *Incisura Semilunaris* (2),—lies between the processes, and is divided by a vertical ridge into two unequal parts. It articulates with the trochlear surface of the humerus.

Fig. 29.

Lesser Sigmoid Cavity or *Incisura Radialis* (3),—lies external to the coronoid process; is oval and concave, articulating with the head of the radius, and giving attachment to the orbicular ligament.

Shaft (1),—large and prismatic above, smaller and rounded below, has the *Nutrient Foramen* (6) on its anterior surface (1), and a prominent margin externally, to which is attached the interosseous membrane (7). It gives attachment to 9 of the 12 muscles of the forearm.

Head (8),—at the carpal end, articulates with the lesser sigmoid cavity of the radius, and the fibro-cartilage of the wrist-joint.

Styloid Processes (9),—projecting from the head internally and posteriorly, its apex gives attachment to the ulno-carpal ligament and a depression at its root to the fibro-cartilage of the joint.

Groove,—for the tendon of the extensor carpi ulnaris muscle.

The Radius lies externally to the ulna when the forearm is in supination; it is prismatic in form with the base below where it articulates with the carpus. The bone is curved outward and is shorter than the ulna, by the length of the olecranon. It presents the following points from above downward, viz.—

Head (11),—cylindrical and cup-shaped, articulating with the capitellum of the humerus, and the lesser sigmoid cavity or radial notch, of the ulna, and playing within the orbicular ligament.

Neck (12),—the constricted part below the head.

Bicipital or *Radial Tuberosity* (13),—rough behind for the inser-

tion of the biceps, and smooth in front where it is covered by a
bursa.

Shaft (10),—prismoid in form, presents a sharp border internally for the
attachment of the interosseous membrane; the *Nutrient Foramen* is on
its anterior surface.   It gives attachment to 8 of the 12 muscles of the
forearm.

Ridge (14),—for the insertion of the pronator radii teres muscle.

Ulnar Notch or *Sigmoid Cavity*,—at the ulnar side of the carpal end (15),
is shallow, and articulates with the head of the ulna.

Articular Surface,—is divided by a ridge into 2 facets for articulation
with the semilunar and scaphoid bones of the carpus.

Styloid Process (16),—gives attachment by its apex to the radio-carpal
ligament, and by its base to the supinator longus muscle.

Grooves,—on the posterior surface of the lower extremity, for the
tendons of the 8 extensor muscles of the thumb, and those of the radial
side of the wrist, and fingers.

THE HAND

The Bones of the Hand are divided into the carpus 8, the metacarpus 5,
and the phalanges 14.   Total, 27 bones.

Bones of the Carpus.   The 8 bones are
placed in 2 rows, one row in front of the
other, with 4 bones in each row, as follows,
—the right hand being in supination, nam-
ing from without inward, viz.—

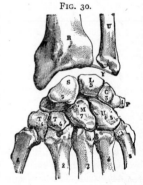

FIG. 30.

    1st or Proximal Row,—Scaphoid, or
      Navicular (s), Semilunar, or Os
      Lunatum (L), Cuneiform, or Os Tri-
      quetrum (c), Pisiform (P).

    2d, or Distal Row,—Trapezium, or
      Greater Multangular (T), Trapezoid or
      Lesser Multangular (T), Os magnum,
      or Os Capitatum (M), Unciform, or
      Os Hamatum (U).

Articulations in the Carpus are 34, as follows:—the number after each
bone representing the number of its articulations, viz.—

Scaphoid, 5.	Semilunar, 5.	Cuneiform 3.	Pisiform, 1.
Trapezium, 4.	Trapezoid, 4.	Os-magnum, 7.	Unciform, 5.

Peculiarities of the Carpal Bones. The first three enter into the formation of the wrist-joint; the pisiform does not, but is wholly without it, and may be considered a mere appendage of the carpus. When the hand is in pronation—

The Scaphoid (navicular), or boat-shaped bone (S)—has a tuberosity on its outer side, its largest facet is uppermost and articulates with the lower end of the radius (R). A transverse groove crosses its posterior surface and serves for the attachment of ligaments.

The Semilunar Bone (os lunatum) (L)—has a crescentic facet externally, and a convex facet superiorly, where it articulates with the radius.

The Cuneiform Bone (os triquetrum) (C)—is wedge-shaped, its convex surface above, articulating with the interarticular fibro-cartilage of the wrist (F). It has an oval facet anteriorly for articulation with the pisiform.

The Pisiform Bone (os pisiforme) (P)—is the smallest, and has but one facet, which lies posteriorly when the bone is in position.

The Trapezium (os multangulum majus) (T)—has a deep groove for the tendon of the flexor carpi radialis, and a saddle-shaped facet, inferiorly for the base of the 1st metacarpal.

The Trapezoid (os multangulum minus) (T)—is small and quadrilateral, bent on itself, with a saddle-shaped facet looking downward, for the base of the 2d metacarpal bone.

The Os-magnum (os capitatum) (M)—has a head looking upward, a neck, and a body; is the largest bone of the carpus, and has 3 facets on the inferior surface for articulation with the 2d, 3d, and 4th metacarpal bones.

The Unciform Bone (os hamatum) (U)—is wedge-shaped, with a concavity which lies to the outer side, and the unciform process, long and curved, projecting from its palmar surface.

OSSA METACARPALIA

The Metacarpus consists of the 5 metacarpal bones which are placed between the carpus and the phalanges. They are long bones, and each has a head, shaft and base. Their heads articulate with the respective phalanges.

The Thumb or *1st Metacarpal Bone* (1),—articulates with the trapezium, (*greater multangular*), is shorter than the others by one-third, and its base has but 1 articular facet.

The Index or *2d Metacarpal Bone* (2),—articulates with 3 bones of the carpus, the trapezium, (*greater multangular*) trapezoid (*lesser mult-*

angular) and os-magnum (*capitate*); its base is large, and has 4 articular facets.

The Middle or *3d Metacarpal Bone* (3),—articulates with 1 bone of the carpus, the os-magnum (*capitate*); its base has a projecting process on the radial side, and 2 small facets on the opposite side.

The Ring or *4th Metacarpal Bone* (4),—articulates with 2 bones of the carpus and with the adjacent metacarpal bones; its base is small and has 2 circular facets 1 on each side.

The Little or *5th Metacarpal Bone* (5),—articulates with 1 carpal bone, the unciform (*hamate*), its base has 1 lateral articular facet.

The Phalanges Digitorum Manus or finger-bones, are 14 in number, 3 to each finger, and 2 to the thumb. They are long bones, and each has a base, a shaft, and a digital extremity. The *Bases* of the first row articulate with the heads of the metacarpal bones. The *Digital Extremities* of the first and second rows have each 2 small lateral condyles, while in the terminal row they are rough, for the attachment of the sensitive pulp of the fingers.

THE THIGH

The Femur or thigh-bone, is the longest, largest and strongest bone in the body, and is nearly cylindrical in the greater part of its extent. In the vertical position of the skeleton it forms one side of a triangle, of which the base is the breadth of the pelvis, and the apex at the knee-joints. The base of this triangle is longest in the female, and consequently that sex is usually knock-kneed. The—

Head (5),—articulates with the acetabulum, forms about two-fifths of a sphere, and has an oval depression (6) below its centre for the attachment of the ligamentum teres.

Neck (7),—connects the head with the shaft, is pyramidal and flattened; its obliquity varies with age, being less before puberty, about 120 to 125 degrees in the adult, and nearly horizontal to the shaft in old or debilitated subjects, the cancellous bone forming the neck is condensed centrally into a hard core known as the *calcar femorale*.

Great Trochanter (8),—a broad, rough, quadrilateral process directed outward and backward from the summit of the shaft to within three-fourths of an inch of the level of the head. On its outer surface the tendon of the gluteus maximus plays over a bursa. It gives insertion to the obturator internus, two gemelli, pyriformis, and gluteus minimus and medius muscles.

Trochanteric or *Digital Fossa* (9),—on the inner or medial surface of the great trochanter, gives insertion to the obturator externus muscle.

Lesser Trochanter (10),—at the inferior root of the neck posteriorly, is small and conical, and affords insertion to the tendon of the psoas magnus muscle, the tendon of the iliacus being inserted immediately below it.

Inter-trochanteric Line,—at the base of the neck in front runs from one trochanter to the other, to it is attached the front part of the capsule of the hip-joint.

Inter-trochanteric Ridge or Crest,—at the base of the neck behind, to its middle portion is attached the quadratus femoris muscle.

Shaft,—is slightly curved forward, broad and cylindrical at each end, and narrow and triangular in the centre. Its nutrient foramen perforates its posterior surface below the centre, and is directed toward the hip. From its anterior surface arise the crureus or vastus-intermedius, and subcrureus or articularis genu muscles.

Linea Aspera (1),—a crest lying along the central third of the shaft posteriorly; bifurcating above (2) towards each trochanter, also below (4) towards the 2 condyles. To its outer lip is attached the vastus externus, or lateralis, to its inner lip, the vastus internus, or medialis; and between them, the pectineus, ad-ductor brevis, and gluteus maximus above the short head of the biceps below, and the adductors longus and magnus along the greater portion of the space.

Groove,—crossing the internal condylar ridge, lodges the femoral artery.

Popliteal Space,—triangular and smooth, lying between the condylar ridges, for the popliteal artery.

Lateral or *External Condyle* (11),—broader and shorter than the internal, so as to form a horizontal articulation, the bone being inclined towards the median line. It gives attachment to the external lateral ligament, the popliteus, and the lateral head of the gastrocnemius.

Medial or *Internal Condyle* (12),—the longer by half an inch; it gives

Fig. 31.

attachment to the internal lateral ligament and medial head of the gastrocnemius muscle.

Intercondylar Notch (13),—lodges the crucial, or cruciate, ligaments. In front the condyles are continuous with each other, forming a concave depression or trochlea for the patella.

Lateral Epicondyle or *Outer Tuberosity* (14),—on the external condyle, for the attachment of the external lateral ligament.

Groove,—below the outer tuberosity, for the tendon of the popliteus muscle, terminating in a depression whence the muscle takes its origin.

Medial Epicondyle or *Inner Tuberosity* (15),—on the internal condyle, for the attachment of the internal lateral ligament.

Adductor Tubercle,—above the inner tuberosity, for the insertion of the tendon of the adductor magnus muscle.

Depression,—behind the tubercle, for the tendon of the inner head of the gastrocnemius.

THE PATELLA

The Patella is flat and triangularly ovoidal with its apex directed downward.

Subcutaneous Surface,—convex, presenting longitudinal ridges and many nutrient foramina.

Apex,—very rough on its deep surface for attachment of ligamentum patellæ. Articular surface presents a longitudinal articular ridge flanked by concave facets of which the lateral one is the larger. The medial facet often presents a "third facet" along its medial border.

THE LEG

The skeleton of the leg consists of 3 bones, the *tibia*, the *fibula*, and the *patella*, the latter being a large, sesamoid bone placed in front of the knee.

The Tibia, or shin-bone, ranks next to the femur in respect to size and length. Its form is prismoidal, the upper extremity being much larger than the lower. It presents the following points:—

Head,—expands into two *tuberosities*, internal (2) and external (3) which articulate with the condyles of the femur. In spite of their being *receiving cavities*, the tuberosities of the tibia are sometimes called *condyles*.

Spine or *Eminentia Intercondyloidea* (4),—projects vertically between the 2 articular surfaces, is bifid, affording attachment to the semilunar fibro-cartilages (semilunar menisci), and by depressions in front and behind its base to the crucial ligaments of the joint.

Extensor Tuberosity (5),—on the head, anteriorly between the tuberosities, for the insertion of the ligamentum patellæ.

Popliteal Notch or *Posterior Intercondylar Fossa,*—posteriorly between the tuberosities, affords attachment to the posterior crucial ligament.

Groove,—on the inner tuberosity (2) posteriorly, for the insertion of the tendon of the semi-membranosus muscle.

Facet,—on the outer tuberosity (3) posteriorly and looking downward, for articulation with the head of the fibula.

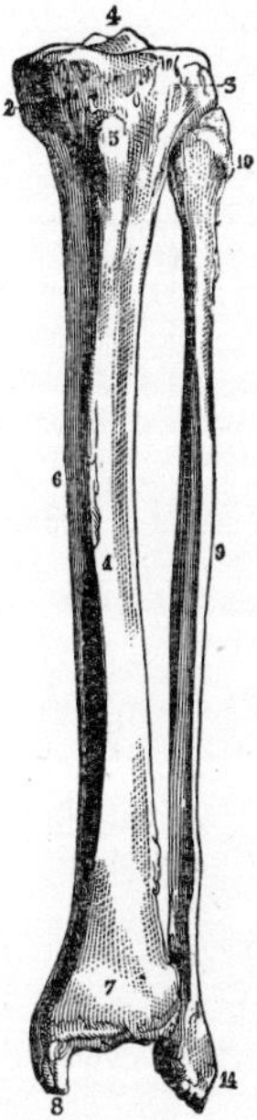

Soleus Ridge or *Popliteal Line,*—obliquely across the upper part of the shaft posteriorly, affords attachment to the soleus.

Nutrient Canal,—the largest in the skeleton, opens just below the popliteal line, and is directed downward.

Shaft (1),—has 3 sharp ridges,—1 in front, the *Crest* (6) or *Shin*, and 1 on either side, to the external of which is attached the interosseous membrane.

Lower Extremity (7),—is smaller than the upper, grooved posteriorly for the tendon of the flexor longus pollicis; externally has a rough triangular depression for articulation with the fibula, and for the attachment of the inferior interosseous ligament. Its inferior surface is concave and smooth for articulation with the upper surface of the astragalus or talus.

Internal Malleolus (8),—projects downward from the internal side of the lower extremity. It articulates with the astragalus (talus), is grooved posteriorly for the tendons of the tibialis posticus and flexor longus digitorum muscles, and affords attachment to the internal lateral ligament.

FIG. 32.

The Fibula, is a long slender bone, placed nearly parallel with the tibia on the outer side of the leg. It is also called the *Peroneus*, or peroneal bone.

Head (10),—articulates with the external tuberosity (*lateral condyle*) of the tibia by a flat facet. Externally, it has a prominence for the attachment of the long external lateral ligament of the knee-joint.

Styloid Process, or *Apex Capituli,*—projects upward from the head posteriorly, and gives insertion to the tendon of the biceps muscle, and the short external lateral ligament of the knee-joint.

Shaft (9),—is twisted about ninety degrees on its long axis. It is often very irregular and may present numerous longitudinal ridges which seem to give it many surfaces. However, it always presents certain characteristics which are constant. On the outer or lateral surface at its distal end, it presents a long smooth *subcutaneous triangle*. The ridge running from the apex of this triangle to the front of the head of the bone, is the **anterior border** or crest. The very first ridge internal (medial) to anterior border, no matter how near or distant it may be, is the **interosseous border** or crest. This border runs upward from the rough *interosseous triangle* to the inner (medial) side of the head. It may, for part of its length, join the anterior border. Running spirally upward from the groove for the peroneal tendons to the styloid process (*apex capituli*), is the **posterior border** (*lateral crest*). The interval between the anterior border and the interosseous border, however narrow it may be, is the **extensor surface** (*anterior part of the medial surface*), from above downward it gives attachment to extensor digitorum communis, extensor hallucis longus, and peroneus tertius. The interval between the anterior border and the posterior border (lateral crest) is the **peroneal surface** (*lateral surface*). The upper third of this surface gives attachment to the peroneus longus, the middle third, to the peroneus brevis; lower third is free. The entire interval between the posterior border and the interosseous border is the **flexor surface.** Running from the back of the head downward and forward and finally joining the interosseous border, is the oblique ridge (not border) also called the medial crest. This oblique ridge divides the flexor surface into *two portions;* one which is close to the interosseous border (*posterior portion of the medial surface*) for the tibialis posticus; the remainder of the flexor surface which is distant from the interosseous ridge (*posterior* surface), from above downward gives attachment to the soleus and flexor hallucis longus.

Nutrient Canal,—opens about the centre of the shaft posteriorly, its canal running downwards.

External Malleolus (11),—is the lower extremity of the bone. It is larger and longer than the internal, articulates with the astragalus by a triangular facet, and is grooved posteriorly for the tendons of the peroneus longus and peroneus brevis muscles. Its edge affords attachment to the external lateral ligaments of the ankle-joint.

THE FOOT

The Bones of the Foot are divided into those of the tarsus 7, metatarsus 5, and phalanges 14. Total, 26 bones.

Bones of the Tarsus are placed in 2 rows side by side, 2 bones in the external row, 5 in the internal, as follows, viz.—

Internally,—Astragalus or Talus (5). Scaphoid or Navicular (8). 3 Cuneiform (10, 11, 12).

Externally,—Os calcis (1), or Calcaneum. Cuboid (6).

(The illustration, Fig. 33, shows the plantar surface of the skeleton of the foot.)

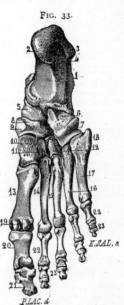

FIG. 33.

Articulations in the Tarsus are 28 in number, each bone articulating with 4 others, except the os calcis (calcaneus), which articulates with 2, and the external (third) cuneiform with 6 bones.

Peculiarities of the Tarsal Bones. They may be divided transversely at the astragalo-scaphoid-calcaneo-cuboid articulation, the site of Chopart's operation. The—

Astragalus or *Talus* (5),—has a rounded head, a convex surface on which is a broad articular facet, and on its inferior surface a deep groove between 2 articular facets.

Os Calcis or *Calcaneus* (1),—is a large bone, having on its upper surface a deep groove for the interosseous ligament, between 2 articular surfaces; anteriorly a large irregular portion, the head; and posteriorly an elongated portion forming *the Heel* (2). On its internal surface is a projection, the *Sustentaculum Tali*, which supports the internal articulating surface; below which process the bone is deeply grooved for the plantar vessels and nerves and the flexor tendons. To the os calcis are attached 8 muscles and the plantar fascia.

Navicular or *Scaphoid Bone* (8),—is boat-shaped, has 3 facets anteriorly for the cuneiform bones, a concave surface posteriorly for the astragalus, and a facet externally for the cuboid bone. A tubercle (9) is situated on the lower surface internally, for the insertion of the tibialis posticus muscle.

Cuboid Bone (6),—has 3 articular surfaces, and a groove inferiorly for the tendon of the peroneus longus.

Internal or *First Cuneiform Bone* (10), the largest of the 3, has a tubercle on its plantar surface for the insertion of parts of the tendons of the tibialis anticus and tibialis posticus muscles.

Middle or *Second Cuneiform Bone* (11),—is small and wedge-shaped with the narrow end downward. Its anterior surface is considerably behind the line of the tarso-metatarsal articulation, thus forming a recess into which the base of the second metatarsal bone fits.

External or *Third Cuneiform Bone* (12),—is also wedge-shaped, but longer than the middle one; and affords origin to 1 muscle, the flexor brevis pollicis.

The Metatarsus consists of 5 metatarsal bones, which are long bones, having each a shaft and two extremities. Their bases articulate with the tarsal bones and with each other; their heads with the first row of phalanges.

1st Metatarsal (13),—is large but shorter than the others, and forms the inner border of the foot, articulating with the internal cuneiform. The head is large and has two grooved facets on its plantar surface, over which glide 2 sesamoid bones (19).

2d Metatarsal (14),—is the longest; its base has 3 facets for articulation with the 3 cuneiform bones in the recess formed by the shortness of the middle or second cuneiform.

3d Metatarsal (15),—has 2 facets on the inner side of its base, besides the facets for the internal cuneiform and the 4th metatarsal bone.

4th Metatarsal (16),—articulates with the cuboid bone, and also with the internal or first cuneiform.

5th Metatarsal (17),—articulates obliquely with the cuboid bone, and has a tubercular projection (18) on the outer surface of its base, which forms the guide in Hey's operation.

The Phalanges of the Foot number 14 as in the hand, the great toe having two (20, 21), the other toes three each. They are long bones, each having a base, a shaft, and an anterior extremity. They are convex above, concave below, and articulate by the bases of the first row with the bones of the metatarsus. The anterior extremities of the distal phalanges (21, 23) are expanded into surfaces for the support of the nails and pulp of the toes.

THE ARTICULATIONS

An Articulation or Joint is a connection between two bones of the skeleton, and has entering into its formation the following-named structures — bone, cartilage, fibro-cartilage, ligament and synovial membrane.

Articulations are divided into three classes,—*Synarthrosis*, immovable joint; *Amphiarthrosis*, mixed articulation, having limited motion; and *Diarthrosis*, movable joint, having free motion.

Synarthroses are subdivided into—*Sutura*, formed by processes and indentations; *Schindy'lesis*, by a plate of bone entering into a fissure of another; and *Gompho'sis*, by a conical process into a socket. The *Sutura* are again subdivided into—*S. dentata*, having tooth-like processes; *S. serrata*, with serrated edges; *S. limbosa*, having beveled margins and dentated processes; *S. squamosa*, with thin beveled margins overlapping each other; *S. harmonia*, contiguous rough surfaces opposed to each other. The first 3 are also named *Sutura Vera* (true sutures) having indented borders; the last 2 *Sutura Notha* (false sutures) being formed by rough surfaces.

Amphiarthroses are subdivided into—*Symphysis*, connected by fibro-cartilage and not separated by synovial membrane; *Syndesmosis*, united by an interosseous ligament.

Diarthroses are subdivided into—*Ginglymus*, hinge-joint; *Trochoides*, pivot-joint, formed by a ring surrounding a pivot; *Condyloid*, by an ovoid head in an elliptical cavity; *Reciprocal Reception*, saddle-joint, by surfaces inversely convex and concave; *Enarthrosis*, ball-and-socket joint; *Arthrodia*, gliding joint.

Examples of each of the above-named articulations, as follows:—

Synarthrosis,—joints of the cranium and face, except the lower jaw.

Sutura Dentata,—the inter-parietal suture.

Sutura Serrata,—the inter-frontal suture.

Sutura Limbosa,—the fronto-parietal suture.

Sutura Squamosa,—the temporo-parietal suture.

Sutura Harmonia,—the intermaxillary suture.

Schindylesis,—rostrum of sphenoid with the vomer.

Gomphosis,—the teeth in their alveoli.

Amphiarthrosis,—the joints between the bodies of the vertebræ (*symphyses*), the inferior tibio-fibular articulation (*syndesmosis*).

Diarthrosis, movable joint, as follows:—

Ginglymus,—inter-pharyngeal joints and the elbow-joint.

Trochoides,—superior radio-ulnar, atlanto-axial joint. (Articulatio Atlanto-epistrophica.)

Condyloid,—the wrist-joint.

Reciprocal Reception,—the carpo-metacarpal joint of the thumb.

Enarthrosis,—the hip- and shoulder-joints.

Arthrodia,—the carpal and tarsal articulations.

Varieties of Motion in Joints are 4 in number, viz.—gliding, angular movement (including adduction, abduction, flexion and extension), circumduction and rotation. These movements are often more or less combined in the various joints.

Structures entering into the formation of Joints are 5, viz.,—the articular lamella of bone, cartilage, fibro-cartilage, ligaments and synovial membrane.

    Articular Lamella of Bone—differs from ordinary bone tissue in being more dense, containing no Haversian canals nor canaliculi, and having larger lacunæ.

    Cartilage,—a non-vascular structure, is divisible into temporary and permanent varieties. The first forms the original frame-work of the skeleton, and becomes ossified. Permanent cartilage is not prone to ossification, and is divided into 4 groups,—*Articular*, covering the ends of bones in joints; *Interarticular*, between the bones in a joint; *Costal*, forming part of the skeleton; and *Membraniform*. According to its minute structure, cartilage is divided into *Hyaline Cartilage*, *White Fibro-cartilage* and *Yellow* or *Elastic Fibro-cartilage*.

    Fibro-cartilages,—in joints and osseous grooves are of the white variety and may be arranged in 4 groups, the—*Interarticular* (menisci), separating the bones of a joint; *Connecting*, binding bones together; *Circumferential*, deepening cavities; *Stratiform*, lining grooves.

    Ligaments—are bands of white fibrous tissue, except the ligamenta subflava and the ligamentum nuchæ, which consist entirely of yellow elastic tissue.

    Synovial Membranes—secrete the synovia, a viscid, glairy fluid, and resemble the serous membranes in structure. They are *Articular*, lubricating joints; *Bursal*, forming closed sacs (bursæ), interposed between surfaces which move upon each other; *Vaginal*, ensheathing tendons.

ARTICULATIONS OF THE TRUNK

√ **The Temporo-mandibular Articulation** is a ginglymo-arthrodial joint between the condyle of the lower jaw and the anterior part of the glenoid cavity of the temporal bone. It has 2 synovial membranes with an interarticular fibro-cartilage between them, and 4 ligaments, viz.—

    External Lateral,—from the tubercle of the zygoma to the outer side of the neck of the condyle of the lower jaw.

    Spheno-mandibular or Internal Lateral (d),—from the alar spine of the sphenoid to the mandibular spine or lingula on the margin of the dental foramen.

Stylo-mandibular (*f*),—from the styloid process of the temporal bone to the angle and posterior border of the ramus of the lower jaw.

Capsular (*c*),—from the edge of the glenoid cavity and the eminentia articularis to the neck of the condyle of the lower jaw.

Its Nerves are derived from the auriculo-temporal and masseteric branches of the mandibular. *Arteries* from the temporal branch of the external carotid.

Fig. 34.

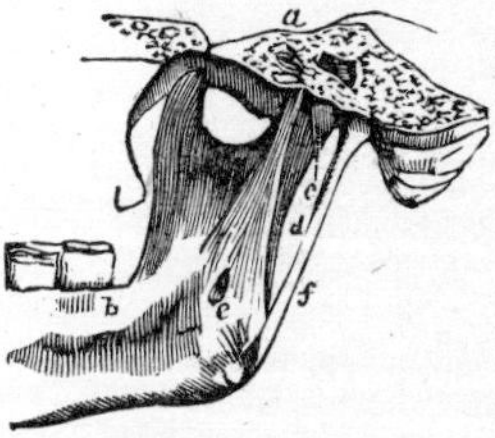

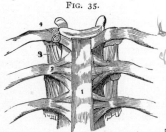

The Vertebral Articulations are formed by the adjacent surfaces of the bodies of the vertebræ and their processes, and are connected by the following ligaments, etc.—

Anterior Common Ligament (1),—along the fronts of the bodies.

Posterior Common Ligament,—along the backs of the bodies.

Ligamenta Subflava,—connect the laminæ of adjacent vertebræ.

Capsular (4),—surround the articular processes and are lined by synovial membrane.

Supra-spinous and Inter-spinous, —connect the spinous processes. In the cervical region they form what is called the Ligamentum Nuchæ.

Fig. 35.

Inter-transverse (3),—connect the transverse processes.

Intervertebral Substance,—in lenticular disks between the bodies of the vertebræ, from the axis to the sacrum.

The Atlanto-axial Articulation is a double arthrodia or gliding joint between the articular processes and a pivot articulation between the atlas and the odontoid process. It has 6 ligaments and 4 synovial membranes, as follows:—

Anterior 2, and *Posterior* 1, *Atlanto-axial,*—continuations of the anterior and posterior common spinal ligaments.

Capsular 2,—surrounding the articular surfaces, each lined by a synovial membrane.

Transverse Ligament,—divides the spinal foramen of the atlas into two portions, stretching across between the tubercles on the inner sides of the articular processes. It holds the odontoid process in place, having a synovial membrane interposed. Another synovial membrane is situated between the process and the anterior arch. The transverse ligament sends two vertical slips, one upward, the other downward, from which it is often named the *Cruciform Ligament.*

The Occipito-atlantal Articulation is a double condyloid formed by the condyles of the occipital bone with the superior articular surfaces of the atlas, and has 6 ligaments, viz.—

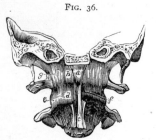

FIG. 36.

Anterior Occipito-atlantal (*a*),—from the anterior margin of the foramen magnum to the anterior arch of the atlas.

Posterior Occipito-atlantal,—from the posterior margin of the foramen magnum to the posterior arch of the atlas. It is perforated by the vertebral and suboccipital nerves.

Lateral 2,—from the jugular processes of the occipital bone to the bases of the transverse processes of the atlas.

Capsular 2 (*d*),—around the articular surfaces, lined by synovial membrane.

The Occipito-axial Articulation is formed by the occipital bone and the odontoid process of the axis, which do not articulate with each other strictly, but are connected with 4 ligaments, the—

Occipito-axial (1) (*Membrana Tectoria*),—a continuation of the posterior common spinal ligament to the basilar process of the occipital bone.

Lateral Occipito-odontoid (5) (*Check Ligaments*) 2,—from the head of the odontoid process to the inner sides of the occipital condyles.

Middle Odontoid (*Ligamentum Suspensorium*),—from the anterior margin of the foramen magnum to the odontoid apex.

The Costo-vertebral Articulations are each a double arthrodia between the head of the rib and the bodies of 2 adjacent vertebræ, except in the 1st, 10th, 11th, and 12th ribs, which are single, as they articulate with but 1 vertebra each. Their ligaments are 3, viz.—

Anterior Costo-central (2), *or Stellate Ligament,*—consists of 3 bundles, which fasten the anterior part of the head of the rib to the intervertebral disk and the 2 adjacent bodies.

Intra-articular,—in the interior of the joint, from the crest on the head of the rib to the intervertebral disk; on each side there is a separate synovial membrane. In the 1st, 10th, 11th and 12th ribs it does not exist, hence there is but one synovial membrane.

Capsular,—surrounding the articular surfaces.

The Costo-transverse Articulations are 10 arthrodial articulations between the tubercles of the first 10 ribs and the transverse processes of the vertebræ next below. Their ligaments are 4, viz.—*Anterior superior, Middle* (interosseous), *Posterior Costo-transverse and Capsular.*

The Chondro-sternal Articulations are 7 in number, 1 of which (the first) is a synarthrodial and 6 are arthrodial articulations, between the costal cartilages and the margin of the sternum. The first has no synovial membrane, the second only has an intra-articular ligament. Each has 4 ligaments,—the *Anterior and Posterior Chondro-sternal,* a *Capsular,* and an *Interarticular.* The *Chondro-xiphoid Ligaments* connect the xiphoid appendix to the cartilage of the 6th or 7th rib.

The Costo-chondral and **Interchondral Articulations** connect the costal cartilages with the ribs and with each other respectively. With the ribs by a depression on the end of each rib, strengthened by the blending together of the periosteum and the perichondrium. The 6th, 7th and 8th, and sometimes the 9th and 10th costal cartilages articulate with each other by their borders and each has a *Capsular* and an *Interchondral* ligament, with 3 synovial membranes for the 3 articulations between the 6th and the 9th cartilages.

The Ligaments of the Sternum are an *Anterior Sternal* and a *Posterior Sternal* ligament, with a layer of cartilage between the manubrium and the gladiolus.

The Sacro-vertebral Articulation is similar to the other vertebral articulations, but has 2 additional ligaments on each side, the—

Lumbo-sacral,—from the transverse process of the 5th lumbar vertebra to the base of the sacrum laterally and anteriorly.

Ilio-lumbar,—from the apex of the transverse processes of the 5th lumbar vertebra to the crest of the ilium in front of the sacro-iliac articulation.

The Sacro-coccygeal Articulation is an amphiarthrodial joint, and has 4 ligaments, viz.—

Anterior Sacro-coccygeal.

Posterior Sacro-coccygeal.

Two Lateral Sacro-coccygeal.

Fibro-cartilage, interposed in the joint.

The Sacro-iliac Articulation is an amphiarthrodial joint, formed by the lateral surfaces of the sacrum and ilium. Its ligaments on each side are the—

Anterior Sacro-iliac.

Posterior Sacro-iliac (8),—which consists of a *short* transverse part (8) and a long part known as the—

Oblique Sacro-iliac.

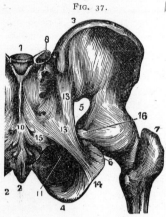

FIG. 37.

The Sacro-ischiatic Articulation is an amphiarthrosis between the sacrum and the ischium. Its ligaments convert the sacro-sciatic notches into foramina, the greater notch (5) being crossed by the lesser ligament, the lesser notch (6) by the greater ligament. These foramina are described on page 13 *ante*.

Posterior or Great Sacro-sciatic Ligament (l. sacrotuberosum) (13), is the divorced tendon of the biceps femoris muscle, it extends from the posterior inferior spine of the ilium and the posterior surface and margins of the sacrum and coccyx (2), to the inner margin of the tuberosity (4) and the ascending ramus (14) of the ischium, the latter portion being known as the *Falciform Ligament.*

Anterior or Lesser Sacro-sciatic Ligament (l. sacrospinosum) (15),—from the margins of the sacrum and coccyx, into the spine of the ischium (16).

The Pubic Articulation or **Symphysis Pubis**, is an amphiarthrodial joint formed by the junction of the two pubic bones with each other. It has an interpubic disk and 4 ligaments, the—

Anterior Pubic. *Posterior Pubic.* *Superior Pubic.*

Sub-pubic, forming a fibrous arch between the rami.

ARTICULATIONS OF THE UPPER EXTREMITY

The Sterno-clavicular Articulation is an arthrodial joint, formed by the sternal end of the clavicle with the sternum and the cartilage of the 1st rib. It has an interarticular fibro-cartilage, 2 synovial membranes and 5 ligaments, the—-

Anterior Sterno-clavicular,	*Interclavicular.*
Posterior Sterno-clavicular,	*Costo-clavicular* or *Rhomboid.*

Capsular,—Formed by the anterior and posterior.

The Acromio-clavicular Articulation is an arthrodial joint, formed by the outer extremity of the clavicle and the acromion process of the scapula. It frequently has an interarticular fibro-cartilage and 2 synovial membranes (usually but 1 is present). It has 3 ligaments, the—

Superior Acromio-clavicular(1). *Coraco-clavicular*(2) { Trapezoid, externally.
Inferior Acromio-clavicular.   divided into—   { Conoid, internally.

Proper Ligaments of the Scapula are 2, the Coraco-acromial, and the Transverse, as follows:—

Coraco-acromial (3),—completes the vault partially formed by the coracoid and acromion processes over the head of the humerus.

Transverse (4),—from the base of the coracoid process to the margin of the suprascapular notch, converting it into a foramen for the suprascapular nerve.

FIG. 38.

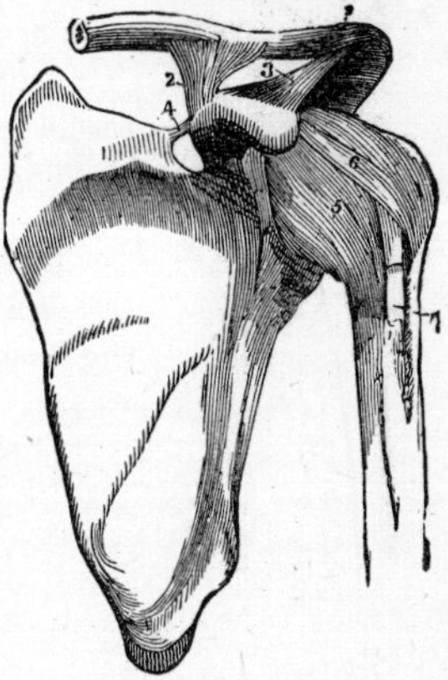

The Shoulder-joint, Articulatio Humeri, is an enarthrodial or ball-and-socket joint, formed by the head of the humerus and the glenoid cavity of the scapula. It has a *Synovial Membrane* which is reflected upon the tendons of the biceps, subscapularis, and infraspinatus muscles, and communicates with bursæ beneath the 2 latter tendons. Its *Arteries* are derived from the anterior and posterior circumflex and the suprascapular; its *Nerves* from the circumflex (n. axillaris) and the suprascapular. It has 3 ligaments, the—

Capsular (5), from the margin of the glenoid cavity to the anatomical neck of the humerus; has 3 openings for the reflexions of the synovial membrane over the tendons.

Coraco-humeral (6), intimately united with the capsular, extends from the coracoid process to the greater tuberosity of the humerus.

Glenoid, a fibro-cartilaginous ring, continuous above with the tendon of the long head of the biceps (7), and attached around the margin of

5

the glenoid cavity in order to deepen the articular surface and pad
its edge.

The Elbow-joint, Articulatio Cubiti, is a ginglymus or hinge articulation,
formed by the lower end of the humerus with the greater sigmoid cavity
of the ulna (2) and the head of the radius (3). Its *Synovial Membrane*
is reflected over the ligaments, and includes the superior radio-ulnar
articulation. Its *Arteries* are derived from the anastomotica magna,
brachial, radial, ulnar, and interosseous recurrent, superior and inferior
profunda arteries. Its *Nerves* are branches of the ulnar, the musculo-
cutaneous and the median. It has 4 ligaments, the—

FIG. 39

Anterior,—from the internal condyle (7) and anterior
surface of the humerus to the orbicular ligament
of the radius and the coronoid process of the ulna.

Posterior (6),—from the posterior surface of the
humerus to the olecranon process of the ulna.

External Lateral (l. collaterale radiale) (4),—from the
external condyle of the humerus passing obliquely
downward and backward behind the orbicular
ligament and the head of the radius to be attached
strongly to the ulna at a point opposite the attachment of the internal lateral ligament.

Internal Lateral (l. collaterale ulnare),—from the internal condyle of the humerus (7) to the inner side
of the juncture of the coronoid and olecranon processes of the ulna.

The Radio-ulnar Articulations are 3 in number, as
follows:—

SUPERIOR RADIO-ULNAR ARTICULATION—is a trochoid
or pivot-joint, formed by the head of the radius and the
lesser sigmoid cavity of the ulna. Its synovial membrane is a continuation of that in the elbow-joint. It
has only one ligament, the—

Orbicular Ligament (5), consists of two distinct portions, the orbicular
and the capsular. The orbicular portion is very thick,—forms
four-fifths of a circle and surrounds the neck of the radius. It is
attached to the margins of the lesser sigmoid cavity of the ulna, and
to the external lateral ligament of the elbow-joint. The Capsular
portion is loose and thin, its fibres run from the lower margin of the
true orbicular ligament to the neck of the radius.

MIDDLE RADIO-ULNAR ARTICULATION—is formed by the shafts of the radius and ulna, which do not touch each other, but are connected by 2 ligaments, as follows:—

Oblique Ligament,—from the tubercle at the base of the coronoid process of the ulna to the shaft of the radius. Its fibres run from the ulna obliquely downward to the radius, whereas the fibers of the interosseous membrane run from the radius downwards to the ulna.

Interosseous Membrane (9),—obliquely downward from the interosseous ridge on the radius to that on the ulna. Through the interval between its upper border and the oblique ligament, the posterior interosseous vessels pass.

INFERIOR RADIO-ULNAR ARTICULATION—is a pivot-joint, formed by the head of the ulna and the sigmoid cavity of the radius. Its *Synovial Membrane* (membrana sacciformis) is very loose, and sometimes communicates with that of the wrist-joint through an opening in the triangular *fibro-cartilage* which separates the head of the ulna from the wrist-joint. It is a capsule but is often considered as consisting of two portions which are then called,

Anterior Radio-ulnar.	*Posterior Radio-ulnar.*

The Radio-carpal Articulation, or Wrist-joint, is a condyloid articulation formed by the lower end of the radius and the triangular fibro-cartilage with the scaphoid (os naviculare), semilunar (os lunatum), and cuneiform, (os triquetrum) bones of the carpus. Its *Arteries* are the anterior and posterior carpal from both the radial and ulnar, the anterior and posterior interosseous and ascending branches from the deep palmar arch. Its *Nerves* are derived from the ulnar and posterior interosseous. It is lined by a *synovial membrane,* and is connected by a *capsule,* which is divided into the following-named 4 ligaments, the—

External Lateral (radio-carpal).	*Anterior Ligament.*
Internal Lateral (ulno-carpal).	*Posterior Ligament.*

The Carpal Articulations are in 3 sets,—between the bones of the first row, between the bones of the second row, between the 2 rows of bones with each other.

The scaphoid, semilunar, and cuneiform bones are connected together by *Dorsal, Palmar (volar),* and 2 *Interosseous Ligaments.* The pisiform bone has a separate capsular ligament and synovial membrane and 2 *Palmar Ligaments* connecting it with the unciform and the 5th metacarpal.

The 4 bones of the second row are connected together by *Dorsal, Palmar* and 3 *Interosseous Ligaments.*

The two rows of bones are united to each other by *Dorsal, Palmar, and 2 Lateral Ligaments*, the last named being continuous with the lateral ligaments of the wrist-joint.

The Carpo-metacarpal Articulations. That of the thumb with the trapezium is a joint of reciprocal reception, and has a *Capsular Ligament* and a separate *synovial membrane*. The 4 inner metacarpal bones form 4 arthrodial joints with the adjacent carpal bones by 6 *Dorsal*, 8 *Palmar, and 2 Interosseous Ligaments*, irregularly disposed.

The Synovial Membranes of the Wrist are 5 in number, and are situated as follows:—

The First, or Membrana Sacciformis,—between the head of the ulna, the sigmoid cavity of the radius, and the triangular interarticular fibro-cartilage.

The Second,—between the lower end of the radius, the triangular fibro-cartilage, and the scaphoid, semilunar, and cuneiform bones of the carpus.

The Third,—between all the carpal bones except the pisiform and between the bases of the inner 4 metacarpal bones; but it extends only halfway into the 2 intervals between the 3 proximal bones of the carpus.

The Fourth,—between the trapezium and the metacarpal bone of the thumb.

The Fifth,—between the cuneiform and pisiform bones.

The Metacarpo-metacarpal Articulations. The 4 inner metacarpal bones are connected together at their bases by *Dorsal, Palmar, and Interosseous Ligaments*, and at their digital extremities by the *Transverse Ligament*, a narrow fibrous band which crosses them anteriorly.

Remaining Articulations of the Hand. The metacarpo-phalangeal are condyloid joints formed by the rounded heads of the metacarpal bones and the shallow cavities in the extremities of the first phalanges. The phalangeal articulations are ginglymus joints. Both sets have for each joint an *Anterior* and 2 *Lateral Ligaments*, the former being lined each with a synovial membrane. There are no posterior ligaments to these articulations, the extensor tendons of the hand supplying their places.

ARTICULATIONS OF THE LOWER EXTREMITY

The Hip-joint is a true enarthrodial or ball-and-socket articulation, formed by the head of the femur with the acetabulum of the os innominatum. Its *Synovial Membrane* is extensive, investing most of the head and neck of the femur, the capsular, cotyloid and teres ligaments, and the cavity of the acetabulum. Its *Arteries* are derived from the obturator, sciatic, internal circumflex, and gluteal. Its *Nerves* are branches from the sacral plexus, great sciatic, obturator, and accessory obturator. It has 5 ligaments as follows: the—

Capsular,—from the margin of the acetabulum and the transverse ligament into the base of the neck of the femur above, the anterior intertrochanteric line in front, and to the middle of the neck of the bone, behind. Superadded to and strengthening it are 3 auxiliary bands, the fibres of which form part of the capsule,—the *ilio-femoral* (described below), the *ischio-femoral* and the *pectineo-femoral* bands.

Ilio-femoral or Y-ligament,—from the anterior inferior spine of the ilium, into the anterior inter-trochanteric line by two fasciculi. It is a dissected portion of the capsular ligament which is very strong anteriorly.

Ligamentum Teres,—from a depression on the head of the femur into the margins of the cotyloid notch of the acetabulum and into the transverse ligament, by two fasciculi.

Cotyloid,—a fibro-cartilaginous band surrounding the margin of the acetabulum in order to deepen its cavity and pad its edge.

Transverse,—that part of the cotyloid ligament which crosses over the cotyloid notch converting it into a foramen.

The Knee-joint is a complicated articulation, formed by the condyles of the femur with the head of the tibia and the patella in front. It consists of 3 articulations in one; those between the condyles of the femur and the tuberositis of the tibia are condylar joints, while that between the patella and the femur is partly trochlear. Its *Synovial Membrane* is the largest in the body, being reflected for 2 or 3 inches over the anterior surface of the femur, where it is supported by the subcrureus muscle; also over its condyles, the patella, semilunar cartilages, crucial ligaments, and the head of the tibia; and it is prolonged through an opening in the capsular ligament beneath the tendon of the popliteus. Its *Arteries* are derived from the anastomotica magna, the articular branches of the popliteal, the recurrent branches of the anterior tibial and the external circumflex of the profunda. Its *Nerves* are derived from the obturator, anterior crural, external and internal popliteal. It has 14 ligaments, of which 6 are external and 8 internal, as follows:—

Anterior, or Ligamentum Patellæ,—is the central portion of the common tendon of the extensor muscles of the thigh, continued from the patella to the tubercle of the tibia (9, Fig. 41).

Posterior, the oblique portion of which is often called *Ligamentum Winslowii* (1),—from the upper margin of the intercondyloid notch of the femur to the posterior margin of the head of the tibia, being

FIG. 40.

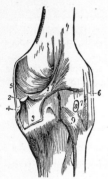

partly derived from the tendon of the semi-membranosus muscle (2):

Internal Lateral (l. collaterale tibiale) (5),—from the internal condyle of the femur to the inner tuberosity of the tibia and the internal semilunar cartilage.

External Lateral 2,—from the external condyle of the femur to the head of the fibula. These ligaments are *a Long* (l. collaterale fibulare) (6) is a divorced portion of the peroneus longus muscle. The short external lateral ligament (l. laterale externum breve seu posticum). (7) is often wanting, when present, it is behind the long external lateral and separated from it by the tendon of the biceps.

Capsular,—is a thin but very strong membrane, which fills in the intervals left between the preceding ligaments and is inseparably connected with them.

The Internal Ligaments are as follows:—

FIG. 41.

Anterior Crucial (2),—from the depression in front of the spine of the tibia to the inner side of the *outer condyle* of the femur.

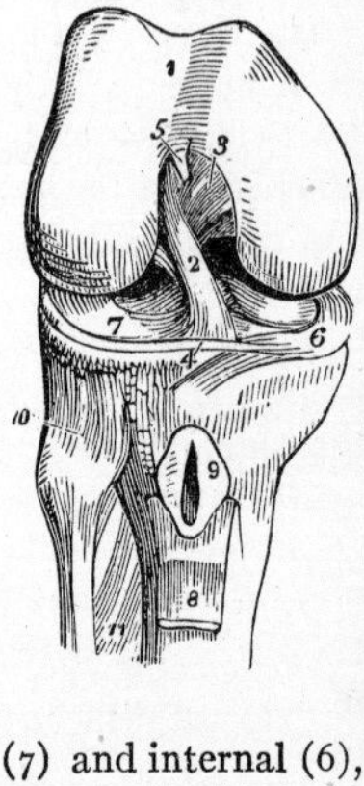

Posterior Crucial (3),—from the depression behind the spine of the tibia and the popliteal notch, to the outer side of the *inner condyle* of the femur. [To remember the positions and insertions of these crucial ligaments, let the student cross his index fingers over each knee in succession; when over the right knee placing the right finger in front, when over the left knee the left finger in front. The positions of the fingers will in each case correspond with those of the respective crucial ligaments.]

Semilunar Fibro-cartilages (menisci) 2,—external (7) and internal (6), are situated between the articular surfaces, and attached to the depressions in front and behind the spine of the tibia. The external one forms nearly an entire circle and gives off posteriorly a strong fasciculus, the *ligament of Wrisberg*, which is inserted into the inner condyle of the femur.

Transverse (4),—is a connecting slip between the semilunar fibro-cartilages anteriorly.

Coronary or *Coronal* (7),—are short bands connecting the outer margins of the fibro-cartilages with the margin of the head of the tibia.

Ligamentum Mucosum (plica synovialis patellaris),—is a triangular fold of the synovial membrane which at the lower border of the patella is given off to the intercondylar notch of the femur.

Ligamenta Alaria (plicæ alares),—are two fringe-like folds on the sides of the ligamentum mucosum, and are attached to the semilunar cartilages.

Bursæ,—in the vicinity of this joint are 12 in number; 3 in front, 4 on the outer side, and 5 on the inner side. Some of these are expansions from others, some often communicate with the joint, and some are only occasionally present. That between the patella and the skin is the one implicated in the affection called "house-maid's knee."

The Tibio-fibular Articulations are 3 in number, as follows, viz.—

SUPERIOR TIBIO-FIBULAR ARTICULATION, in an arthrodial joint, formed by the contiguous surfaces of the bones. It has a *Synovial Membrane* which is sometimes continuous with that of the knee-joint, and 3 ligaments, the—

Capsular,—a membranous bag surrounding the joint and much thicker in front than behind.

Anterior and Posterior Superior Tibio-fibular (10),—which connect the head of the fibula with the outer tuberosity of the tibia.

MIDDLE TIBIO-FIBULAR ARTICULATION. The shafts of these bones do not touch each other, but are connected by an *Interosseous Membrane* extending between their contiguous borders, and perforated, above for the anterior tibial vessels, below for the anterior peroneal vessels.

INFERIOR TIBIO-FIBULAR ARTICULATION, is an amphiarthrodial joint, of the subdivision syndesmosis, and is formed by the contiguous rough surfaces on the lower ends of these bones. Its *Synovial Membrane* is derived from that of the ankle-joint, and it has 4 ligaments, the—

Inferior Interosseous,—continuous with the interosseous membrane.

Anterior and Posterior Inferior Tibio-fibular,—from the margins of the external malleous to the front and back of the tibia.

Transverse,—posteriorly between the 2 malleoli.

The Ankle-joint is a ginglymus or hinge-joint articulation, formed by the lower ends of the tibia and fibula and their malleoli, with the astragalus.

Its *Synovial Membrane* is prolonged upward between the tibia and fibula for a short distance. Its *Arteries* are derived from the malleolar branches of the anterior tibial and peroneal arteries; and its *Nerves* from the anterior and posterior tibial nerves. It has 4 ligaments; the—

Anterior,—connecting the anterior margins of the tibia and astragalus or talus.

Posterior,—a very thin band of transverse fibres, connecting the posterior margins of the tibia and astragalus.

Internal Lateral or *Deltoid Ligament* (l. calcaneotibiale),—from the internal malleolus to the 3 adjacent tarsal bones.

External Lateral,—by anterior (l. talofibulare anterius), posterior (l. talofibulare posterius) and middle (l. calcaneofibulare) fasciculi, from the external malleolus to the astragalus and os calcis.

The Tarsal Articulations are connected by the following-named ligaments, viz., the—

Calcaneo-astragaloid 3, external, internal and posterior,—connecting the os calcis with the astragalus.

Calcaneo-cuboid 4, superior, internal, long and short,—connecting the os calcis with the cuboid.

Calcaneo-navicular 2, superior and inferior,—connceting the os calcis with the scaphoid or navicular bone.

Astragalo-navicular, superior,—connecting the astragalus with the scaphoid or navicular bone.

Dorsal and *Plantar Ligaments,*—connecting the scaphoid with the three cuneiform and with the cuboid, the three cuneiform with each other, and the external cuneiform with the cuboid.

Interosseous Ligaments,—connecting the os calcis with the astragalus, the scaphoid with the cuboid, the cuneiform bones with each other, and the external cuneiform with the cuboid.

Nerves. All the joints of the tarsus are supplied by the anterior tibial nerve.

The Tarso-metatarsal Articulations are 5 arthrodial joints formed by the bases of the metatarsal bones with the adjacent bones of the tarsus, the 2d metatarsal bone articulating with all 3 cuneiform in the recess formed by the shortness of the second cuneiform. They are united by *Dorsal, Plantar, and 3 Interosseous Ligaments*. The 2d metatarsal bone has 3 dorsal ligaments, 1 from each cuneiform bone. The interosseous ligaments pass from the 2d and 3d metatarsal bones to the internal and external cuneiform.

Synovial Membranes of the Tarsus and Metatarsus are 6 in number, and are situated as follows, viz.—

First,—between the os calcis and the astragalus, behind the interosseous ligament.

Second,—between the same bones in front of the interosseous ligament, also between the astragalus and the scaphoid.

Third,—between the os calcis and the cuboid.

Fourth,—between the scaphoid and the 3 cuneiform bones, running backward between the scaphoid and the cuboid, forward between the cuneiform bones, between the external cuneiform and the cuboid, between the middle and external cuneiform and the bases of the 2d and 3d metatarsal, passing also between the bases of these bones and the 4th metatarsal.

Fifth,—between the internal cuneiform and the base of the 1st metatarsal bone.

Sixth,—between the cuboid and the 4th and 5th metatarsal bones, also running forward between their bases,

The Metatarso-metatarsal Articulations. The metatarsal bones are connected together, except the first, at their bases by *Dorsal, Plantar, and Interosseous Ligaments*. The base of the first metatarsal is not connected with the base of the second by any ligaments, resembling the thumb in this respect.

Remaining Articulations of the Foot. The metatarso-phalangeal and the phalangeal articulations are similar to those in the hand, each having a *Plantar* and 2 *Lateral Ligaments*. The extensor tendons supply the places of the posterior ligaments.

THE MUSCLES AND FASCIÆ

The Muscles are the active organs of locomotion, formed of bundles of reddish fibres endowed with the property of shortening themselves upon irritation, which is called *muscular contractility*, and chemically consisting of 75 per cent. of water, 20 of proteids, 2 of fat, 1 of nitrogenous extractives and carbohydrates, and 2 per cent. of salts, mainly potassium phosphate and carbonate.

The Muscles are divided into 2 great classes,—*Voluntary, Striped, or Muscles of animal life*, comprise those which are under the control of the will. *Involuntary, Unstriped, or Muscles of organic life*, are those which are not under the control of the will.

Voluntary Muscular Fibre consists of *fasciculi* enclosed in a delicate web, the *perimysium*, connected together by a delicate connective tissue, the *endomysium*, aggregated into muscular fibres, from $\frac{1}{600}$ inch to $\frac{1}{200}$ inch in diameter, which are enclosed in tubular sheaths, the *sarcolemma*, and are marked by fine *striæ* passing around them transversely or somewhat obliquely. The fasciculi are formed of longitudinal fibrillæ or *sarcostyles*, made up of successive portions called *sarcomeres*, each of which consists of a central dark part the *sarcous element*, and a clear layer which is most visible when the fibre is extended (Schäfer).

Involuntary Muscular Fibre is made up of spindle-shaped cells, the *contractile fibre-cells*, averaging $\frac{1}{450}$ inch long and $\frac{1}{4000}$ inch broad, collected into bundles and held together by a cement-like substance. These are aggregated into larger bundles or flattened bands, bound together by ordinary connective tissue. Involuntary muscular fibres are found in the walls of the alimentary canal, in the posterior wall of the trachea, in the bronchi, the ducts of certain glands, in the ureters, bladder, urethra, genitalia of both sexes, walls of all arteries and most veins and lymphatics, in the iris and ciliary muscle, and in the skin.

Tendons and Aponeuroses. *Tendons* are white, glistening cords or bands formed of white fibrous tissue almost entirely, have few vessels and no nerves in the smaller ones. They serve to connect the muscles with the structures on which they act. *Aponeuroses* are fibrous membranes, of similar structure and appearance, and serve the same purpose.

Fasciæ are laminæ of variable thickness which invest (*fascia*, a bandage) the softer structures. The superficial fascia or subcutaneous tela consists of two layers, a superficial fatty layer (panniculus adiposus) which is closely adherent to the true skin, covering over almost the entire body. Except on the eyelids, penis, and scrotum, it contains much fat. The deep layer of the superficial fascia is a fibro-muscular layer (panniculus carnosus) it envelops the entire trunk. On the sides of the neck and upper part of the chest it is muscular and is there called the platysma, it is also muscular in the scrotum where it is called the dartos. The *deep fascia* is of aponeurotic structure, dense, inelastic, and fibrous, ensheathing the muscles and affording some of them attachment, it also forms the sheaths of the vessels and nerves, and binding down the whole into a shapely mass.

Muscles are attached to the periosteum and perichondrium of bone and cartilage, to the subcutaneous areolar tissue, and to ligaments. In the latter case only are their tendons in direct contact with the tissue on which they are to act.

Double-bellied Muscles are 4 in number, the—occipito-frontalis, digastric, omo-hyoid, and the diaphragm.

Orinjin Semitian actian (handwritten)
mere (handwritten)
Epidemni (handwritten)

MUSCLES OF THE HEAD

CRANIAL REGION

Occipito-frontalis (*a*), arises *from* the external two-thirds of the superior curved line of the occipital bone and the mastoid process of the temporal; also from the pyramidalis nasi, corrugator supercilii, and orbicularis palpebrarum fibres; and is inserted *into* an aponeurosis or "galea capitis," which covers the vertex of the skull. *Action*, chiefly as a muscle of facial expression. *Nerves*, the frontal portion (m. frontalis) by the facial nerve, the occipital portion (m. occipitalis) by the posterior auricular branch of the facial.

AURICULAR REGION

Auricularis anterior, or Attrahens Auriculam,—*from* the lateral cranial aponeurosis: *into* the helix of the ear anteriorly. *Action*, to draw the pinna forward. *Nerve*, temporal branch of the facial.

Auricularis superior, or Attollens Auriculam,—*from* the occipito-frontalis aponeurosis: *into* the pinna of the ear superiorly. *Action*, to raise the pinna. *Nerve*, temporal branch of the facial.

Auricularis posterior, or Retrahens Auriculam,—*from* the mastoid process of the temporal bone: *into* the concha. *Action*, to retract the pinna. *Nerve*, posterior auricular branch of the facial.

PALPEBRAL REGION

Orbicularis Palpebrarum (m. orbicularis oculi),—*from* the internal angular process of the frontal bone, the nasal process of the superior maxillary, and the borders of the tendo oculi; *into* the skin of the eyelids, forehead, temple, and cheek, blending with the occipito-frontalis and the corrugator supercilii. *Action*, to close the eyelids. *Nerve*, facial; perhaps also the 3d nerve.

Corrugator Supercilii,—*from* the inner end of the superciliary ridge of the frontal bone: *into* the orbicularis palpebrarum. *Action*, to draw eyebrow downward and inward. *Nerve*, facial; perhaps by the 3d nerve.

Tensor Tarsi (is classed by some as a portion (pars lacrimalis) of the orbicularis) it arises,—*from* the crest of the lacrimal bone *into* the tarsal cartilages by two slips. *Action*, to compress the puncta lacrimalia against the globe of the eye and to compress the lacrimal sac. *Nerve*, facial; perhaps also the 3d nerve.

Orbital Region

Levator Palpebræ Superioris (9),—*from* the lesser wing of the sphenoid: *into* the upper tarsal cartilage. *Action*, to lift the upper lid. *Nerve*, 3d cranial, or motor oculi.

The fibrous ring (annulus tendineus communis) from which arise the recti oculi muscles, is divisible into an upper common tendon and a lower common tendon.

Rectus Superior (5),—*from* the superior common tendon (ligament of Lockwood): *into* the sclerotic coat. *Action*, to rotate the eyeball upward. *Nerve*, 3d cranial.

Rectus Inferior (4),—*from* the inferior common tendon (ligament of Zinn):

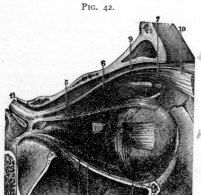

Fig. 42.

into the sclerotic coat. *Action*, to rotate the eyeball downward. *Nerve*, 3d cranial.

Rectus Internus (3),—*from* the inferior common tendon (ligament of Zinn): *into* the sclerotic coat. *Action*, to rotate the eyeball inward. *Nerve*, 3d cranial.

Rectus Externus (or lateralis) (2),—by 2 heads, the upper from the superior common tendon (ligament of Lockwood), the lower from the inferior common tendon (ligament of Zinn) and a bony process at lower margin of the sphenoidal fissure: *into* the sclerotic coat. *Action*, to rotate the eyeball outward. *Nerve*, 6th cranial, or abducens.

Between the 2 heads of the external rectus pass the 3d, nasal branch of the 5th, and 6th cranial nerves, and the ophthalmic vein.

Obliquus Oculi Superior (6),—*from* about a line above the inner margin of the optic foramen, its tendon passing through a pulley (7) near the internal angular process of the frontal bone and thence beneath the rectus superior: *into* the sclerotic coat at right angles to the insertion of the rectus superior. *Action*, to rotate the eyeball on its antero-posterior axis. *Nerve*, 4th cranial, or patheticus.

Obliquus Oculi Inferior (8),—*from* the orbital plate of the maxilla: *into* the sclerotic coat below the insertion of the external rectus and at right angles thereto. *Action*, to rotate the eye on its antero-posterior axis. *Nerve*, 3d cranial.

NASAL REGION

Pyramidalis Nasi (m. procerus) (*c*),—*from* the occipito-frontalis: *into* the compressor naris. *Action*, to depress the eyebrow. *Nerve*, facial.

Levator Labii Superioris Alæque Nasi (caput angulare of the m. quadratus labii superioris) (*e*),—*from* the nasal process of the maxilla bone: *into* the cartilage of the ala of the nose and into the upper lip. *Action*, to elevate the upper lip, and dilate the nostril. *Nerve*, facial.

Dilator Naris Anterior,—*from* the cartilage of the ala: *into* the border of its integument. *Action*, to dilate the nostril. *Nerve*, facial.

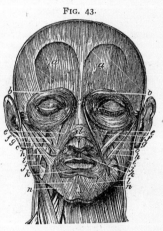

FIG. 43.

Dilator Naris Posterior,—*from* the nasal notch of the maxilla and the sesamoid cartilages: *into* the integument at the margin of the nostril. *Action*, to dilate the nostril. *Nerve*, facial.

Compressor Nasi (m. nasalis) (*d*),— *from* the maxilla above the incisive fossa: *into* the fibro-cartilage of the nose, being continuous with its fellow and the pyramidalis nasi aponeurosis. *Action*, to dilate the nostril. *Nerve*, facial.

Compressor Narium Minor,—*from* the alar cartilage: *into* the skin at the end of the nose. *Action*, to dilate the nostril. *Nerve*, facial.

Depressor Alæ Nasi (m. depressor septi),—*from* the incisive fossa of the maxilla: into the septum and ala of the nose. *Action*, to contract the nostril. *Nerve*, facial.

MAXILLARY REGION

Levator Labii Superioris (caput infra-orbitale of the m. quadratus labii superioris) (*f*),—*from* the lower margin of the orbit: *into* the upper lip. *Action*, to elevate the lip. *Nerve*, facial.

Levator Anguli Oris (m. Caninus) (*o*),—*from* the canine fossa of the maxilla: *into* the angle of the mouth. *Action*, as named. *Nerve*, facial.

Zygomaticus Major (m. zygomaticus) (*h*),—*from* the malar bone: *into* the angle of the mouth. *Action*, to raise the lip outward. *Nerve*, facial.

Zygomaticus Minor (caput zygomaticum of the m. quadratus labii superioris) (*g*),—*from* the malar bone anteriorly: *into* the angle of the mouth, blending with the levator labii superioris. *Action*, to raise the lip outward. *Nerve*, facial.

Musculus Quadratus Labii Superioris (B. N. A.) comprises three muscles, each one of which is called a head or caput. The three heads are called respectively, caput angulare, caput infra-orbitale, and caput zygomaticum. The regular names for these three heads, are, in the order given, levator labii superioris alæquæ nasi, levator labii superioris, and zygomaticus minor.

MANDIBULAR REGION

Levator Menti (m. mentalis) (*m*),—*from* the incisive fossa of the mandible bone: *into* the integument of the chin. *Action*, as named. *Nerve*, facial.

Depressor Labii Inferioris (m. quadratus labii inferioris) (*l*),—*from* the external oblique line of the mandible: *into* the lower lip. *Action*, as named. *Nerve*, facial.

Depressor Anguli Oris (m. triangularis) (*n*),—*from* the external oblique line of the mandible: *into* the angle of the mouth. *Action*, as named. *Nerve*, facial.

BUCCAL REGION

Orbicularis Oris (*k*),—is the sphincter of the lips, the upper portion, in the upper lip, is attached in the mid-line to the septum of the nose (naso-labial band), laterally it is attached to the incisor fossa of the maxilla (superior incisive bundle). The lower portion, in the lower lip, is attached to the mandible immediately above the mental protuberance (inferior incisive bundle). At the corner of the mouth, the upper and lower portions decussate with each other and, deeply, with the buccinator. *Action*, to close the mouth. *Nerve*, facial.

Buccinator (*j*),—*from* the alveolar arches of both the maxillæ and mandible and from the pterygo-mandibular ligament: *into* the orbicularis oris. It forms the lateral walls of the mouth; it is pierced by the parotid duct.

Action, to compress the cheeks.   *Nerves* (motor) facial, and (sensory) the long buccal branch of the mandibular.

Risorius,—*from* the fascia over the masseter muscle: *into* the angle of the mouth.   *Action*, the laughing muscle.   *Nerve*, facial.

TEMPORO-MANDIBULAR REGION

Masseter (*i*),—*from* the anterior two-thirds and the inner surface of the zygoma and the malar process of the maxilla: *into* almost all of the outer surface of the angle, ramus, and coronoid process of the lower jaw. *Action*, to raise the back part of the lower jaw; a muscle of mastication. *Nerve*, masticator portion of mandibular.

Temporal,—*from* the temporal fossa and temporal fascia: *into* the coronoid process of the mandible.   *Action*, to bring the incisor teeth together; the biting muscle.   *Nerve*, masticator portion of mandibular.

PTERYGO-MANDIBULAR REGION

External Pterygoid,—by 2 heads, *the upper*, from the pterygoid ridge on the greater wing of the sphenoid, *the lower* from the external pterygoid plate, and the tuberosities of the palate and maxilla: *into* a depression in front of the condyle of the mandible, and the inter-articular fibro-cartilage.   *Action*, to draw the jaw forward; a triturating muscle of mastication.   *Nerve*, masticator portion of mandibular.

Between the two heads of the external pterygoid muscle passes the internal maxillary artery.

Internal Pterygoid,—*from* the pterygoid fossa of the sphenoid bone, and the tuberosity of the palate: *into* the angle and inner surface of the ramus of the jaw, as high as the dental foramen.   *Action*, raises and draws forward the lower jaw; a triturating muscle of mastication. *Nerve*, masticator portion of mandibular.

MUSCLES OF THE EAR

The muscles of the ear include those of the pinna and those of the tympanum.   The former are divided into two sets: *Extrinsic*,—the attrahens, attollens and retrahens auriculam (see page 75); and the *Intrinsic*, as follows:—

INTRINSIC MUSCLES OF THE PINNA

Helicis Major,—*from* the cauda helicis: *into* the anterior border of the helix.   *Nerve*, facial.

Helicis Minor,—an oblique fasciculus which covers the crus helicis. *Nerve*, facial.

Tragicus,—a short, vertical band of muscular fibres, on the outer surface of the tragus. *Nerve*, facial.

Antitragicus,—*from* the antitragus: *into* the cauda helicis and antihelix. *Nerve*, facial.

Transversus Auriculæ,—on the cranial surface of the pinna, *from* the convexity of the concha: *into* the prominence corresponding to the groove of the helix. *Nerve*, facial.

Obliquus Auriculæ.—from the upper and back part of the concha: *into* the convexity immediately above it. *Nerve*, facial.

Muscles of the Tympanum

Tensor Tympani,—*from* the under surface of the petrous portion of the temporal bone, the cartilaginous Eustachian tube, and its own osseous canal: *into* the handle of the malleus. *Action*, to draw the membrana tympani inward and tense. *Nerve*, branch from otic ganglion.

Laxator Tympani,—*from* the base of the alar spine of the sphenoid, its tendon passing through the petro-tympanic fissure to be attached to the processus gracilis (anterior processus) of the malleus. *Nerve*, branch from otic ganglion (see page 301).

Stapedius,—*from* the interior of the pyramid, through the orifice at its apex: *into* the neck of the stapes. *Action*, to rotate the base of the stapes and compress the contents of the vestibule. *Nerve*, tympanic branch of the facial.

MUSCLES OF THE NECK

Superior Cervical Region

Platysma Myoides (panniculus carnosus),—is a muscular fascia covering the pectoral and cervical region; it is loosely attached to the lower jaw, the angle of the mouth, the skin, and the cellular tissue of the face. *Action*, to wrinkle the skin, and depress the mouth. *Nerve*, facial.

Sterno-cleido-mastoid (11),—by two heads from the sternum (12) and the clavicle (13) at its inner third: *into* the mastoid process of the temporal bone, and the outer half of the superior curved line of the occipital. *Action*, to depress and rotate the head. *Nerves*, spinal accessory, and deep branches of the cervical plexus.

Infra-hyoid Region

Sterno-hyoid (14),—*from* the posterior surface of the sternum and the sternal end of the clavicle: *into* the body of the hyoid bone. *Action,* to depress the hyoid bone. *Nerve,* a branch from the communicating loop (ansa hypoglossi) between the descendens and communicans hypoglossi.

Sterno-thyroid (m. sterno-thyreoideus) (15),—*from* the posterior surface of the sternum and the cartilage of the 1st rib: *into* the oblique line on the ala of the thyroid cartilage. *Action,* to depress the thyroid (thyreoid) cartilage. *Nerve,* a branch from the communicating loop (ansa hypoglossi) between the descendens and communicans hypoglossi.

Fig. 44.

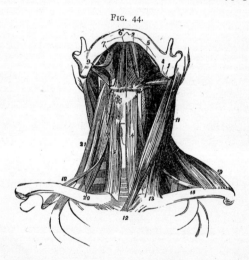

Thyro-hyoid (m. thyreohyoideus) (16),—*from* the oblique line on the thyroid cartilage: *into* the body and greater cornu of the hyoid bone. *Action,* to depress the larynx and the hyoid bone. *Nerve,* hypoglossal.

Omo-hyoid (17, 18),—*from* the upper border of the scapula and the transverse ligament: *into* the body of the hyoid bone. It has a tendon in its centre which is bound down to the clavicle and the 1st rib by a loop of the deep cervical fascia. *Action,* to depress the hyoid bone, and draw it backward. *Nerve,* branch from the communicating loop (ansa hypoglossi) between the descendens and communicans hypoglossi.

6

Supra-hyoid Region

Digastric,—by 2 bellies, the *posterior one* (1) from the digastric groove of the mastoid process of the temporal bone; the *anterior* (2) from a fossa on the inner surface of the mandible near its symphysis: *into* a central tendon (3) which perforates the stylo-hyoid muscle, and is bound down to the body of the hyoid bone by an aponeurotic loop. *Action*, to raise the hyoid bone and tongue. *Nerves*, anterior belly is supplied by a branch of the mylo-hyoid nerve, the posterior belly by the facial nerve.

Stylo-hyoid (4),—*from* the styloid process of the temporal bone near its base: *into* the body of the hyoid bone. *Action*, to elevate and retract the hyoid bone. *Nerve*, facial. This muscle is perforated by the digastric.

Mylo-hyoid (5),—*from* the mylo-hyoid ridge of the lower jaw: *into* the body of the hyoid bone and a median fibrous raphé line running from the hyoid bone to the lower jaw. *Action*, elevates the hyoid bone and draws it forward, also forms the floor of the mouth. *Nerve*, mylo-hyoid branch of inferior dental (inferior alveolar).

Genio-hyoid (6),—*from* the inferior genial tubercles (mental spines) of the mandible *into* the body of the hyoid bone. *Action*, same as that of the mylo-hyoid. *Nerve*, hypoglossal.

Lingual Region

Genio-hyo-glossus (m. genioglossus),—*from* the superior genial tubercles (mental spines) of the mandible: *into* the body of the hyoid bone, the side of the pharynx, and the whole length of the under surface of the tongue, forming a fan-like muscle. *Action*, to retract and protrude the tongue. *Nerve*, hypoglossal.

Hyo-glossus (8),—*from* the side of the body of the hyoid bone, and the whole length of its greater cornu: *into* the side of the tongue. *Action*, to draw down the side of the tongue. *Nerve*, hypoglossal.

Chondro-glossus,—sometimes described as a part of the hyo-glossus, *from* the lesser cornu and the body of the hyoid bone: *into* the intrinsic muscular fibres of the tongue, between the hyo-glossus and the genio-hyo-glossus. *Action*, as the hyo-glossus. *Nerve*, hypoglossal.

Stylo-glossus (9),—*from* the styloid process and the stylo-mandibular ligament: *into* the side of the tongue and the hyo-glossus muscle. *Action*, to elevate and retract the tongue. *Nerve*, hypoglossal.

Palato-glossus (m. glossopalatinus),—is one of the muscles of the tongue, serving to draw its base upward, but is described with the muscles of the palatal region.

Lingualis (the tongue-muscle), in 4 strata,—*longitudinalis linguæ superior*, composed of fibres passing forward and outward; *stratum* derived principally from the extrinsic muscles, the stylo-glossus, hyo-glossus, etc.; *transversus linguæ* and *verticalis linguæ*, the latter found only at the borders of the fore part of the tongue; *longitudinalis linguæ inferior* and fibres from the stylo-glossus. *Action*, to give the tongue its various forms. *Nerve*, the hypoglossal is the motor nerve of the tongue.

Pharyngeal Region

Inferior Constrictor,—*from* the sides of the cricoid and thyroid cartilages *into* the fibrous raphé of the pharynx. *Action*, to contract the pharyngeal calibre. *Nerves*, branches from the pharyngeal plexus, external laryngeal, recurrent laryngeal.

Middle Constrictor,—*from* the cornua of the hyoid bone and the stylo-hyoid ligament: *into* the fibrous pharyngeal raphé. *Action*, to constrict the pharynx. *Nerves*, branches from the pharyngeal plexus.

Superior Constrictor,—*from* the lower third of the margin of the internal pterygoid plate and its hamular process, the contiguous part of the palate bone, the tendon of the tensor palati, the pterygo-mandibular ligament, part of the alveolar process of the lower jaw and the side of the tongue: *into* the fibrous pharyngeal raphé and the pharyngeal spine of the occipital bone. *Action*, to constrict the pharynx. *Nerves*, branches from the pharyngeal plexus.

Stylo-pharyngeus (10),—*from* the inner side of the base of the styloid process: *into* the constrictor and palato-pharyngeus muscles, and the thyroid cartilage. *Action*, to elevate the pharynx. *Nerve*, glosso-pharyngeal nerve which crosses this muscle in passing to the tongue.

Palatal Region

Levator Palati (m. Levator veli palatini),—*from* the under surface of the apex of the petrous portion of the temporal bone and from the Eustachian tube: *into* the posterior surface of the soft palate. *Action*, to elevate the soft palate. *Nerve*, pharyngeal plexus.

Tensor Palati (m. tensor veli palatini),—*from* the scaphoid fossa and the spine of the sphenoid bone and the Eustachian tube, reflected around the hamular process: *into* the anterior surface of the soft palate, and the horizontal portion of the palate bone. *Action*, to make tense the soft palate. *Nerve*, a branch from the otic ganglion.

Azygos Uvulæ (m. uvulæ),—*from* the posterior nasal spine of the palate bone, and from the soft palate: *into* the uvula. *Action*, possibly to raise the uvula. This muscle is wrongly named, as it is a double muscle. *Nerve*, pharyngeal plexus.

Palato-glossus (m. glossopalatinus) (constrictor isthmi faucium),—*from* the anterior surface of the soft palate on the side of the uvula: *into* the side and dorsum of the tongue. *Action*, to constrict the fauces. It forms the anterior pillar of the fauces. *Nerve*, pharyngeal plexus of the spinal accessory.

Palato-pharyngeus (m. pharyngopalatinus) (posterior pillar of the fauces), —*from* the soft palate: *into* the side of the pharynx and the posterior border of the thyroid cartilage, having joined the stylo-pharyngeus. *Action*, to close the posterior nares. *Nerve*, pharyngeal plexus.

Salpingo-pharyngeus,—*from* the Eustachian tube near its orifice: *into* the posterior fasciculus of the palato-pharyngeus. *Action*, to raise the upper and lateral part of the pharynx. *Nerve*, pharyngeal plexus.

Prevertebral Region

Rectus Capitis Anti'cus Major (m. longus capitis),—*from* the anterior tubercles of the transverse processes of the 3d, 4th, 5th, and 6th cervical vertebræ by 4 slips: *into* the basilar process of the occipital bone. *Action*, to flex and rotate the head. *Nerves*, first cervical and the loop between it and the second. This muscle seems to be a continuation of the scalenus anticus.

Rectus Capitis Anti'cus Minor (m. rectus capitis anterior),—*from* the anterior surface of the lateral mass of the atlas, and the root of its transverse process,—*into* the basilar process of the occipital bone. *Action*, to flex and rotate the head. *Nerves*, as the rectus capitis anticus major.

Rectus Capitis Lateralis,—*from* the upper surface of the transverse process of the atlas: *into* the jugular process of the occipital bone. *Action*, to draw the head laterally. *Nerves*, as the preceding muscles.

Longus Colli, 3 portions,—*the superior oblique*, from the anterior tubercles of the transverse processes of the 3d, 4th, and 5th cervical vertebræ, into a tubercle on the anterior arch of the atlas:—*inferior oblique*, from the bodies of the first 2 or 3 dorsal vertebræ, into the transverse processes of the 5th and 6th cervical:—*vertical portion*, from the bodies of the lower 3 cervical and upper 3 thoracic vertebræ, to the bodies of the 2d, 3d, and

4th cervical. *Action*, to flex and slightly rotate the cervical portion of the spine. *Nerves*, branches from the anterior divisions of the lower cervical nerves.

Lateral Vertebral Region

Scalenus Anti'cus (m. scalenus anterior) (20),—*from* the transverse processes of the cervical vertebræ, from the 3d to the 6th inclusive: *into* the scalene tubercle on the upper surface of the 1st rib. *Action*, to flex the neck laterally, or to raise the 1st rib. *Nerves*, branches from the lower cervical. (See Fig. 44.)

Scalenus Medius (22),—*from* the transverse processes of the lower 6 cervical vertebræ: *into* the upper surface of the 1st rib, behind the subclavian groove. *Action*, same as the scalenus anticus. *Nerves*, branches from the lower cervical.

Scalenus Posti'cus (m. scalenus posterior) (21),—*from* the posterior tubercles on the transverse processes of the lower 2 or 3 cervical vertebræ: *into* the outer surface of the 2d rib, behind the serratus magnus. *Action*, to flex the neck laterally, or to elevate the 2d rib. *Nerves*, branches from lower cervical.

MUSCLES OF THE LARYNX AND EPIGLOTTIS

Muscles of the Vocal Cords and Rima Glottidis

Crico-thyroid (m. cricothyreoideus),—*from* the front and side of the cricoid cartilage (*b*): *into* the lower and inner borders of the thyroid cartilage (*c*). *Action*, to elongate and make tense the vocal cords. *Nerve*, external laryngeal.

Fig. 45.

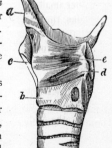

Crico-arytenoideus Posticus (posterior),—*from* the cricoid cartilage posteriorly: *into* the outer angle of the base of the arytenoid cartilage. *Action*, to rotate the arytenoid cartilages outward and open the glottis, while keeping the vocal cords tense. *Nerve*, recurrent laryngeal.

A small fasciculus, called *Kerato-cricoideus*, is sometimes found below the arytenoideus, extending from the cricoid cartilage to the inferior cornu of the thyroid. It occurs once in 5 cases, usually on one side only, but occasionally on both, and acts to fix the lower horn of the thyroid cartilage backward and downward. [Sir Wm. Turner.]

Crico-arytenoideus Lateralis (*d*),—*from* the upper border of the cricoid cartilage laterally: *into* the outer angle of the base of the arytenoid cartilage. *Action*, to rotate the arytenoid cartilages inward and close the glottis. *Nerve*, recurrent laryngeal.

Arytenoideus,—*from* the posterior surface and outer border of one arytenoid cartilage: *into* the corresponding parts of the opposite cartilage. A single muscle which fills the posterior concave surface of these cartilages. *Action*, by approximating the arytenoids, to close the back part of the glottis. *Nerves*, internal and recurrent laryngeal.

A fairly constant muscle, the *Arytenoideus rectus*, is found beneath the arytenoideus, extending from the posterior surface of the arytenoid cartilage to the posterior surface of the cartilage of Santorini [Luschka].

Thyro-arytenoideus (*e*),—*from* the receding angle of the thyroid cartilage and the crico-thyroid membrane: *into* the base and anterior surface of the arytenoid cartilage. *Action*, to shorten and relax the vocal cords by approximating the cartilages. *Nerve*, recurrent laryngeal.

MUSCLES OF THE EPIGLOTTIS

Thyro-epiglottideus,—*from* the inner surface of the thyroid cartilage: *into* the margin of the epiglottis and the aryteno-epiglottidean fold. *Action*, a depressor of the epiglottis. *Nerve*, recurrent laryngeal.

Aryteno-epiglottideus Superior,—*from* the apex of the arytenoid cartilage: *into* the aryteno-epiglottidean folds. *Action*, to constrict the superior laryngeal aperture. *Nerve*, recurrent laryngeal.

Aryteno-epiglottideus Inferior,—*from* the arytenoid cartilage anteriorly: *into* the anterior surface of the epiglottis. *Action*, to compress the sacculus laryngis. *Nerve*, recurrent laryngeal.

Another small muscle is frequently found, though rarely described in the books, the *Triticeo-glossus*. It arises from the cartilaginous nodule in the posterior thyro-hyoid ligament, and passes forward and upward to enter the tongue along with the hyo-glossus muscle. [Bochdalek, jun.]

MUSCLES OF THE TRUNK

The muscles of the trunk may be arranged in four groups, corresponding to the regions in which they are situated, viz.—those of the Back, the Thorax, the Abdomen, and the Perineum.

MUSCLES OF THE BACK

The muscles of the back are in seven layers; these muscles can be divided into two groups. First, those that are *appendicular*, *i.e.*, those that actuate the upper extremity, and second, those that are *axial*, *i.e.*, those that act on the pelvis, ribs, vertebræ, and skull.

The First or Appendicular Group constitutes the first two layers of the muscles of the back.

FIRST LAYER,—

Trapezius, and *Latissimus Dorsi*.

SECOND LAYER,—

Levator Anguli Scapulæ (m. levator scapulæ).

Rhomboideus Minor.

Rhomboideus Major.

The Second or Axial Group includes the remaining five layers, two that are superficial and three that are covered in and surrounded by the lumbo-dorsal fascia (vertebral aponeurosis).

THIRD LAYER,—

Serratus Posticus Superior (m. serratus posterior superior).

Serratus Posticus Inferior (m. serratus posterior inferior).

FOURTH LAYER,—

Splenius Capitis.

Splenius Cervicis (splenius colli).

LUMBO-DORSAL FASCIA OR VERTEBRAL APONEUROSIS

FIFTH LAYER,—consists of two distinct muscular masses, the sacro-spinal mass and the semi-spinal mass both of which used to be included by the term erector spinæ mass.

The Sacrospinal Mass divides into three longitudinal bundles.

OUTER OR ILIO-COSTAL DIVISION,—

Ilio-costalis Lumborum (ilio-costalis or sacro-lumbalis).

Ilio-costalis Dorsi (accessorius ad ilio-costalem).

Ilio-costalis Cervicis (cervicalis ascendens).

MIDDLE OR LONGISSIMUS DIVISION,—

Longissimus Dorsi.

Longissimus Cervicis (transversalis colli).

Longissimus Capitis (trachelo-mastoid).

INNER OR SPINAL DIVISION,—

Spinalis Dorsi.

Spinalis Cervicis (spinalis colli).

THE SEMI-SPINAL MASS,—

Semi-spinalis Dorsi.

Semi-spinalis Cervicis (semi-spinalis colli).

Semi-spinalis Capitis (complexus, the inner portion of which was sometimes called the biventer cervicis).

SIXTH LAYER,—
  Multifidus Spinæ (m. multifidus).
  Rotatores Spinæ (mm. rotatores).
SEVENTH LAYER,—
  Inter-spinales.
  Inter-transversales (mm. inter-transversarii).

THE SUB-OCCIPITAL MUSCLES

Rectus Capitis Posticus Major (m. rectus capitis posterior major).
Rectus Capitis Posticus Minor (m. rectus capitis posterior minor).
Obliquus Capitis Inferior.
Obliquus Capitis Superior.
Rectus Capitis Lateralis.

FIRST LAYER

Trapezius (1),—*from* the inner third of the superior curved line of the occipital bone, the ligamentum nuchæ (2), the spinous processes of the last
cervical and all the thoracic vertebræ, and the supra-spinous ligament:
into the outer third of the posterior border of the clavicle, the superior
margin of the acromion process, the whole length of the superior border
of the spine of the scapula (3), and a tubercle at its inner extremity.
Action, to draw the head backward. *Nerves*, spinal accessory (n.
accessorius), cervical plexus.

LIGAMENTUM NUCHÆ (2),—*from* the external occipital protuberance: *to*
the spines of the cervical vertebræ, from the 2d to the 7th inclusive.

Latissimus Dorsi (4),—by an aponeurosis *from* the spines of the 6 lower
thoracic and the lumbar and sacral vertebræ, the supra-spinous ligament,
the crest of the ilium and the lower 3 or 4 ribs: *into* the bicipital groove of
the humerus. *Action*, the *cursor ani* muscle, drawing the arm downward
and backward; or raising the lower ribs and drawing the trunk forward.
Nerve, the middle or long subscapular.

SECOND LAYER.

Levator Anguli Scapulæ (m. levator scapulæ) (10),—by 4 slips from the
transverse processes of the atlas and 3 upper cervical vertebræ: *into* the
vertebral border of the scapula. *Action*, as named. *Nerves*, branches
from the anterior divisions of the 3d, 4th and 5th cervical nerves.

Rhomboideus Minor (11),—*from* the ligamentum nuchæ (2) and spines of
the 7th cervical and 1st thoracic vertebræ: *into* the smooth surface at
the root of the spine of the scapula. *Action*, to draw the scapula back-

ward and upward. *Nerve*, branches from the anterior division of the
5th cervical.

Rhomboideus Major (12),—*from* the spines of the upper 4 or 5 thoracic
vertebræ and the supra-spinous ligament: *into* the scapula at the root of

FIG. 46.

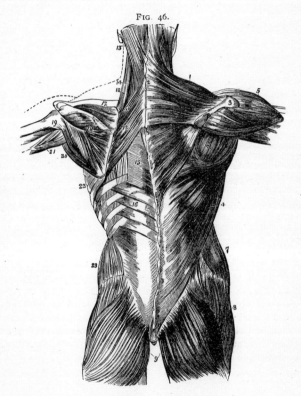

its spine and inferior angle, by a tendinous arch. *Action*, to draw the
scapula upward and backward. *Nerve*, anterior division of the 5th
cervical.

THIRD LAYER

Serratus Posti'cus Superior (m. serratus posterior superior),—*from* the
ligamentum nuchæ (a). and spines of the 7th cervical and upper 2 or 3

thoracic vertebræ: *into* the upper borders of the 2d, 3d, 4th, and 5th ribs, by 4 digitations. *Action*, to raise these ribs in inspiration. *Nerves*, external posterior branches of the upper thoracic nerves.

Serratus Posti'cus Inferior (m. serratus posterior inferior) (16),—*from* the spines of the last 2 thoracic and first 3 lumbar vertebræ: *into* the lower borders of the lower 4 ribs, by 4 digitations. *Action*, to depress these ribs in expiration. *Nerves*, external posterior branches of the lower thoracic nerves.

FOURTH LAYER

Splenius (Capitis et Cervicis) (14),—*from* the lower half of the ligamentum nuchæ (2), the last cervical and upper 6 thoracic spines, and the supra-spinous ligament: the *S. capitis* (13) into the mastoid process of the temporal bone and a rough surface below the superior nuchal line of the occipital bone,—the *S. cervicis* or *colli* (14) into the transverse processes of the upper 2 or 3 cervical vertebræ. *Action*, to draw the head backward and the neck erect. *Nerves*, external posterior branches of the cervical nerves.

Lumbo-dorsal Fascia or Vertebral Aponeurosis,—consists of three layers. Posterior layer is the most extensive, it is attached to the spines of sacral, lumbar, and thoracic vertebræ, its fibres pass out laterally to blend in the lumbar region first with the middle layer and further out, at the origin of the transversalis abdominis, it blends with the anterior layer. The middle layer is in the interval between the sacro-spinal mass and the quadratus lumborum. It is attached to the tips of the transverse processes of the lumbar vertebræ. The anterior layer forms the front part of the sheath of the quadratus lumborum, it then passes between that muscle and the psoas to become attached to the front of the bases of the transverse processes of the lumbar vertebræ.

FIFTH LAYER. (See Fig. 47)

Sacro-spinalis or Erector Spinæ (1),—*from* the sacro-iliac groove, and by the lumbo-sacral tendon from the sacral, lumbar and lower 2 thoracic spines, the iliac crest, and the posterior eminences of the sacrum: *divides* into the ilio-costalis (2) and longissimus dorsi (3) muscles. *Action*, to erect the spine and bend the trunk backward. *Nerves*, external posterior branches of the lumbar nerves.

Ilio-costal Division

Ilio-costalis Lumborum (sacro-lumbalis) (2),—the external portion of the erector spinæ: *into* the inferior borders of the angles of the lower 6 or 7 ribs. *Action*, as the erector spinæ. *Nerves*, branches of the thoracic.

Ilio-costalis Dorsi or Musculus Accessorius ad Ilio-costalem (2),—*from* the angles of 6 lower ribs: *into* the angles of upper 6 ribs. *Action*, as the erector spinæ. *Nerves*, branches of the thoracic.

Ilio-costalis Cervicis or Cervicalis Ascendens (5),—*from* the angles of upper 4 or 5 ribs: *into* the transverse processes of the 4th, 5th, and 6th cervical vertebræ. *Action*, to keep the neck erect. *Nerves*, branches of the cervical.

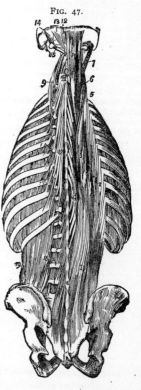

Fig. 47.

Longissimus Division

Longissimus Dorsi (3),—is the middle and largest portion of the erector spinæ, and is inserted *into* the transverse and articular processes of the lumbar vertebræ, into the tips of the transverse processes of all the thoracic vertebræ, and into from lower 7 to 11 ribs between their tubercles and angles. *Action*, as the erector spinæ. *Nerves*, branches of the lumbar and thoracic nerves.

Longissimus Cervicis or Transversalis Colli (6),—*from* the transverse processes of the upper 6 thoracic vertebræ; *into* the transverse processes of the cervical vertebræ (9), from the 2d to the 6th inclusive. *Action*, to keep the head erect. *Nerves*, branches of the cervical.

Longissimus Capitis or Trachelo-mastoid (7),—*from* the transverse processes of the upper 5 or 6 thoracic vertebræ, and the articular processes of the lower 3 or 4 cervical: *into* the posterior margin of the mastoid process of the temporal bone. *Action*, to steady the head. *Nerves*, branches of the cervical.

Spinal Mass

Spinalis Dorsi,—*from* the last 2 thoracic and first 2 lumbar spines: *into* all the remaining thoracic spines. *Action*, to erect the spinal column. *Nerves*, branches of the thoracic.

Spinalis Cervicis or Spinalis Colli,—*from* the 5th, 6th and 7th cervical spines, sometimes from the 1st and 2d thoracic: *into* the spine of the axis and occasionally into the spines of the next two vertebræ below. *Action*, to steady the neck. *Nerves*, branches of the cervical. [This muscle is frequently absent.]

Semi-spinalis Capitis or Complexus (8),—by 7 tendons *from* the tips of the transverse processes of the 7th cervical and upper 6 or 7 thoracic vertebræ, and from the articular processes of the 4th, 5th, and 6th cervical: *into* the inner depression between the curved (nuchal) lines of the occipital bone. *Action*, to retract and rotate the head. *Nerves*, sub-occipital, great occipital, and branches of the cervical nerves.

Biventer Crevicis,—is the inner part of the Complexus, *from* the transverse processes of upper 2 to 4 thoracic vertebræ: *into* the superior curved line of the occipital bone. *Action*, as the complexus. *Nerves*, branches of the cervical.

Semi-spinalis Dorsi (10),—*from* the transverse processes of the thoracic vertebræ, from about the 5th to the 11th: *into* the last 2 cervical and upper 4 thoracic spines. *Action*, to erect the spinal column. *Nerves*, branches of the thoracic nerves.

Semi-spinalis Cervicis or Semi-spinalis Colli (11),—*from* the transverse processes of the upper 5 or 6 thoracic vertebræ: *into* the 2d, 3d, 4th, and 5th cervical spines. *Action*, to erect the spinal column. *Nerves*, branches of the cervical.

Sixth Layer

Multifidus Spinæ (m. multifidus) (16),—*from* the back of the sacrum, posterior superior spine of the ilium, posterior sacro-iliac ligaments, articular processes of lumbar and lower 3 or 4 cervical vertebræ, and the transverse processes of the thoracic: *into* the spines of the next 4 vertebræ above. *Action*, to erect and rotate the spinal column. *Nerves*, branches of the spinal nerves.

Rotatores Spinæ (mm. rotatores),—*from* the transverse processes of the thoracic vertebræ, from the 2d to the 12th inclusive: each *into* the lamina of the next thoracic vertebræ above. *Action*, to rotate the spinal column. *Nerves*, branches of the posterior thoracic.

Inter-spinales,—placed in pairs between the spines of contiguous vertebræ, 6 pairs in the cervical region, 3 in the thoracic, 4 sometimes 6 in the lumbar. *Nerves,* branches of the posterior spinal.

Extensor Coccygis,—*from* the last bone of the sacrum or first of the coccyx: *into* the lower part of the coccyx, posteriorly. *Action,* as named. *Nerves,* branches of the posterior sacral.

Inter-transversales (mm. intertransversarii) (18),—placed between the transverse processes of contiguous vertebræ, 7 in the cervical region, 12 in the thoracic, and 4 in the lumbar. *Nerves,* branches of the posterior spinal.

SUBOCCIPITAL MUSCLES

Rectus Capitis Posti′cus Major (m. rectus capitis posterior major) (13),—*from* the spine of the axis: *into* the inferior curved or nuchal line of the occipital bone and the surface below. *Action,* to rotate the head. *Nerves,* suboccipital.

Rectus Capitis Posti′cus Minor (m. rectus capitis posterior minor) (12),—*from* the tubercle on the posterior arch of the atlas: *into* a rough surface between the foramen magnum and the inferior curved or nuchal line of the occipital bone. *Action,* to draw the head backward. *Nerves,* suboccipital.

Obliquus Capitis Inferior (15),—*from* the spinous process of the axis: almost horizontally into the transverse process of the atlas. *Action,* to rotate the atlas and cranium. *Nerves,* suboccipital.

Obliquus Capitis Superior (14),—*from* the transverse process of the atlas. upward and inward *into* the occipital bone between the curved lines. *Action,* draws the head backward. *Nerves,* suboccipital.

Rectus Capitis Lateralis,—from upper surface of lateral mass of atlas: *into* under surface of the jugular process of the occipital bone. *Action,* to flex the head laterally. *Nerve,* the anterior branch of the first cervical.

MUSCLES OF THE THORAX

External Intercostals,—each *from* the lower border of each rib: *into* the upper border of the next rib below directed obliquely downward and forward. *Action,* to raise and evert the ribs in inspiration. *Nerves,* intercostal.

Internal Intercostals,—each *from* the ridge on the inner surface of each rib: *into* the upper border of the rib below, directed obliquely downward and backward. *Action*, at sides of thorax to depress the ribs in expiration; anteriorly they raise the costal cartilages. *Nerves*, intercostals.

Infra-costales,—obliquely *from* inner surface of each rib: *into* the inner surface of the 1st, 2d, or 3d rib below. *Action*, muscles of inspiration. *Nerves*, intercostal. [These muscles vary in number and length.]

Triangularis Sterni,—*from* the posterior surface of the ensiform cartilage and lower third of the sternum, also from the sternal ends of the costal cartilages of the lower 3 or 4 true ribs: *into* the lower border and inner surfaces of the 2d, 3d, 4th, 5th, and 6th costal cartilages. *Action*, to draw down the cartilages in expiration. *Nerves*, intercostal.

Fig. 48.

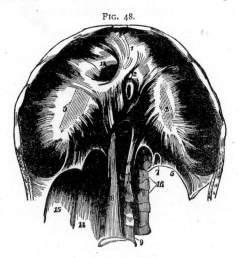

Levatores Costarum (17 Fig. 47),—each *from* the transverse process of the 7th cervical and upper 11 thoracic vertebræ: *into* the upper surface of the next rib below, near its angle. *Action*, to raise the ribs. *Nerves*, intercostal.

Diaphragm,—*from* the ensiform cartilage (4), inner surfaces of lower 6 or 7 ribs, ligamenta arcuata (5), and by its crura (8, 10), from the bodies of the lumbar vertebræ: *into* the central or cordiform tendon (2, 3). *Action*, the great muscle of respiration and expulsion. *Nerves*, the two phrenic, lower intercostals and phrenic plexus of the sympathetic.

OPENINGS OF THE DIAPHRAGM,—include several small openings and 3 large ones; the

Aortic (11), in the middle line posteriorly, and behind the diaphragm; transmits the aorta, vena azygos major, and thoracic duct. *Œsophageal* (12), in the muscular structure, transmits the œsophagus and pneumogastric nerves. *Opening for the Vena Cava* (13) is the highest, and has 4 tendinous margins.

The *Right Crus* (8) transmits the greater and lesser splanchnic nerves of that side: the *Left Crus* (10), the greater and lesser splanchnic nerves of the left side and the vena azygos minor.

Descent of the Diaphragm. Its central tendon does not descend during inspiration, being connected with the deep cervical fascia by the fibrous pericardium.

MUSCLES OF THE ABDOMEN

Obliquus Abdominis Externus or **External Oblique** (12),—from 8 lower ribs by 8 fleshy digitations: *into* the anterior half of the outer lip of the crest of the ilium, and by a broad aponeurosis (13) into the ensiform cartilage, linea alba, symphysis and spine of the pubes, and the ilio-pectineal line. Its *aponeurosis* is continuous with that of the pectoralis major above; below it forms Poupart's (l. inguinale) (14) and Gimbernat's (l. lacunare) ligaments, and by the separation of its fibres the external abdominal ring (15). *Action,* to compress the viscera, and flex the thorax on the pelvis, and *vice versâ*. *Nerves,* lower intercostal.

Obliquus Internus Abdominis or **Internal Oblique** (18),—*from* the lumbo-dorsal fascia, the anterior two-thirds of the middle lip of the crest of the ilium, and the outer half of Poupart's ligament (l. inguinale): *into* the cartilages of 4 lower ribs; by its aponeurosis into the linea alba; and leaving an arched border (20) over the spermatic cord, by the *conjoined tendon* (falx aponeurotica inguinalis) (19) with the transversalis into the pubic crest and the pectineal line. Its aponeurosis passes in front of the rectus abdominis; the lowermost portion, from the level of the semilunar fold of Douglas downward, is called the *conjoined tendon* because it serves for the transversalis as well. It blends in the linea alba with the tendons of its fellow of the opposite side and the external oblique and transversalis of both sides. *Action,* same as the external oblique. *Nerves,* lower intercostals, ilio-hypogastric, and sometimes from the ilio-inguinal.

Cremaster,—*from* the inner part of Poupart's ligament (l. inguinale), forming a series of loops along the outer side of the spermatic cord: *into* the crest of the pubis and the front of the sheath of the rectus. Its origin and insertion is precisely similar to that of the lower fibres of the internal oblique, from which it is derived by the descent of the testicle. *Action,* to raise the testicle. *Nerve,* the genital branch of the genito-crural.

Transversalis Abdominis or **Transversalis,**—*from* the outer third of Poupart's ligament (l. inguinale), the anterior two-thirds of the inner lip of the crest of the ilium, the cartilages of 6 lower ribs, and by its dorsal aponeurosis (middle layer of the lumbodorsal fascia) from the spines and transverse processes of the lumbar vertebræ: by its ventral aponeurosis *into* the linea alba, and by the conjoined tendon (falx ap-

FIG. 49.

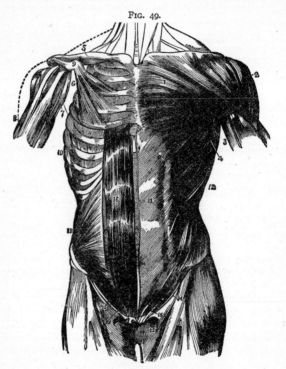

oneurotica inguinalis) (19) with the internal oblique, into the pubic crest and the pectineal line. Its *ventral aponeurosis* passes behind the rectus abdominis for about its upper three-fourths; the lower edge of this tendon is the *so-called* "semilunar" fold of Douglas. *Action*, as the external oblique. *Nerves*, as the internal oblique.

Rectus Abdominis (16),—by 2 tendons from the pubic crest and the ligaments covering the symphysis; *into* the cartilages of the 5th, 6th, and

7th ribs. It lies in a sheath formed by the aponeuroses of the internal oblique and transversalis muscles for its upper three-fourths, and is crossed by 3 tendinous lines, the *Lineæ Transversæ*. At its outer border is a similar line placed vertically, the *Linea Semilunaris*, formed by the blending of the aponeuroses of the internal oblique and transversalis. *Action*, to flex the thorax on the pelvis and *vice versâ*, also to compress the abdominal viscera. *Nerves*, lower intercostal nerves.

Pyramidalis (17),—lies in front of the rectus, but in the same sheath; arises *from* the front of the pubic bone and the anterior pubic ligament: *into* the linea alba, half-way to the umbilicus. *Action*, a tensor of the linea alba. *Nerves*, lower intercostal nerves.

Quadratus Lumborum (19 Fig. 47),—*from* the ilio-lumbar ligament, and the adjacent 2 inches of the crest of the ilium: *into* one-half of the lower border of the last rib, and the transverse processes of the 4 upper lumbar vertebræ. *Action*, to flex the thorax laterally on the pelvis and *vice versâ*. *Nerves*, anterior branches of the last thoracic and 1st lumbar.

The Psoas Magnus, the Psoas Parvus and the Iliacus muscles may be considered deep muscles of the abdomen, but are described with the muscles of the lower extremity.

MUSCLES OF THE PELVIC OUTLET

The muscles of this region are situated at the pelvic outlet in the ischio-rectal region and the perinæum.

Muscles of the Ischio-rectal Region

Corrugator Cutis Ani,—A thin stratum of involuntary muscular fibre around the anus, radiating from its orifice and serving to raise the skin into ridges around the anal margin.

External Sphincter Ani (4),—*from* the tip of the coccyx and superficial fascia: *into* the tendinous center of the perinæum. *Action*, to close the anus. *Nerves*, inferior hemorrhoidal branch of the internal pudic, also a branch from the anterior division of the 4th sacral.

Internal Sphincter Ani,—an aggregation of the involuntary circular fibres of the intestine, forming a muscular ring around the rectum about an inch above the margin of the anus. *Action*, to occlude the anal aperture.

[A third sphincter, the *Sphincter Tertius*,—from the sacrum, encircling the rectum about 4 inches above the anus, was demonstrated by Velpeau, Nelaton and Hyrtl, but is denied by other anatomists.]

7

Levator Ani (5),—*from* the body and ramus of the pubis posteriorly, the pelvic fascia and the spine of the ischium: *into* the tendinous centre of the perinæum, the sides of the rectum (and vagina), apex of the coccyx and a fibrous raphé extending from the coccyx to the anus. *Action*, to support the lower end of the rectum and vagina and the bladder, and assist in forming the floor of the pelvis. *Nerves*, branches from the 4th sacral and pudic.

Coccygeus,—*from* the spine of the ischium and the lesser sacro-sciatic ligament: *into* the margin of the coccyx and the side of the last sacral segment. *Action*, to support the coccyx, and close the outlet of the pelvis posteriorly. *Nerves*, branches from the 4th and 5th sacral.

Fig. 50.

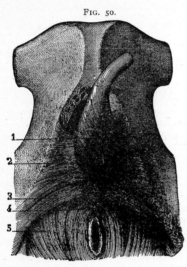

MUSCLES OF THE PERINÆUM IN THE MALE

Superficial Transversus Perinæi (3),—*from* the tuberosity of the ischium: *into* the central tendon of the perinæum. *Action*, to draw tense the central tendon. *Nerve*, perineal branch of the pudic.

Transversus Perinæi Profundus (Compressor Urethræ),—*from* the junction of the rami of the pubis and ischium: *into* its fellow of the opposite side after encircling the membranous portion of the urethræ. *Action*, to compress the veins of the penis, the membranous urethra, and Cowper's glands. *Nerve*, perineal branch of the pudic.

Bullo-cavernosus (Accelerator Urinæ) (1),—*from* the central tendon of the perinæum and the median raphé anteriorly: the fibres spread over the bulb, corpus spongiosum, corpus cavernosum and the dorsal vessels of the penis. *Action*, to accelerate the flow of urine and erect the penis. *Nerve*, perineal branch of the pudic.

Ischio-cavernosus or **Erector Penis** (2),—from the tuberosity and ramus of the ischium and the crus penis: *into* the crus penis laterally and inferiorly. *Action*, to maintain erection of the penis. *Nerve*, perineal branch of the pudic.

FASCIÆ OF THE PERINÆUM,—are described under the title Perinæum at the end of the book.

MUSCLES OF THE PERINÆUM IN THE FEMALE

Superficial Transversus Perinæi (3),—*from* the tuberosity of the ischium internally: *into* the central point of the perinæum, joining with its fellow of the opposite side. *Action*, to fix the central tendinous point of the perinæum. *Nerve*, the perineal branch of the pudic.

Bulbo-cavernosus or **Sphincter Vaginæ**,—surrounds the orifice of the vagina, and is analogous to the accelerator urinæ of the male. Arising *from* the central tendon of the perinæum, its fibres are inserted *into* the corpora cavernosa of the clitoris, a fasciculus crossing over the body of the organ so as to compress the dorsal vein. *Action*, to diminish the orifice of the vagina. *Nerve*, perineal branch of the pudic.

Ischio-cavernosus or **Erector Clitoridis**,—*from* the tuberosity and ramus of the ischium internally: *into* the crus clitoridis by an aponeurosis. *Action*, to erect the clitoris by retarding the return of its blood supply. *Nerve*, perineal branch of the pudic.

Deep Transversus Perinæi or **Compressor Urethræ**,—from the margin of the descending ramus of the pubic bone: *into* its fellow in front of the urethra and into the wall of the vagina behind the urethra. *Action*, as indicated by its name. *Nerve*, perineal branch of the pudic.

MUSCLES OF THE UPPER EXTREMITY

MUSCLES OF THE THORACIC REGION

Pectoralis Major (1, 2, 3),—*from* the sternal half of the clavicle, by an aponeurosis from the front of the sternum as low as the 6th or 7th rib, the cartilages of all the true ribs (5), and the aponeurosis of the external oblique: the fibres converge, cross and are inserted by a flat tendon (4) *into* the external bicipital ridge (crest of the great tubercle) of the humerus, having crossed the bicipital groove (intertubercular sulcus). *Action*, to draw the arm forward and downward; also to elevate the ribs in forced inspiration. *Nerves*, anterior thoracic.

Pectoralis Minor (6),—*from* the 3d, 4th, and 5th ribs, and the intercostal aponeurosis: *into* the coracoid process of the scapula. *Action*, to depress the point of the shoulder, also to elevate the ribs in forced inspiration. *Nerves*, anterior thoracic.

Subclavius (7),—*from* the cartilage of the 1st rib: *into* a deep groove on the under surface of the clavicle. *Action*, to draw the clavicle downward. *Nerve*, a branch from the 5th cervical.

Serratus Magnus (m. serratus anterior),—by 9 digitations (10) *from* the 8 upper ribs (the 2d rib having 2) and from the intercostal aponeurosis: *into* the whole length of the ventral aspect of the vertebral border of the scapula. *Action*, to elevate the ribs in inspiration, also to raise the

FIG. 51.

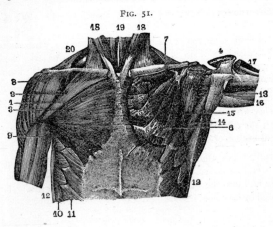

point of the shoulder. In the lower animals it is the great sling-muscle, slinging the body between the upper extremities. *Nerve*, posterior thoracic.

MUSCLES OF THE SHOULDER AND ARM

Deltoid (8),—*from* the outer third of the anterior and superior surfaces of the clavicle, the outer margin and upper surface of the acromion, and the lower border of the spine of the scapula: *into* a prominence on the outer side of the shaft of the humerus, about its middle. *Action*, to raise the arm. *Nerve*, circumflex (n. axillaris).

Subscapularis (15),—*from* the inner two-thirds of the subscapular fossa: *into* the lesser tuberosity of the humerus. *Action*, to rotate the head of the humerus inward. *Nerves*, subscapular.

Supraspinatus,—*from* the inner two-thirds of the supraspinous fossa and the fascia covering the muscle: *into* the upper facet of the greater tuberosity of the humerus. *Action*, to support the shoulder-joint, and to raise the arm. *Nerve*, suprascapular.

Infraspinatus,—*from* the inner two-thirds of the infraspinous fossa and the covering fascia: *into* the middle facet on the greater tuberosity of the humerus. *Action*, to rotate the humerus outward. *Nerve*, suprascapular.

FIG. 52.

Teres Minor (14),—*from* the upper two-thirds of the dorsal surface of the axillary border of the scapula: *into* the lowest facet on the greater tuberosity of the humerus, and the bone below. *Action*, to rotate the humerus outward. *Nerve*, circumflex (n. axillaris).

Teres Major,—*from* the dorsal aspect of the inferior angle of the scapula: *into* the internal bicipital ridge (crest of the small tubercle) of the humerus. *Action*, to assist the latissimus dorsi. *Nerve*, subscapular.

Coraco-brachialis (11),—*from* the apex of the coracoid process (2) of the scapula: *into* a ridge on the inner side of the shaft of the humerus, about its middle. *Action*, elevates the humerus forward and inward. *Nerve*, musculo-cutaneous, which perforates this muscle.

Biceps (15) (biceps flexor cubiti),—*Long head* (8) from the upper margin of the glenoid cavity; *short head* (12) from the apex of the coracoid process (2), in common with the coraco-brachialis: *into* the back of the tuberosity of the radius, and the fascia (20) of the forearm. *Action*, to flex and supinate the forearm, and to make tense its fascia. *Nerve*, the musculo-cutaneous.

Brachialis Anti'cus (m. brachialis) (17),—*from* the lower half of the shaft of the humerus anteriorly and laterally, embracing the insertion of the deltoid (9): *into* the base of the coronoid process (19) of the ulna. *Action*, a flexor of the forearm. *Nerves*, musculo-cutaneous and musculo-spiral (n. radialis).

Triceps (16) (triceps extensor cubiti),—by three heads, *the outer* (lateral) *and inner* (medial) from the posterior surface of the shaft of the humerus, the outer above, the inner below the musculo-spiral (radial) groove; the *middle or long head* from a depression (infra-glenoid tuberosity) below the glenoid cavity of the scapula; by a common tendon *into* the upper end of the olecranon process of the ulna. *Action*, to extend the forearm. *Nerve*, musculo-spiral (n. radialis).

Sub-anconeus,—*from* the humerus above the olecranon fossa: *into* the posterior ligament of the elbow-joint. *Action*, probably a tensor of the ligament. *Nerve*, musculo-spiral (n. radialis).

MUSCLES OF THE FOREARM

Muscles of the Forearm, arranged in groups of 5 and 3. (Pancoast.)
ANTERIORLY, 5 flexors, 2 pronators, 1 tensor of palmar fascia:—

Flexor Carpi Radialis.	*Pronator Radii Teres* (m. pronator
Flexor Carpi Ulnaris.	*Pronator Quadratus.* teres.
Flexor Longus Pollicis.	*Palmaris Longus.*

Flexor Sublimis Digitorum.
Flexor Profundus Digitorum.

POSTERIORLY 12 muscles in 4 sets of threes:—

Brachio-radialis (*Supinator Longus*).	*Extensor Indicis.*
Extensor Carpi Radialis Longior.	*Extensor Communis Digitorum.*
Extensor Carpi Radialis Brevior.	*Extensor Minimi Digiti.*
Extensor Ossis Metacarpi Pollicis.	*Extensor Carpi Ulnaris.*
Extensor Brevis Pollicis.	*Anconeus.*
Extensor Longus Pollicis.	*Supinator Brevis.*

Pronator Radii Teres (m. pronator teres) (4),—by 2 heads, one *from* above the medial or internal condyle of the humerus, the common tendon, fascia, and the intermuscular septum; the other from the medial or inner side of the coronoid process of the ulna: *into* a rough ridge on the radial or outer side of the shaft of the radius, about its middle. *Action*, to pronate the hand. *Nerve*, median, which passes between the 2 heads of the muscle.

Flexor Carpi Radialis (5),—*from* the medial or internal condyle of the humerus by the common tendon, the fascia, and the intermuscular septa: *into* the base of the metacarpal bone of the index finger. *Action*, to flex the wrist. *Nerve*, median.

Palmaris Longus (6),—*from* the same origin as the flexor carpi radialis:

into the annular ligament (l. carpi transversum) and the palmar fascia (9). *Action,* to make the palmar fascia tense. *Nerve,* median.

Flexor Carpi Ulnaris (8),—by 2 heads, *one* from the inner or medial condyle of the humerus by the common tendon, the *other* from the inner or medial margin of the olecranon, the upper two-thirds of the posterior border of the ulna, and the intermuscular septum: *into* the pisiform bone, the annular ligament (l. carpi transversum), and the 5th metacarpal and unciform (hamate) bones. *Action,* to flex the wrist. *Nerve,* ulnar.

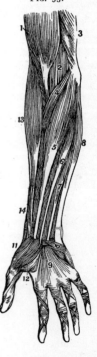

FIG. 53.

Flexor Sublimis Digitorum (Perforatus) (7),—by 3 heads, *one* from the medial or inner condyle of the humerus by the common tendon, the internal lateral or ulnar collateral ligament, and the intermuscular septum; the *second* from the inner side of the coronoid process of the ulna; the *third* from the oblique line of the radius: *into* the lateral margins of the second phalanges by 4 tendons which are split for the passage of the deep flexor tendons. *Action,* to flex the second phalanges. *Nerve,* median.

Flexor Profundus Digitorum (Perforans),—*from* the upper three-fourths of the shaft of the ulna, a depression on the inner side of the coronoid process, and the interosseous membrane: *into* the bases of the last phalanges, by 4 tendons which perforate the tendons of the superficial flexor. *Action,* to flex the phalanges. *Nerves,* ulnar, anterior interosseous branch of the median.

Flexor Longus Pollicis,—*from* the upper two-thirds of the shaft of the radius and the interosseous membrane: *into* the base of the last phalanx of the thumb, which it flexes. *Nerve,* anterior interosseous branch of the median.

Pronator Quadratus,—*from* the oblique line on the lower fourth of the ulna, and the anterior border of the ulna: *into* the lower fourth of the anterior border of the shaft of the radius. *Action,* to pronate the hand. *Nerve,* anterior interosseous branch of the median.

Brachio-radialis or Supinator Longus (13),—*from* the upper two-thirds of the lateral or external condylar ridge of the humerus, and the intermuscular septum; *into* the base of the styloid process of the radius. *Action*, to supinate the hand. *Nerve*, musculo-spiral (n. radialis).

Extensor Carpi Radialis Longior (*e*),—*from* the lower third of the lateral or external condylar ridge of the humerus, and the intermuscular septum: *into* the base of the metacarpal bone of the index finger (*g*), on its radial side. *Action*, to extend the wrist. *Nerve*, musculo-spiral (n. radialis).

FIG. 54.

Extensor Carpi Radialis Brevior (*f*),—*from* the lateral or external condyle of the humerus by the common tendon, the external lateral ligament, and the intermuscular septa: *into* the radial side of the base of the 3d metacarpal bone (*g*). *Action*, to extend the wrist. *Nerve*, posterior interosseous.

Extensor Communis Digitorum (*h*),—*from* the lateral or external condyle of the humerus by the common tendon, the deep fascia, and the intermuscular septa: *into* the 2d and 3d phalanges of all the fingers, by 3 tendons, one of which divides into two. *Action*, to extend the fingers. *Nerve*, posterior interosseous.

Extensor Minimi Digiti (m. extensor digiti quinti proprius) (*i*),—*from* the common tendon and the intermuscular septa: *into* the 2d and 3d phalanges of the little finger, with the tendon derived from the common extensor. *Action*, as named. *Nerve*, posterior interosseous.

Extensor Carpi Ulnaris (*j*),—*from* the common tendon, the middle third of the posterior border of the ulna, and the deep fascia of the forearm: *into* the base of the 5th metacarpal bone. *Action*, to extend the wrist. *Nerve*, posterior interosseous.

Anconeus (*k*),—*from* the lateral or external condyle of the humerus, posteriorly: *into* the side of the olecranon, and upper fourth of the posterior surface of the shaft of the ulna. *Action*, to extend the forearm. *Nerve*, the musculo-spiral (n. radialis).

Supinator Brevis (m. supinator)—*from* the external condyle of the humerus, the external lateral and orbicular ligaments and an oblique line on the ulna: *into* the inner surface of the neck of the radius, the outer edge of its bicipital tuberosity, and the oblique line. *Action*, to supinate the hand. *Nerve*, posterior interosseous, which pierces it.

Extensor Ossis Metacarpi Pollicis (m. abductor pollicis longus) (14),—*from* the posterior surfaces of the shafts of the radius and ulna, and the interosseous membrane: *into* the base of the metacarpal bone of the thumb. *Action*, to extend the thumb. *Nerve*, posterior interosseous.

Extensor Brevis Pollicis (Extensor Primi Internodii Pollicis) (*n*),—*from* the posterior surface of the shaft of the radius and the interosseous membrane: *into* the base of the 1st phalanx of the thumb. *Action*, to extend the thumb. *Nerve*, posterior interosseous.

Extensor Longus Pollicis (Extensor Secundi Internodii Pollicis) (*m*),—*from* the shaft of the ulna posteriorly and the interosseous membrane: *into* the base of the last phalanx of the thumb. *Action*, to extend the thumb. *Nerve*, posterior interosseous.

Extensor Indicis (m. extensor indicis proprius),—*from* the shaft of the ulna posteriorly and the interosseous membrane: *into* the 2d and 3d phalanges of the index finger with the tendon of the common extensor. *Action*, to extend the index finger. *Nerve*, posterior interosseous.

FASCIÆ OF THE HAND

Anterior Annular Ligament (l. carpi transversum),—*from* the pisiform and unciform (hamate) bones: *to* the tuberosity of the scaphoid (navicular) and the ridge on the trapezium (great multangular). Inserted into its anterior surface are parts of the tendons of the palmaris longus and the flexor carpi radialis, and beneath it pass the tendons of the superficial and deep flexors of the fingers and the flexor longus pollicis, also the median nerve. It is continuous with the palmar fascia and the deep fascia of the forearm.

Posterior Annular Ligament (l. carpi dorsale) (*o*),—*from* the ulna, cuneiform and pisiform bones: *to* the margin of the radius and the ridges on its posterior surface. It has 6 canals for the passage of the extensor tendons, each lined by a synovial membrane. It is continuous with the deep fascia of the forearm.

Deep Palmar Fascia,—ensheaths the muscles of the hand, and divides into 4 slips for the four fingers, each slip dividing and forming tendinous arches for the passage of the flexor tendons of the fingers.

Muscles of the Hand

Abductor Pollicis (m. abductor pollicis brevis) (11),—*from* the ridge of the trapezium (great multangular) the tuberosity of the scaphoid (navicular) and the annular ligament (l. carpi transversum): *into* the radial side of the base of the 1st phalanx of the thumb. *Action*, to draw the thumb from the median line. *Nerve*, median.

Opponens Pollicis,—*from* the palmar surface of the trapezium (great multangular) and the annular ligament (l. carpi transversum): *into* the radial side of the metacarpal bone of the thumb, for its whole length. *Action*, as a flexor ossis metacarpi pollicis. *Nerve*, median.

Flexor Brevis Pollicis (12),—the outer portion from the lower border of the annular ligament (l. carpi transversum), the inner and deeper portion from the ulnar side of the 1st metacarpal bone: *into* both sides of the base of the 1st phalanx of the thumb, by two tendons, each having a sesamoid bone in it. *Action*, to flex the thumb. *Nerves*, median and ulnar.

Adductor Obliquus Pollicis (m. adductor pollicis),—*from* the os magnum, the bases of the 2d and 3d metacarpal bones, the anterior carpal ligaments and the sheath of the tendon of the flexor carpi radialis: *into* the ulnar side of the base of the 1st phalanx of the thumb, having a sesamoid bone in the tendon of insertion. *Action*, to draw the thumb toward the median line. *Nerve*, ulnar.

Adductor Transversus Pollicis,—*from* the lower two-thirds of the metacarpal bone of the middle finger: *into* the ulnar side of the base of the 1st phalanx of the thumb. *Action*, as the preceding muscle. *Nerve*, ulnar. [The above-mentioned 5 muscles of the thumb occupy the radial side of the hand and form the *Thenar Eminence;* the first 4 of the following-mentioned muscles occupy the ulnar side of the hand and form the *Hypothenar Eminence.*]

Palmaris Brevis (10),—*from* the annular ligament and palmar fascia: *into* the skin on the ulnar border of the palm of the hand. *Action*, to corrugate the skin of the hand. *Nerve*, ulnar.

Abductor Minimi Digiti (m. abductor digiti quinti),—*from* the pisiform bone and the tendon of the flexor carpi ulnaris: *into* the ulnar side of the base of the 1st phalanx of the little finger and the aponeurosis of the extensor minimi digiti. *Action*, as indicated by its name. *Nerve*, ulnar.

Flexor Brevis Minimi Digiti (m. flexor digiti quinti brevis),—*from* the hook of the unciform bone and the annular ligament (l. carpi transversum): *into* the base of the proximal phalanx of the little finger, with the preceding muscle. *Action,* as named. *Nerve,* ulnar.

Opponens Minimi Digiti (m. opponens digiti quinti),—*from* the unciform or hamate bone and the annular ligament (l. carpi transversum): *into* the whole ulnar margin of the 5th metacarpal bone. *Action,* a flexor of the 5th metacarpal bone. *Nerve,* ulnar.

Lumbricales 4,—*from* the tendons of the deep flexor: *into* the expanded tendons of the common extensor on the dorsi of the phalanges. *Action,* to dorsiflex the proximal phalanges. *Nerves,* median and ulnar. These muscles have no sheaths.

Dorsal Interossei 4,—by 2 heads *from* the adjacent sides of the metacarpal bones: *into* the bases of the proximal phalanges of the index, middle, and ring fingers, the middle finger having two. *Action,* abductors of the fingers from the median line of the hand. *Nerve,* ulnar.

Palmar Interossei (mm. interossei volares) 3,—*from* the palmar surfaces of the 2d, 4th, and 5th metacarpal bones: *into* the bases of the proximal phalanges of the same fingers. *Action,* adductors of the fingers. *Nerve,* ulnar.

MUSCLES OF THE LOWER EXTREMITY

MUSCLES AND FASCIÆ OF THE ILIAC REGION

ILIAC FASCIA,—is an aponeurotic layer which lines the back of the abdominal cavity and covers the psoas and iliacus muscles throughout their whole extent. It is attached above to the ligamentum arcuatum internum (medial lumbo-costal arch), internally by arched processes to the bodies of the vertebræ, also to the sacrum and the brim of the true pelvis; externally it is continuous with the lumbar fascia above and is attached to the whole length of the inner border of the crest of the ilium; below it is continuous with the fascia transversalis and the pubic part of the fascia lata of the thigh, is intimately connected to Poupart's (l. inguinale) ligament, and is prolonged backward and inward therefrom as a band, the *Ilio-pectineal Ligament,* to the ilio-pectineal eminence. It descends behind the femoral vessels into the thigh, forming the posterior wall of the femoral sheath. *Transversalis Fascia* lines the anterior abdominal wall.

Psoas Magnus (m. psoas major) (11),—*from* the bodies, transverse processes, and intervertebral substances of the last thoracic and all the lumbar vertebræ: *into* the lesser trochanter of the femur, by a common tendon with the iliacus. *Action,* to flex the thigh upon the pelvis, and when the femur is fixed to bend the trunk forward. *Nerves,* anterior branches of the 2nd and 3rd lumbar.

Psoas Parvus (m. psoas minor),—*from* the bodies of the last thoracic and first lumbar vertebræ and the intervertebral substance: *into* the ilio-pectineal eminence and the iliac fascia. *Action*, when present it is a tensor of the iliac fascia. *Nerve*, anterior branch of the 1st lumbar.

Iliacus (10),—*from* the iliac fossa, inner margin of the iliac crest, ilio-lumbar ligament, base of the sacrum, anterior spinous processes of the ilium and the notch between them: *into* the outer side of the tendon of the psoas magnus, and the capsule of the hip-joint. *Action*, the same as that of the psoas magnus. *Nerve*, anterior crural.

Muscles and Fasciæ of the Thigh

Superficial Fascia,—forms a continuous fatty covering over the whole thigh, in which lie the superficial vessels and nerves. The *superficial* layer is continuous above with Camper's fascia of the abdomen. The *deep* fibrous layer (Scarpa's fascia) covers the saphenous opening in the fascia lata (see below), where it is perforated for the internal saphenous vein and numerous vessels, and is therefore called the *Cribriform Fascia* in this situation. It forms one of the coverings of a femoral hernia.

Fascia Lata,—the *deep fascia* of the thigh, extends from Poupart's ligament to the prominent points around the knee-joint, and from the margin of the sacrum and coccyx around the limb to the pubic arch and pectineal line. It sends two strong intermuscular septa down to the linea aspera, and contains the *Saphenous Opening* (fossa ovalis), which is formed by the reflected margins of its pubic and iliac portions. The structure named *Poupart's Ligament* (l. inguinale) is made by the knife, and is only the line of junction between the aponeurosis of the external oblique muscle and the fascia lata; extending from the anterior superior spine of the ilium to the spine of the pubic bone.

Tensor Vaginæ Femoris (m. tensor fasciæ latæ) (4),—*from* the anterior part of the outer lip of the iliac crest, the anterior superior spinous process and part of the notch below it, also from the fascia covering the gluteus medius: *into* the fascia lata, between its two layers, about one-fourth down the outer side of the thigh. *Action*, a tensor of the fascia lata. *Nerve*, superior gluteal.

Sartorius (5),—*from* the anterior superior spine of the ilium (2) and half of the notch below it: *into* the upper internal surface of the shaft of the tibia. *Action*, to flex and cross the legs. *Nerve*, anterior crural.

Quadriceps Extensor (m. quadriceps femoris),—including the 4 remaining muscles on the front of the thigh,—the rectus femoris, vastus externus (m. vastus lateralis), vastus internus (m. vastus medialis), and the crureus (m. vastus intermedius). Its tendon is inserted into the patella. *Action*, the great extensor of the leg. *Nerve*, anterior crural.

Rectus Femoris (6),—by two tendons, *the Straight* from the anterior inferior spine of the ilium, *the Reflected* from a groove above the brim of the acetabulum: *into* the patella by a flattened tendon (9) which is common to this and the next 3 muscles. *Action*, to extend the leg. *Nerve*, anterior crural (n. femoralis).

Fig. 55.

Vastus Externus (m. vastus lateralis) (7),—*from* the anterior border of the great trochanter and part of the linea aspera of the femur: *into* the outer border of the patella, by a flat tendon which blends with the great extensor tendon. *Action*, to extend the leg. *Nerve*, anterior crural (n. femoralis).

Vastus Internus (m. vastus medialis) (8),—*from* the anterior intertrochanteric line, the spiral line, the linea aspera, the internal supracondylar line, the tendon of the adductor magnus and the intermuscular septum: *into* the inner border of the patella and the great extensor tendon. *Action*, to extend the leg. *Nerve*, anterior crural (n. femoralis).

Crureus (m. vastus intermedius),—*from* the upper two-thirds of the shaft of the femur and the intermuscular septum: *into* the great extensor tendon. *Action*, to extend the leg. *Nerve*, anterior crural. This muscle and the vastus internus appear to be inseparably united, but they can be separated.

Subcrureus (m. articularis genu),—often blended with the crureus: *from* the lower part of the shaft of the femur anteriorly;—*into* the capsular ligament behind the patella. *Action*, to draw up the capsular ligament. *Nerve*, anterior crural.

Gracilis (15),—*from* the margin of the symphysis and the anterior half of the pubic arch: *into* the inner surface of the shaft of the tibia below the tuberosity (medial condyle). *Action*, to flex the leg and rotate it inward, also to adduct the thigh. *Nerve*, obturator.

Pectineus (12),—*from* the ilio-pectineal line, and the bone in front thereof, also from the fascia covering the muscle: *into* the rough line extending from the trochanter minor to the linea aspera. *Action*, to adduct the thigh and rotate it outward. *Nerves*, accessory obturator, anterior crural (n. femoralis).

Adductor Longus (13),—*from* the front of the os pubis: *into* the middle third of the linea aspera. *Action*, to adduct the thigh powerfully. *Nerve*, obturator.

Adductor Brevis,—*from* the body and descending ramus of the os pubis; *into* the upper part of the linea aspera. *Action*, to adduct the thigh. *Nerve*, obturator.

FIG. 56.

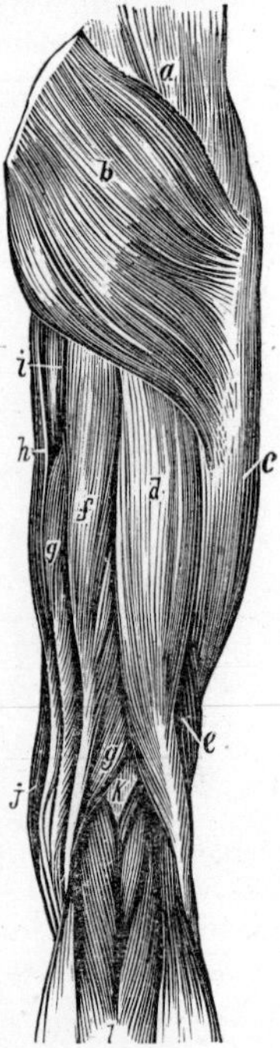

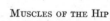

Adductor Magnus (14),—*from* the descending ramus of the os pubis, the ramus of the ischium, and the outer margin and under surface of the tuberosity of the ischium: *into* the rough line leading from the great trochanter to the linea aspera, the whole length of the linea aspera, and by a tendon into the tubercle on the inner condyle of the femur. *Action*, to adduct the thigh and rotate it outward. *Nerves*, obturator and great sciatic. This muscle is pierced by 4 *apertures* for the 3 superior perforating and the profunda arteries, and about the lower one-third of its insertion an angular interval is left therein, the lower opening of *Hunter's canal* (femoral canal), for the passage of the femoral vessels into the popliteal space.

MUSCLES OF THE HIP

Gluteus Maximus (m. glutæus maximus) (*b*),— *from* the posterior gluteal line of the ilium, the crest behind it, the last piece of the sacrum, the side of the coccyx, the great sacro-sciatic ligament, the aponeurosis of the erector spinæ and the fascia covering the gluteus medius: *into* the fascia lata and the rough line leading from the great trochanter to the linea aspera. *Action*, to extend and abduct the thigh and rotate it outward, also to maintain the trunk erect. *Nerves*, inferior gluteal from the sacral plexus.

Gluteus Medius (m. glutæus medius) (*a*),—*from* the ilium between the posterior gluteal and the anterior gluteal lines, the crest between them, and the fascia of the part: *into* the oblique lines on the great trochanter. *Action*, its posterior fibres rotate the thigh outward, its anterior fibres rotate inward. It also abducts the thigh and draws it forward, and assists to maintain the trunk erect. *Nerve*, superior gluteal.

Gluteus Minimus (m. glutæus minimus) (8),—*from* the ilium between the anterior and inferior gluteal lines, and the margin of the great sacro-sciatic notch: *into* the anterior border of the great trochanter. *Action*, to rotate the thigh inward, also to abduct and draw it forward, and to maintain the trunk erect. *Nerve*, superior gluteal.

Pyriformis (9),—by 3 digitations from the front of the sacrum, from the margin of the great sacro-sciatic foramen and the great sacro-sciatic ligament (l. sacro-tuberosum): *into* the upper border of the great trochanter (7), having passed through the great sacro-sciatic foramen. *Action*, an external rotator of the thigh. *Nerves*, first and second sacral.

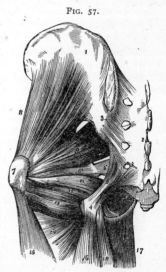

FIG. 57.

Obturator Internus (11),—*from* the posterior bony margin of the obturator foramen and the inner surface of the obturator membrane: *into* the great trochanter (7), passing through the lesser sacro-sciatic foramen. *Action*, an external rotator of the thigh. *Nerve*, a special nerve from sacral plexus to the obturator internus.

Gemellus Superior (10), *from* the outer surface of the spine of the ischium: *into* the great trochanter, being blended with the tendon of the obturator internus. *Action*, an external rotator of the thigh. *Nerve*, the special nerve to the obturator internus from the sacral plexus.

Gemellus Inferior (12), *from* the tuberosity of the ischium: *into* the tendon of the obturator internus and the great trochanter. *Action*, an external rotator of the thigh. *Nerve*. the special nerve from the sacral plexus to the quadratus femoris.

Quadratus Femoris (13),—*from* the tuberosity of the ischium: *into* the upper part of the linea quadrata on the trochanter major posteriorly. *Action*, an external rotator of the thigh. *Nerves*, a special branch of the sacral plexus.

Obturator Externus,—*from* the anterior inner bony margin of the obturator foramen, and the inner two-thirds of the anterior surface of the obturator membrane: *into* the trochanteric or digital fossa of the femur. *Action*, an external rotator of the thigh. *Nerve*, obturator.

Biceps (m. biceps femoris) (16),—by 2 heads, the *Long Head* (*d*) from the tuberosity of the ischium posteriorly, the *Short Head* (*e*) from the outer lip of the linea aspera, and the intermuscular septum: *into* the outer side of the head of the fibula; its tendon embracing the external lateral (fibular collateral) ligament of the knee-joint and forming the *Outer Hamstring*, the tendons of the semi-tendinosus, semi-membranosus, gracilis and sartorius forming the *Inner Hamstring*. *Action*, to flex the leg and rotate it outward. *Nerve*, great sciatic.

Semi-tendinosus (*f*),—*from* the tuberosity of the ischium by a tendon (4) common to it and the long head of the biceps, and from the adjacent aponeurosis: *into* the shaft of the tibia at its upper and inner surface, its tendon curving around the inner tuberosity (medial condyle). *Action*, to flex the leg upon the thigh. *Nerve*, great sciatic.

Semi-membranosus (*g*),—*from* the tuberosity of the ischium above the origin of the above-named two muscles: *into* the inner tuberosity (medial condyle) of the tibia; its tendon of insertion giving off fibrous expansions one to the outer condyle of the femur forming part of the posterior ligament of the knee-joint, another to the fascia covering the popliteus muscle, and fibres to the internal lateral (tibial collateral) ligament of the joint. *Action*, to flex the leg, and rotate it inward. *Nerve*, great sciatic.

External Rotators of the Hip-joint are 13½,—the 3 adductors, pyriformis, 2 obturators, 2 gemelli, quadratus femoris, pectineus, psoas magnus, iliacus, sartorius, and posterior half of the gluteus medius.

Internal Rotators of the Hip-joint are 2½,—the tensor vaginæ femoris, gluteus minimus, and the anterior half of the gluteus medius.

MUSCLES OF THE LEG

Tibialis Anti'cus (m. tibialis anterior) (3),—*from* the outer tuberosity (lateral condyle) and upper two-thirds of the shaft of the tibia externally, the interosseous membrane, deep fascia, and intermuscular septum; through the inner canal in the anterior annular ligament (ll. transversum et cruciatum cruris): *into* the inner and plantar surface of the internal cuneiform bone, and the base of the 1st metatarsal. *Action*, to flex the tarsus on the leg, and elevate the inner border of the foot. *Nerve*, anterior tibial.

Extensor Proprius Hallucis (m. extensor hallucis longus) (5),—*from* the middle two-fourths of the fibula anteriorly and the interosseous membrane, through the 2d canal in the anterior annular ligament: (l. transversum cruris et l. cruciatum cruris): *into* the base of the terminal or distal phalanx of the great toe. *Action*, to extend that toe. *Nerve*, anterior tibial (deep peroneal nerve).

FIG. 58.

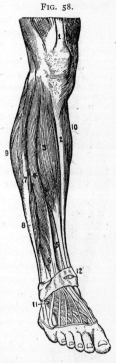

Extensor Longus Digitorum (m. extensor digitorum longus) (4),—*from* the outer tuberosity (lateral condyle) of the tibia the upper three-fourths of the extensor surface of the shaft of the fibula anteriorly, interosseous membrane, deep fascia, and intermuscular septa: *into* the 2d and 3d phalanges of the 4 lesser toes, by 4 tendons which pass over the dorsum of the foot from the outer canal in the anterior annular ligament (ll. transversum et cruciatum cruris). *Action*, to extend the lesser toes. *Nerve*, anterior tibial (deep peroneal).

Peroneus Tertius (m. peronæus tertius) (6),—*from* the outer lower fourth of the extensor surface of the fibula, interosseous membrane and intermuscular septum: *into* the base of the 5th metatarsal bone. This muscle is a part of the last-named, and passes through the same canal in the annular ligament (ll. transversum et cruciatum cruris). *Action*, to dorsiflex the tarsus. *Nerve*, anterior tibial (deep peroneal).

Gastrocnemius,—by 2 heads (9, 10), *from* the condyles of the femur, and the supra-condylar ridges: unites with the tendon of the soleus to form the *tendo Achillis*, into the posterior tuberosity of the os calcis (calcaneus). *Action*, to extend the foot or flex the calcaneus. *Nerve*, internal popliteal (n. tibialis).

Soleus,—*from* the head and upper third of the flexor surface of the shaft

8

of the fibula posteriorly, the oblique line of the tibia, and the tendinous arch: unites with the tendon of the gastrocnemius as the *tendo Achillis* (see above). *Action,* to extend the foot and flex the heel. *Nerves,* internal popliteal, posterior tibial (nn. tibialis).

Plantaris,—*from* the outer bifurcation of the linea aspera and the posterior ligament of the knee-joint: by a very long, delicate tendon *into* the posterior surface of the os calcis. *Action,* to extend the foot and flex the heel. *Nerve,* internal popliteal (n. tibialis).

Popliteus (6 Fig. 59),—*from* a depression on the external (lateral) condyle of the femur, and the posterior ligament of the knee-joint: *into* the inner two-thirds of the triangular surface on the shaft of the tibia (2) posteriorly and above the oblique line. *Action,* to flex the leg. *Nerve,* internal popliteal (n. tibialis).

FIG. 59.

Flexor Longus Hallucis (m. flexor hallucis longus) (9),—*from* the lower two-thirds of the flexor surface of the shaft of the fibula, the interosseous membrane, fascia, and intermuscular septum, its tendon passing through grooves in the tibia, astragalus and os calcis: *into* the base of the last phalanx of the great toe. *Action,* to flex the great toe. *Nerve,* posterior tibial (n. tibialis).

Flexor Longus Digitorum (m. flexor digitorum longus) (7),—*from* the shaft of the tibia posteriorly and below the oblique line; its tendon passing behind the inner malleolus in a groove (13) with the tibialis posticus (m. tibialis posterior): *into* the bases of the last phalanges of the lesser toes by 4 tendons which perforate the tendons of the flexor brevis digitorum. *Action,* to flex the phalanges and extend the foot. *Nerve,* posterior tibial (n. tibialis).

Tibialis Posti′cus (m. tibialis posterior) (8),—by two processes between which pass the anterior tibial vessels, *from* the upper half of shaft of the tibia posteriorly, the upper two-thirds of the flexor surface of the shaft of the fibula internally, the interosseous membrane, deep fascia, and intermuscular septa; its tendon passes behind the inner malleolus in a groove (13) with the long flexor: *into* the tuberosity of the scaphoid and internal cuneiform bones. *Action,* to extend the tarsus and invert the foot. *Nerve,* posterior tibial (n. tibialis).

Peroneus Longus (m. peronæus longus) (10),—*from* the head of the fibula, and the upper two-thirds of the peroneal surface of its shaft externally, the deep fascia and intermuscular septa, passes behind the outer malleolus in a groove with the peroneus brevis, through a groove in the cuboid bone: *into* the outer side of the base of the metatarsal bone of the great toe and the internal cuneiform bone, having crossed the sole of the foot obliquely. *Action,* to extend and evert the foot and flex the heel. *Nerve,* musculo-cutaneous branch of the external popliteal (n. peronæi superficialis).

Peroneus Brevis (m. peronæus brevis) (11),—*from* the middle third of the peroneal surface of the shaft of the fibula externally and the intermuscular septa: its tendon passes behind the external malleolus in a groove with the long peroneal, *into* the dorsum of the base of the 5th metatarsal bone. *Action,* to extend the foot. *Nerve,* musculo-cutaneous branch of the external popliteal (n. peronæi superficialis).

FASCIÆ OF THE FOOT

ANTERIOR ANNULAR LIGAMENT (ll. transversum et cruciatum cruris) (12 Fig. 58),—consists of vertical and horizontal portions, is attached to the lower ends of the fibula and tibia, the os calcis and the plantar fascia. It contains sheaths lined by synovial membranes for the tendons of the extensor muscles (that of the extensor proprius hallucis passing beneath it), as also the anterior tibial vessels and nerve.

INTERNAL ANNULAR LIGAMENT (l. laciniatum),—*from* the inner malleolus *to* the os calcis (calcaneus), converting 4 bony grooves into canals lined by synovial membranes for the flexor tendons and the posterior tibial vessels and nerves.

EXTERNAL ANNULAR LIGAMENT (l. peronæi retinaculum superior),—*from* the outer malleolus *to* the os calcis, binding down the peronei tendons in one synovial sac.

PLANTAR FASCIA,—the densest in the body, divided into a central and two lateral portions, and attached to the inner tuberosity of the os calcis, divides into 5 processes, 1 for each toe, and several intermuscular septa.

DORSAL FASCIA,—is a thin membranous layer continuous above with the anterior margin of the annular ligament, and becoming gradually lost opposite the heads of the metatarsal bones, and on each side blending with the plantar fascia. It forms a sheath for the tendons on the dorsum of the foot.

MUSCLES OF THE FOOT

Extensor Brevis Digitorum (m. extensor digitorum brevis) (11 Fig. 58),— the only muscle on the dorsum of the foot, arises *from* the os calcis

externally, the calcaneo-astragaloid and the anterior annular ligaments
(l. cruciatum cruris):—by 4 tendons, 1 into the proximal phalanx of
the great toe, and the others into the outer sides of the long extensor
tendons of the 2d, 3d, and 4th toes. *Action*, to extend the toes. *Nerve*,
anterior tibial (deep peroneal).

Muscles on the sole of the foot number 19; arranged by layers:—

1st Layer

Abductor Hallucis.

Flexor Brevis Digitorum (m.
flexor digitorum brevis).

Abductor Minimi Digiti (m.
abductor digiti quinti).

2d Layer

Flexor Accessorius (m. quadratus plantæ).

Lumbricales, 4.

3d Layer

Flexor Brevis Hallucis (m. flexor hallucis brevis).

Adductor Obliquus Hallucis (caput obliquum m. adductoris hallucis).

Flexor Brevis Minimi Digiti (m. flexor
digiti quinti brevis).

Adductor Transversus Hallucis (caput
transversum m. adductoris hallucis).

4th Layer

Interossei (4 *Dorsal*, 3 *Plantar*).

Abductor Hallucis,—*from* the inner tubercle of the os calcis (calcaneus),
the internal annular ligament (l. laciniatum), plantar fascia, and intermuscular septum: *into* the inner side of the base of the 1st phalanx of
the great toe. *Action*, to abduct the great toe. *Nerve*, internal plantar
(n. plantaris medialis).

Flexor Brevis Digitorum (m. flexor digitorum brevis),—*from* the inner
tubercle of the os calcis (calcaneus) (11), the plantar fascia and intermuscular septa: *into* the sides of the 2d phalanges of the lesser toes by 4
tendons (5) which are perforated for the long flexor tendons (2). *Action*,
to flex the lesser toes. *Nerve*, internal plantar (n. plantaris medialis).

Abductor Minimi Digiti (m. abductor digiti quinti),—*from* the tubercles
and under surface of the os calcis (calcaneus) (11), the plantar fascia and
the intermuscular septum: *into* the base of the proximal phalanx of the
little toe with the tendon of its short flexor. *Action*, to abduct the little
toe. *Nerve*, external plantar (n. plantaris lateralis).

Flexor Accessorius (m. quadratus plantæ) (1),—by 2 heads, *from* the os
calcis (calcaneus) and the long plantar ligament: *into* the tendon of the
flexor longus digitorum. *Action*, accessory flexor of the toes. *Nerve*,
external plantar (n. plantaris lateralis).

Lumbricales (4), four, *from* the long flexor tendons: each *into* the dorsum of
the proximal phalanx of the corresponding toe. *Action*, accessory

flexors of the toes and to dorsiflex the proximal phalanges.
ternal plantar (n. plantaris medialis) to the innermost
external plantar (n. plantaris lateralis) to the other three.

Flexor Brevis Hallucis (m. flexor hallucis brevis) (7),—*from* th
and external cuneiform bones, and the prolonged tendon of the ......us
posticus (m. tibialis posticus): *into* both sides of the base of the proximal
phalanx of the great toe, by 2 portions, of which one blends with the
abductor hallucis, the other with the adductor ob-
liquus hallucis. *Action*, to flex the great toe.
Nerve, internal plantar (n. plantaris medialis).

Fig. 60.

Adductor Obliquus Hallucis (caput obliquum m.
adductoris hallucis),—*from* the tarsal ends of
the three middle metatarsal bones, and the
sheath of the tendon of the peroneus longus:
into the base of the proximal phalanx of the
great toe, externally. *Action*, to adduct the
great toe. *Nerve*, external plantar (n. plantaris
lateralis).

Flexor Brevis Minimi Digiti (m. flexor digiti quinti
brevis) (6),—*from* the base of the 5th metatarsal
bone (9) and the sheath of the tendon of the peroneus longus: *into* the base of the proximal
phalanx of the little toe externally. *Action*, to
flex the little toe. *Nerve*, external plantar (n.
plantaris lateralis.)

Adductor Transversus Hallucis (caput transversum
m. adductoris hallucis) (Transversus Pedis),—*from*
the inferior metatarso-phalangeal ligaments of
the three outer toes and the transverse ligament of the metatarsus:
into the outer side of the proximal phalanx of the great toe, blending with
the tendon of the adductor obliquus hallucis. *Action*, to adduct the
great toe. *Nerve*, external plantar (n. plantaris lateralis).

Dorsal Interossei (4),—each by two heads *from* the adjacent sides of
two metatarsal bones: *into* the base of the proximal phalanx of the
corresponding toe. *Action*, to abduct the toes. *Nerve*, external plantar.

Plantar Interossei 3,—*from* the shafts of the 3d, 4th, and 5th metatarsal
bones: *into* the bases of the proximal phalanges of the same toes. *Action*, to adduct the toes toward the median line. *Nerve*, external plantar
(n. plantaris lateralis).

THE BLOOD-VASCULAR SYSTEM

THE HEART OR COR

The Pericardium is a conical membranous sac, containing the heart and the roots of the great vessels. It lies behind the sternum and between the pluræ, its apex upward, its base attached to the central tendon of the diaphragm. It is composed of an outer fibrous coat, and an inner serous one; the former is prolonged on the outer surfaces of the great vessels, except the inferior vena cava, and becomes continuous with the deep layer of the cervical fascia; the latter consists of a parietal layer, lining the inner surface of the fibrous coat, and a visceral layer, which is reflected over the heart and vessels. The serous portion secretes a thin fluid, about 1 drachm in quantity normally, for the lubrication of its surfaces. *Arteries*, are derived from the internal mammary and its musculo-phrenic branch, and from the descending thoracic aorta. *Nerves*, are branches from the vagus, the phrenic and the sympathetic.

The Endocardium is a thin, smooth, transparent membrane, which lines the internal surface of the heart; assisting by its reduplications in forming the valves, and being continuous with the lining membrane of the great blood-vessels.

The Heart (cor) is a hollow muscular organ, conoidal in shape, placed obliquely in the chest between the lungs, base upward, apex to the left and front, corresponding to the space between the 5th and 6th costal cartilages, $\frac{3}{4}$ inch inside of and $1\frac{1}{2}$ inch below the left nipple. In the adult its size is about 5 inches by $3\frac{1}{2}$ by $2\frac{1}{2}$, and from 10 to 12 oz. in weight in the male, 8 to 10 oz. in the female.

The Cavities of the Heart are 4 in number, an atrium and ventricle on each side of the heart; the cavities on one side being separated from those of the other side by a longitudinal muscular septum. The division into 4 cavities is indicated on the external surface of the organ by grooves, named, from their contiguous cavities, the *auriculo-ventricular groove* transversely, and the *inter-ventricular grooves* longitudinally.

Structure of the Heart. The muscular fibres forming the heart take origin from four fibrous rings at the auriculo-ventricular and aortic openings. The fibres of the auricles are arranged in two layers, a superficial and a deep one, the latter having looped fibres and annular fibres. In the ventricles the fibres are also superficial and deep, the latter being arranged circularly, the former spirally, coiling inward at the apex of the heart into a whorl-like form, the *vortex*.

Vessels and Nerves. The *Arteries* are the right and left coronary from the aorta. The *Veins* accompany the arteries and terminate in the right auricle. The *Lymphatics* terminate in the thoracic and right lymphatic ducts. The *Nerves* are derived from the cardiac plexuses, which are formed partly from the cranial nerves and partly from the sympathetic.

THE RIGHT HEART

The Right Auricle (atrium dextrum) is slightly larger than the left, its walls somewhat thinner, being about one line in thickness; its cavity contains about 2 fluidounces. It consists of two parts, a principal cavity, the *sinus venosus* (1) or *atrium*, situated posteriorly, and a smaller portion, the *appendix auriculæ* (auricula dextra) (2), situated anteriorly. It receives the venous blood by the superior (3) and inferior (4) venæ cavæ and the coronary sinus, and presents interiorly the following points for examination:—

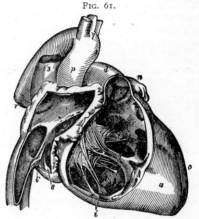

FIG. 61.

Appendix Auriculæ (auricula dextra) (*n*),—a conical pouch projecting from the sinus to the front and left, its margins being dentated.

Openings—of the superior and inferior venæ cavæ and the coronary sinus (7), the latter having a valve in two segments.

Foramina Thebesii (**foramina venarum minimarum**),—several minute orifices, the mouths of veins from the substance of the heart.

Auriculo-ventricular Opening (ostium venosum dextrum) (9),—communicates with the right ventricle, is oval, about 1½ inch broad, surrounded by a fibrous ring, and is guarded by the tricuspid valve.

Fossa Ovalis (5),—a depression on the inner wall, corresponding to the situation of the foramen ovale in the fœtus.

Annulus Ovalis (limbus fossæ ovalis [Vieussenii]),—the oval margin of the fossa ovalis.

Musculi Pectinati,—muscular columns on the inner surface of the appendix and the inner wall of the auricle.

Tubercle of Lower (tuberculum intervenosum [Loweri]),—a very small projection on the right wall, supposed to influence the direction of the blood-current.

Eustachian Valve (valvula venæ cavæ inferioris [Eustachii]) (6),—at the anterior margin of the inferior vena cava; large in the fœtus, to direct the blood to the foramen ovale.

Coronary Valve (valvulæ sinus coronarii [Thebesii]) (Valve of Thebesius) (8),—a semicircular fold which protects the orifice of the coronary sinus and prevents regurgitation of blood into the sinus.

The Right Ventricle (ventriculus dexter) (*a*) is triangular in form and extends from the right auricle to near the apex of the heart. Its anterior surface is rounded and convex and forms the larger part of the front of the heart. Its under surface is flattened and rests upon the diaphragm. Its cavity (*b c*) can contain about 3 fluidounces, and presents the following points for examination:—

Tricuspid Valve (valvula tricuspidalis) (*e, f*),—consists of 3 triangular segments connected by their bases with the auriculo-ventricular orifice, and by their sides with each other, the largest being on the left side.

Semilunar Valves (valvulæ semilunares a. pulmonalis) (*m*),—are 3 in number, and guard the orifice of the pulmonary artery; each about the middle of its free margin has a fibrocartilaginous nodule, the *corpus Arantii* (noduli valvarum semilunarum [Arantii]), which more perfectly closes the orifice.

Opening of the Pulmonary Artery (ostium arteriosum pulmonis),—at the superior and internal angle of the ventricle, the *conus arteriosus*. It is circular in form, surrounded by a fibrous ring, and is guarded by three semilunar valves.

Sinuses of Valsalva,—are 3 pouches, one behind each valve, between it and the commencement of the pulmonary artery.

Columnæ Ccrneæ (trabeculæ carnæ) (*g*),—muscular columns projecting from the surface of the ventricle, of which 3 or 4, called *musculi papillares*, give attachment to the chordæ tendinæ.

Chordæ Tendinæ (*l*),—delicate tendinous cords which connect the margins and lower surfaces of the tricuspid valve with the columnæ.

The Left Heart

The Left Auricle (atrium sinistrum) is smaller than the right, but has thicker walls, being about 1½ line. Like the right auricle it consists of a principal cavity (1) or *sinus* (atrium) and an *appendix auriculæ* (auricula

sinistra, (2), which overlaps the root of the pulmonary artery.   Internally
the auricle presents the following parts:—

Openings (3) *of the Pulmonary Veins*,—are 4 in number, sometimes 3, as
the two left veins (5) frequently end in a common opening.   They
have no valves.

Left Auriculo-ventricular Opening (ostium venosum ventriculi sinistri)
(6),—is smaller than the right one.

Musculi Pectinati,—on the inner surface of the appendix.

Depression,—corresponding to the fossa ovalis in the right auricle.

The Left Ventricle (ventriculus sinister) (8) is longer, thicker and more
conical in shape than the right ventricle (*h*), and it forms a small part of
the anterior surface of the heart but
a considerable part of its posterior
surface. By its projection beyond
the apex of the right ventricle it
forms the apex of the heart. Its walls
are the thickest of those in the heart,
being thrice as thick as those of the
right ventricle. Its interior (9) presents the following:—

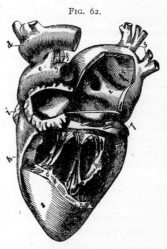

Fig. 62.

Left Auriculo-ventricular Opening
(ostium venosum ventriculi sinistri),—is surrounded by a dense
fibrous ring (annulus fibrosus sinister) and is guarded by the mitral
valve (valvula bicuspidalis).

Aortic Opening (ostium arteriosum),—is small and circular, placed in
front and to the right of the auriculo-ventricular, a segment of the
mitral (bicuspid) valve being between them.   It is surrounded by a
fibrous ring, and guarded by the semilunar valves (valvulæ semilunares aortæ).

Mitral Valve (valvula bicuspidalis) (*a*),—consists of two unequal-
sized segments, and is attached to the fibrous ring which surrounds
the auriculo-ventricular opening (ostium venosum ventriculi sinistri).
Its margins are connected with the ventricular walls by chordæ
tendinæ and musculi papillares.

Semilunar Valves (valvulæ semilunares aortæ),—3 in number, guard the
aortic orifice, and are larger and stronger than those on the right side.

Sinus of Valsalva,—a pouch in the wall of the aorta opposite each segment of the semilunar valves.

Columnæ Carneæ (b),—are smaller and more numerous than those on the right side; the *musculi papillares* are but two in number, one connected to the anterior, the other to the posterior wall.

THE ARTERIES

The Arteries are cylindrical tubular vessels which carry blood from the ventricles of the heart to every part of the body. The *Aorta* and its branches, together with the returning veins, constitute the greater or systemic circulation. The *Pulmonary Artery* and its branches to the lungs, together with the returning veins, constitute the lesser or pulmonic circulation. The arteries anastomose or communicate freely with each other everywhere throughout the body, permitting the establishment of collateral circulations.

Structure of the Arteries. They are dense in structure, very elastic, preserving their cylindrical form, and are composed of 3 coats, an *Internal* or serous (tunica intima); a *Middle* (tunica media), composed of muscular and elastic tissue; and an *External* (tunica externa or adventitia), composed of connective tissue. They are generally included in a fibro-areolar investment, the *Sheath,* which also encloses the accompanying veins. The larger arteries are nourished by the *Vasa Vasorum,* blood-vessels which ramify in the external and middle coats; and are supplied with nerves, the *Vaso-motor,* derived from both the sympathetic and cerebrospinal systems, and forming intricate plexuses on the larger trunks.

The Capillaries are minute vessels forming a network throughout the tissues of the body between the terminating arteries and the commencing veins. Their average diameter is about the $\frac{1}{3000}$ of an inch, average length $\frac{1}{50}$ of an inch and their walls consist of a transparent homogeneous membrane continuous with the innermost layer of the arterial and venous walls.

The Pulmonary Artery and Aorta

The Pulmonary Artery (a. pulmonalis) alone of the arteries carries venous blood, which it conveys from the right side of the heart to the lungs. It is $1\frac{1}{5}$ inch in diameter and only about 2 inches long, and all within the pericardium; arising from the right ventricle in front of the ascending aorta, passing upward and backward to the under surface of the arch of the aorta, where it bifurcates, and is connected at its root to he aorta by a fibrous cord, the remains of the *ductus arteriosus* of the œtus. Its terminal branches are the—

Right (ramus dexter a. pulmonalis) *and Left* (ramus sinister a. pulmonalis) *Pulmonary Arteries,*—the latter being the shorter of the two; they pass horizontally outward to the roots of their respective lungs, where each divides into two branches, which again and again subdivide to ramify throughout the lung tissue and end in the capillaries of those organs.

The Aorta (arteria magna) is the main trunk of the systemic arteries, commencing at the aortic opening of the left ventricle of the heart, it arches backward over the roof of the left lung into the thorax, where it descends on the left of the spinal column, and after passing through the aortic opening in the diaphragm, it terminates in the right and left common iliac arteries opposite the 4th lumbar vertebra. It is divided into the *Ascending Aorta* (aorta ascendens) (5), the *Arch* (arcus aortæ) (6), and the *Descending Aorta* (aorta descendens) (12), the last-named being again divided into the *Thoracic Aorta* (aorta thoracalis) and the *Abdominal Aorta* (aorta abdominalis) (described under Arteries of the Trunk). The upper border of the arch is generally situated about an inch below the upper margin of the sternum. The branches of the aorta are—

From the Ascending Aorta,—2 *Coronary Arteries* (4).

From the Arch,—*Innominate* (a. anonyma) (7). **Left Common Carotid**

(10). **Left Subclavian** (11).

From the Thoracic,—*Pericardial.* *Œsophageal.* 18 *Intercostals.*
Bronchial. *Posterior Mediastinal.*

From the Abdominal,—2 *Phrenic.*

Cœliac Axis. { *Gastric.* *Hepatic.* *Splenic* (a. lienalis).

2 *Spermatic*, in the male.
2 *Ovarian*, in female.   *Inferior Mesenteric.*
Superior Mesenteric.   8 *Lumbar.*
2 *Supra-renal.*   *Sacra Media.*
2 *Renal.*   2 *Common Iliac.*

The Coronary Arteries are 2 in number, a right and a left (4), arise from the aorta in the sinuses of Valsalva behind the semilunar valves, and run in the vertical grooves of the heart, the left artery in front, to supply the tissue of that organ. Each artery divides into 2 branches, the *transverse* and the *descending*, the latter anastomosing at the apex of the heart with its fellow of the opposite side. The descending branch of the right coronary sends off a *marginal* branch along the margin of the right ventricle, and an *infundibular* branch to the conus arteriosus of the same ventricle.

FIG. 63.

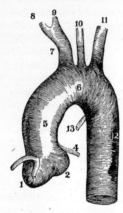

The Innominate Artery (a. anonyma) (7) arises from the summit of the arch of the aorta, is 1½ inch long, and divides behind the right sternoclavicular joint into the *Right Common Carotid* (9) and *Right Subclavian* (8), these arteries on the left side of the body (10, 11) arising directly from the arch of the aorta. It sometimes sends off a small branch, the *Thyroidea ima*, to the thyroid body; which vessel may arise from the arch of the aorta, the right common carotid, the subclavian, or the internal mammary. The Innominate artery is sometimes absent and not infrequently varies in length from ½ inch to 2 inches.

ARTERIES OF THE HEAD AND NECK

The Common Carotid Arteries (Arteræ Carotides Communes). Arising differently (see above) the two carotids are similarly described, except that the left is longer and deeper than the right one. Their course is indicated by a line drawn from a point midway between the angle of the lower jaw and the mastoid process to the sternoclavicular articulation. At the lower part of the neck they are separated only by the width of the trachea, and they are each contained in a sheath of the deep cervical fascia with the internal jugular vein externally and the pneumogastric nerve (n. vagus) between the artery and vein. On the front of the sheath lies the descendens hypo-

FIG. 64.

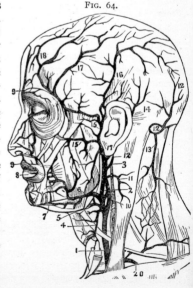

glossi nerve (descending branch of the 12th or hypoglossal). The artery lies beneath the inner border of the sterno-cleido-mastoid muscle, and is crossed about its *middle* by the omo-hyoid muscle and the middle thyroid vein. It is also crossed *above* by the facial, lingual, and superior thyroid veins, *below* by the anterior jugular vein, and on the *left side* often by the internal jugular vein. It bifurcates, at the level of the upper border of the thyroid cartilage, into the *External and Internal Carotids*, of which the internal is the more remote from the median line.

The External Carotid Artery (a. carotis externa) (2) (Fig. 64) commences opposite the upper border of the thyroid cartilage, and passes upward, forward and backward to the space between the neck of the condyle of the lower jaw and the external meatus, where it divides into the temporal and internal maxillary arteries. It has 8 branches, the—

Superior Thyroid (a. thyreoidea superior) (4),—arising below the greater cornu of the hyoid bone; giving off—

Muscular.	Hyoid.	Superior Laryngeal.
Glandular.	Superficial Descending.	Crico-thyroid.

Lingual (a. lingualis) (5),—under the hyo-glossus muscle to the tongue; giving off—

Hyoid.   Dorsalis Linguæ.   Sublingual.   Ranine.

Facial (a. maxillaris externa), should be called *superficial facial* (6),—crosses the lower jaw at the anterior border of the masseter; giving off—

Inferior (Ascending) Palatine.	Submental (7).	2 Coronary (aa. labiales) (8, 9).
Tonsillar.	Muscular.	
Submandibular.	Inferior Labial.	Lateralis Nasi.
		Angular.

Occipital (a. occipitalis) (10),—lies in the occipital groove of the temporal bone.

Muscular.	Auricular.	Arteria Princeps Cervicis (13) (ramus descendens a. occipitalis).
Sterno-mastoid.	Meningeal.	

Posterior Auricular (a. auricularis posterior) (14),—ascends under cover of the parotid gland.

Stylo-mastoid.   Auricular.   Mastoid.   Muscular.   Glandular.

Ascending Pharyngeal, (a. pharyngea ascendens),—lies on the rectus capitis anticus major.

Prevertebral.   Pharyngeal.   Tympanic.   Meningeal.

Superficial Temporal (a. temporalis superficialis) (15),—the smallest of the termini of the external carotid, begins in the parotid gland, crosses the zygomatic arch, and divides into anterior (13) and posterior temporal (16). Its branches are the—

Parotid. Articular. Zygomatico-orbital. Frontal. Parietal.
Transverse Facial (15). Middle Temporal (17). Anterior Auricular.

Fig. 65.

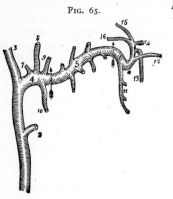

Internal Maxillary (a. maxillaris interna), should be called *deep facial* (4),—the other terminal branch of the external carotid (1), is divided into three portions, Maxillary (4), Pterygoid (5), and Spheno-maxillary (6), which respectively give off the following branches (Fig. 65):

Maxillary

Deep Auricular, to the tragus and canal.
Anterior Tympanic (7), entering the Glaserian (petro-tympanic) fissure.
Middle Meningeal (8).
Small or Accessory Meningeal (9).
Inferior Alveolar or Dental (10), divides into Incisor and Mental.

Pterygoid

Deep Temporal, ant. and posterior.
Pterygoid Branches, to those muscles.
Masseteric, to the masseter muscle.
Buccal, to the buccinator muscle.

Spheno-maxillary

Posterior Superior Alveolar (11).
Infra-orbital (12).
Descend. Palatine (13).
Vidian (a. canalis pterygoidea) (16).
Pterygo-palatine (15).
Spheno-palatine or Naso-palatine (14).
Pharyngeal.

The Internal Carotid Artery (a. carotis interna) commences at the bifurcation of the common carotid and ascends in front of the transverse processes of the three upper cervical vertebræ, and close to the tonsil, traverses the carotid canal in the temporal bone, and after piercing the dura mater close by the anterior clinoid process, divides into its terminal (cerebral) branches. It curves remarkably in different parts of its course, in the carotid canal and alongside the body of the sphenoid bone it describes a double curvature resembling the italic letter *S* placed horizontally. In the cervical portion no branches are given off; in the petrous, cavernous and cerebral portions it gives off the following:—

Tympanic (a. carotico-tympanic),—enters the tympanum from the carotid canal, and anastomoses on the membrana tympani with the tympanic branch of the internal maxillary and the stylo-mastoid.

Arteriæ Receptaculi (aa. cavernosæ),—numerous small vessels going to the walls of the sinuses, the Gasserian (semilunar) ganglion and the pituitary body (hypophysis).

Anterior Meningeal,—a small branch to the dura mater of the anterior fossa, after passing over the lesser wing of the sphenoid.

Ophthalmic,—arises from the cavernous portion, enters the orbit through the optic foramen, terminating at the inner angle of the eye into the frontal and nasal branches. It gives off the following branches:—

Ocular Group	Orbital Group	
Art. Centralis Retinæ.	Lacrimal.	Frontal.
Muscular.	Supra-orbital.	Nasal.
Anterior Ciliary.	Posterior Ethmoidal.	(the
Short Ciliary.	Anterior Ethmoidal.	terminal.
Long Ciliary.	Internal Palpebral.	branches).

Anterior Cerebral,—joined to its fellow by the *Anterior Communicating Artery*, about 2 lines long; then runs alongside its fellow, terminating by anastomosis with the posterior cerebral arteries, and giving off the following branches:—

    Antero-median Ganglionic or Basal.
    Inferior Internal or Medial Frontal.
    Ant. Internal or Medial Frontal.
    Middle Internal or Medial Frontal.
    Posterior Internal or Medial Frontal.

Middle Cerebral (a. cerebri media),—in the fissure of Sylvius; divides into:—

Antero-lateral Ganglionic or Basal.	Ascending Frontal.
Inferior External or Lateral Frontal.	Ascending Parietal.

Parieto-temporal.

Posterior Communicating,—anastomoses with the posterior cerebral, a branch of the basilar, and gives off the:—

Postero-median Ganglionic, branches supplying the optic thalami
and the walls of the 3rd ventricle.

Anterior Choroid,—to the hippocampus major, corpus fimbriatum, etc.
and ends in the choroid plexus.

[The *vertebral Artery*, a branch of the Subclavian, and the *Basilar Artery*,
formed by the junction of the two vertebrals, may be considered arteries
of the head and neck, but they are most conveniently described as branches
of the Subclavian Artery (see below.)]

The Circle of Willis

The Circle of Willis (circulus arteriosus) is a remarkable anastomosis
at the base of the brain, formed by the branches of the vertebral and internal carotid arteries, and giving origin to the 3 trunks which supply
each cerebral hemisphere. Posteriorly, the two *Vertebral* arteries unite
to form the *Basilar*, which ends in the two *Posterior Cerebral*.   Anteriorly,
each *Internal Carotid* gives off the *Anterior Cerebral*, these latter being
connected by the short *Anterior Communicating* artery. The circle is
completed by the *Posterior Communicating* arteries, one on each side,
which connect the posterior cerebral with the internal carotid.

The Circle of Willis gives off,—*anteriorly*, the anterior cerebral arteries;
antero-laterally, the middle cerebral; and *posteriorly*, the posterior cerebral;
each artery giving origin to two very different arterial systems: the *Central Ganglionic System*, supplying the central ganglia of the brain; the
Cortical Arterial System, which ramifies the pia mater and supplies the
cortex and subjacent medullary substance. The two systems, though
having a common origin, do not communicate afterwards, and in their
distribution are entirely independent of each other.   Hence, between the
parts supplied by each, there is a zone of diminished nutritive activity,
where softening may be especially liable to occur in the brains of old people.
By the Circle of Willis the cerebral circulation is equalized and provision
made for carrying it on if one or more of the branches should be
obliterated.

The Triangles of the Neck

Anterior Triangle of the Neck is bounded, in front, by a line extending
from the chin to the sternum; behind, by the anterior margin of the
sterno-mastoid muscle; its base, directed upward, is formed by the lower
border of the body of the jaw and a line extending from the angle of the
jaw to the mastoid process; its apex is below, at the sternum. It is
crossed by the digastric muscle above and the anterior belly of the omo-
hyoid below, dividing it into 3 smaller triangles, named from below up-

ward the Inferior Carotid, the Superior Carotid, and the Submaxillary or Submandibular triangles.

Inferior Carotid Triangle, situated below the anterior belly of the omo-hyoid, contains at its posterior edge in a common sheath the lower portion of the common carotid artery, the pneumogastric nerve and the internal jugular vein, concealed by the sterno-mastoid muscle, also other structures, which with the former may be summarized as follows:—

Muscles,—the sterno-hyoid and sterno-thyroid, covering the common carotid artery.

Arteries,—the common carotid and the inferior thyroid.

Veins,—the internal jugular, as described above.

Nerves,—the pneumogastric (n. vagus) recurrent laryngeal, and sympathetic, also filaments from the loop between the descendens and communicans hypoglossi.

Other Structures,—the trachea, thyroid gland, and the lower part of the larynx.

Superior Carotid Triangle, situated above the anterior belly of the omo-hyoid, contains the upper part of the common carotid artery and its bifurcation into the internal and external carotid, also other structures, all summarized as follows:—

Muscles,—parts of the thyro-hyoid, hyo-glossus, inferior and middle constrictors of the pharynx.

Vessels,—the common carotid artery, the internal and external carotid arteries, and the internal jugular vein; the superior thyroid, lingual, facial (external maxillary), occipital and ascending pharyngeal branches of the external carotid and the veins accompanying them.

Nerves,—the pneumogastric (n. vagus), spinal accessory (n. accessorius), hypoglossal, descendens hypoglossi, sympathetic, internal and external laryngeal.

Other Structures,—the upper part of the larynx, and the lower part of the pharynx.

Sub-mandibular or Sub-maxillary Triangle, immediately below the body of the jaw, and above the posterior belly of the digastric and the stylo-hyoid; contains the following:—

Muscles,—the mylo-hyoid, hyo-glossus, stylo-glossus, and stylo-pharyngeus.

Arteries,—the external and internal carotid; also the facial (external maxillary), posterior auricular, temporal, internal maxillary, sub-mental, and mylo-hyoid arteries.

Veins,—the facial and internal jugular.

9

Nerves,—the pneumogastric (n. vagus), glosso-pharyngeal, facial, and mylo-hyoid.

Glands,—the parotid and sub-maxillary (sub-mandibular).

Posterior Triangle of the Neck is bounded, in front by the sterno-mastoid muscle; behind, by the trapezius; its base corresponds to the middle third of the clavicle, its apex is at the occiput. It is crossed by the posterior belly of the omo-hyoid muscle about an inch above the clavicle, subdividing it into two smaller triangles, the Occipital above, and the Subclavian below.

Occipital Triangle, the larger division of the posterior triangle of the neck, above the posterior belly of the omo-hyoid muscle, contains the following:—

Muscles,—the splenius, levator anguli scapulæ (m. levator scapulæ), middle and posterior scaleni.

Vessels,—the transversalis colli artery and vein.

Nerves,—the spinal accessory (n. accessorius), and descending branches of the cervical plexus.

Glands,—a chain of lymphatic glands.

Subclavian Triangle, the smaller of the divisions of the posterior triangle of the neck, situated below the posterior belly of the omo-hyoid muscle, and above the middle third of the clavicle, contains the following:—

Vessels,—the subclavian artery, the subclavian vein occasionally, the transversalis colli and suprascapular arteries (a. transversa scapulæ), and veins, the external jugular and transverse cervical veins.

Nerves,—the brachial plexus, descending branches of the cervical plexus, nerve to the subclavius muscle.

Glands,—a lymphatic gland.

ARTERIES OF THE UPPER EXTREMITY

The Subclavian Artery (Arteria Subclavia) arises on the right side from the innominate, of the left side from the arch of the aorta, and is divided into 3 portions by the scalenus anticus muscle, which crosses it just external to the origin of the thyroid axis, viz.—the parts internal, behind and external to that muscle. At the outer border of the 1st rib, the subclavian becomes the *Axillary Artery.* Its upper border is a little above the clavicle, and it is separated from the subclavian vein by the scalenus anticus at its origin from the first rib. Its branches are all given from its first portion, except the *Superior Intercostal,* which on the right side arises from the second portion. Its branches are the—

VERTEBRAL (a. vertebralis) (6),—passing up the neck, through the foramina in the transverse processes of six cervical vertebræ, enters the
skull by the foramen magnum, where it joins its fellow to form the
Basilar Artery. Its branches are—

Lateral Spinal Branches.

FIG. 66.

Muscular Branches.

Posterior Meningeal.

Anterior Spinal.

Posterior Spinal.

Posterior Inferior Cerebellar.

Bulbar.

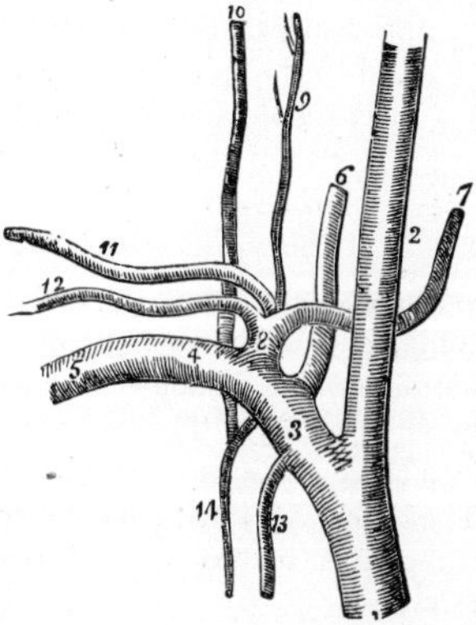

The Basilar (a. basilaris),—formed
by the junction of the vertebrals,
gives off on each side a transverse,
anterior, and superior cerebellar,
and ends in the two posterior cerebral. (See *Circle of Willis*, pages
151 and 158.)

THYROID AXIS (truncus thyreocervicalis) (8),—at once divides into the
three following branches.

Inferior Thyroid (a. thyreoidea inferior) (7),—to the thyroid gland,
giving off—

Inferior Laryngeal.

Œsophageal Branches.

Tracheal.   Muscular.

Ascending Cervical (9).

2 Terminal.

Suprascapular (a. transversa scapulæ) (12),—to the shoulder-joint
and the dorsum of the scapula, anastomosing there with the posterior and subscapular.

Transversalis Colli (11),—divides beneath the margin of the trapezius
into—

Superficial Cervical (ramus ascendens).

Posterior Scapular (ramus descendens).

INTERNAL MAMMARY (a. mammaria interna) (13),—arises opposite the
thyroid axis, descends behind the costal cartilages, and ends at the
6th interval, in the musculo-phrenic and superior epigastric, the
latter anastomosing with the deep epigastric branch of the external
iliac. Its branches are the—

Comes Nervi Phrenici	Paricardiac.	Perforating.
(pericardiaco-phrenic),	Sternal.	Musculo-phrenic.
or Superior Phrenic.	Anterior Intercostal.	Superior Epigastric.
Mediastinal.		

SUPERIOR INTERCOSTAL (a. intercostalis suprema) (14),—gives off branches in the intercostal spaces to the posterior spinal muscles and to the spinal cord.   One branch, the—

> *Profunda Cervicis* (a. cervicalis profunda) (10),—supplies the muscles of the back of the neck, and anastomoses with the arteria princeps cervicis (ramus descendens a. occipitalis) of the occipital. This vessel occasionally arises from the subclavian artery.

The Axillary Artery (a. axillaris) (5), the continuation of the subclavian, commences at the outer border of the first rib, and terminates at the lower border of the tendon of the teres major muscle, where it becomes the brachial artery.   The pectoralis minor crosses it and marks its division into three portions,—1st, above; 2nd behind, and 3rd below that muscle. The brachial plexus is in close relation with the artery, surrounding it on three sides in the second portion.   Its branches are 7 in number as follows:—

Superior Thoracic (a. thoracalis suprema),—from the first portion; supplies the pectoral muscles and the walls of the thorax.

Acromial Thoracic (a. thoraco-acromialis),—from the first portion; divides into the—

Thoracic (pectoral) Branches 2 or 3,—to the serratus magnus (m. serratus anterior) and pectorals.

Acromial Branches,—to the deltoid muscles.

Descending or Humeral (deltoid),—to the pectoralis major and deltoid.

Clavicular,—a very small branch, to the subclavius muscle.

Alar Thoracic,—from the second portion; to the glands and the areolar tissue of the axilla.

Long Thoracic (a. thoracalis lateralis or external mammary),—from the second portion; to the serratus magnus (m. serratus anterior), the pectoral muscles and the mammary gland.

Subscapular (a. subscapularis),—from the third portion; to the inferior angle of the scapula, where it anastomoses with the long thoracic, the intercostal and the posterior scapular (ramus descendens a. transversalis Colli) arteries.   It gives off small branches to the deltoid and triceps muscles, and the

> Dorsalis Scapulæ (a. circumflexa scapulæ),—a large branch, to the subscapular fossa and the axillary border of the scapula.

Posterior Circumflex (a. circumflexa humeri posterior),—from the third portion; winds around the neck of the humerus to the deltoid muscle and the shoulder-joint, anastomosing with the anterior circumflex and other arteries.

Anterior Circumflex (a. circumflexa humeri anterior),—from the third portion; winds around the neck of the humerus, to the head of that bone, the deltoid muscle and the shoulder-joint, anastomosing with the posterior circumflex.

The Brachial Artery (a. Brachialis) is the continuation of the axillary from the lower margin of the teres major tendon to its bifurcation into the radial and ulnar, which is usually about half an inch below the bend of the elbow. The median nerve crosses it from the outside to the inside about its middle. Above its bifurcation it is crossed diagonally by the bicipital fascia (lacertus fibrosus). The basilic vein lies on its inner side but separated from it in the lower part of the arm by the deep fascia. Its branches are the—

Superior Profunda (a. profunda brachii),—winds over the arm in the spiral groove (sulcus radialis), giving off the posterior articular to the elbow anastomosis, and a branch to anastomose with the recurrent branch of the radial, and a nutrient artery to the bone. This artery supplies the triceps muscle.

Nutrient Branch,—enters the nutrient canal of the humerus.

Inferior Profunda (a. collateralis ulnaris superior),—to the elbow-joint anastomosis.

Anastomotica Magna (*a. collateralis ulnaris inferior*),—anastomoses with the posterior articular, inferior profunda (superior ulnar collateral) anterior and posterior ulnar recurrent.

Muscular Branches,—to the muscles in the course of the artery.

The Radial Artery (a. radialis) extends from the bifurcation of the brachial to the deep palmar arch, and gives off the following branches:— In the Forearm,—

Radial Recurrent,—to the supinators, the brachialis anticus and the elbow joint, anastomosing with the terminal branches of the superior profunda (a. profunda brachii).

Muscular Branches,—to the muscles on the radial side of the forearm.

Anterior Carpal (ramus carpeus volaris),—anastomoses with the anterior carpal of the ulnar artery, forming the Anterior Carpal Arch (rete carpi volare).

Superficialis Volæ,—to the muscles of the thumb.

In the Wrist,—

Posterior Carpal (ramus carpeus dorsalis),—anastomoses with the posterior carpal of the ulnar artery forming the Posterior Carpal Arch
(rete carpi dorsale).

Metacarpal,—the first dorsal interosseous branch, divides into two
dorsal digital branches, supplying the adjoining sides of the index
and middle fingers.

Dorsales Pollicis 2,—along the sides of the thumb.

Dorsalis Indicis,—along the radial side of the index finger.

In the Hand,—

Princeps Pollicis,—along the sides of the palmar aspect of the thumb by
two branches forming an arch.

Radialis Indicis (a. volaris indicis radialis),—along the radial side of
the index finger to anastomose with the collateral digital and the
princeps pollicis, giving a communicating branch to the superficial
palmar arch (arcus volaris superficialis).

Perforating 3,—backward from the deep palmar arch to anastomose
with the dorsal interosseous arteries.

Palmar Interosseous 3 or 4,—from the deep palmar arch, on the interossei muscles to anastomose with the digital branches of the superficial arch (arcus volaris superficialis).

Palmar Recurrent,—from the deep palmar arch to the carpal joints,
anastomosing with the anterior carpal arch (rete carpi volare).

The Ulnar Artery (a. ulnaris) extends from the bifurcation of the
brachial just below the bend of the elbow along the ulnar border of the
forearm to the wrist. Immediately beyond the pisiform bone it divides
into two branches which enter into the formation of the superficial and
deep palmar (volar) arches. Its branches are as follows:—

In the Forearm,—

Anterior Ulnar Recurrent (a. recurrentes ulnaris anterior),—anastomoses
in front of the inner condyle of the humerus with the anastomotica
magna (inferior ulnar collateral) and the inferior profunda (superior
ulnar collateral).

Posterior Ulnar Recurrent (a. recurrentes ulnaris posterior),—anastomoses behind the inner condyle of the humerus with the anastomotica
magna (inferior ulnar collateral), inferior profunda (superior ulnar
collateral) and interosseous recurrent.

Interosseous,—about ½ inch long, divides into two branches. The
Anterior Interosseous (volar interosseous) gives off the *Median
Artery* to the median nerve and a *Nutrient* branch to both bones of the

forearm.   The Posterior (dorsal) Interosseous gives off near its origin the *Interosseous Recurrent* to the elbow-joint anastomosis.

Muscular,—to the muscles on the ulnar side of the forearm.

In the Wrist,—

Anterior Carpal, (ramus carpeus volaris),—anastomoses with a corresponding branch of the radial artery in front of the carpus.

Posterior Carpal (ramus carpeus dorsalis),—anastomoses with a corresponding branch of the radial artery forming the posterior carpal arch (rete carpi dorsale).

In the Hand,—

Deep or *Communicating* (ramus volaris profunda),—anastomoses with the termination of the radial artery, completing the deep palmar arch (arcus volaris profundus).

Superficial Palmar Arch (arcus volaris superficialis),—is the continuation of the trunk of the ulnar artery in the hand.

Digital 4,—given off by the superficial palmar arch (arcus volaris superficialis).

THE CARPAL ARCHES

The Anterior Carpal Arch (rete carpi volare) is formed by the anastomosis of the anterior carpal of the radial with the anterior (volar) carpal of the ulnar artery in front of the wrist.   It is joined by branches from the anterior (volar) interosseous above and by recurrent branches from the deep palmar (volar) arch below, and gives off branches to supply the articulations of the wrist and carpus.

The Posterior Carpal Arch (rete carpi dorsale) is formed by the anastomosis of the posterior (dorsal) carpal of the radial with the posterior (dorsal) carpal of the ulnar artery.   It is joined by the termination of the anterior (volar) interosseous artery and gives off *dorsal interosseous arteries* for the third and fourth interosseous spaces, which divide into *dorsal digital* branches which supply the adjacent sides of the middle, ring and little fingers, and communicate with the digital arteries of the superficial palmar (volar) arch, and at their origin with the perforating branches from the deep palmar (volar) arch.

THE PALMAR ARCHES

The Superficial Palmar Arch (arcus volaris superficialis) is formed by the part of the ulnar artery which lies in the palm of the hand, and is completed by that artery anastomosing with a branch from the radialis indicis, at the root of the thumb; sometimes with the superficialis volæ or the princeps pollicis of the radial.   It gives off 4 *Digital Collateral* branches to the sides of the fingers, except the radial side of the index finger, which with the thumb is supplied from the radial artery.

The Deep Palmar Arch (arcus volaris profundus) is formed by the palmar portion of the radial artery, and is completed by the anastomosis of that artery with the deep palmar (communicating) branch of the ulnar. It lies upon the carpal ends of the metacarpal bones and the interosseous muscles, about $\frac{1}{2}$ inch nearer to the carpus than the superficial palmar (volar) arch, from which it is separated by the transverse carpal ligament, the flexor brevis minimi digiti, (m. flexor digiti quinti brevis) the superficial flexor tendons and divisions of the median and ulnar nerves. From it are given off the radialis indicis, palmar (volar) interosseous, perforating and palmar (volar) recurrent branches of the radial artery.

ARTERIES OF THE TRUNK

THE DESCENDING AORTA (AORTA DESCENDENS)

The Descending Aorta is divided into two portions, the *Thoracic Aorta* (aorta thoracalis) and the *Abdominal Aorta* (aorta abdominalis), corresponding to the two great cavities of the trunk in which they are situated.

The Thoracic Aorta (aorta thoracalis) commences at the lower border of the 4th thoracic vertebra on the left of the spine, and descends in the back part of the posterior mediastinum, terminating at the aortic opening in the diaphragm directly in front of the lower border of the last thoracic vertebra. Its branches are—

Pericardial,—irregular in origin, to the pericardium.

Bronchial,—vary in number and origin; generally one on the right side and two on the left. They nourish the lungs, bronchial glands and the œsophagus.

Œsophageal, 4 or 5,—anastomose on the œsophagus with branches of the inferior thyroid, phrenic, and gastric arteries.

Posterior Mediastinal,—numerous small vessels supplying the glands and the areolar tissue in the mediastinum.

Intercostals,—usually 9 on each side, the two superior intercostal spaces being supplied by the superior intercostal branch of the subclavian. They run between the two layers of intercostal muscles, anastomose with the anterior intercostal branches of the internal mammary, and each gives off the following branches:—

Posterior or Dorsal,—to the muscles and skin of the back.

Spinal,—to the spinal cord and its membranes.

Collateral Intercostal,—along the upper border of the rib below.

The Abdominal Aorta (aorta abdominalis) begins where the thoracic aorta ends (see p. 123) and terminates on the body of the 4th lumbar vertebra, where it divides into the two common iliac arteries. Its branches are as follows:—

2 *Inferior Phrenic* (1),—one on each side, but usually only one arises from the aorta, the other springing from either the cœliac axis or the renal artery. They go to the under surface of the diaphragm, where each artery divides into two branches, an external and an internal, the former to the side latter to the front of the thorax and the diaphragm.

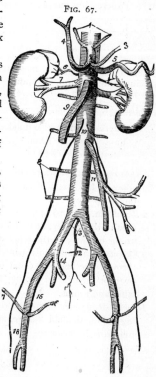

Fig. 67.

Cœliac Axis (a. cœliaca) (2), arises from the aorta, close to the margin of the opening in the diaphragm, runs forward for half an inch, and divides into the Left Gastric, Hepatic, and Splenic (a. lienalis) arteries, occasionally giving off one of the phrenics. The—

Left Gastric (a. gastrica sinistra) (3), —supplies the stomach along its lesser curvature, anastomosing with the aortic œsophageal, splenic (a lienalis), and hepatic branches.

Hepatic (a. hepatica) (4),—forms the lower boundary of the foramen of Winslow (foramen epiploicum), passes upward to the transverse fissure (porta hepatis) of the liver where it divides into two branches, right and left, supplying the corresponding lobes of that organ. Its branches are the—

Pyloric (a. gastrica dextra),—to the pyloric end of the stomach and along the lesser curvature of that viscus.

Gastro-duodenalis,—giving off the Gastro-epiploica Dextra along the greater curvature of the stomach, and the Pancreatico-duo-

denalis Superior to the contiguous margins of the duodenum and
pancreas.

Right Hepatic,—to the right lobe of the liver, giving off the Cystic
Artery to the gall-bladder.

Left Hepatic,—to the left lobe of the liver.

Splenic (a. lienalis) (5),—the largest branch of the cœliac axis, passes by
a very tortuous course to the spleen, giving off the following:—

Pancreaticæ Parvæ.	Gastric (Vasa Brevia) (a.a. gastricæ breves) to the stomach.
Pancreatica Magna.	Gastro-epiploica Sinistra, to the stomach.

Terminal Branches, enter the hilum of the spleen.

Superior Mesenteric (a. mesenterica superior) (9),—supplies the small
intestine, cæcum, ascending and transverse colon. Arising about
¼ inch below the cœliac axis it arches forward, downward, and to
the left, giving off the—

Inferior Pancreatico-duodenal.	Ileo-colic.
Vasa Intestini Tenuis (aa. intestinales), 12 to 15.	Colica Dextra and Media.

Supra-renal (a. supra-renalis media) (6),—arise one on each side,
opposite the origin of the superior mesenteric, passing to the supra-
renal capsules.

2 *Renal* (aa. renales) (7),—one from each side, just below the preceding,
pass to the kidney, at its hilum having the middle place between the
ureter behind and the renal vein in front. U. A. V. (you 'ave!)

2 *Spermatic* (aa. spermaticæ internæ) (10),—one on each side, in the male
through the inguinal canal to the testes; in the female it is called
Ovarian (a. ovarica), going to the ovaries, uterus and skin of the
labia and groins.

Inferior Mesenteric (a mesenterica inferior) (11),—supplies the descending colon, sigmoid flexure, and most of the rectum, giving off the
following branches:—

Colica Sinistra.	Sigmoid (aa. sigmoideæ).	Superior Hemorrhoidal.

Lumbar (aa. lumbales) (8),—usually 4 on each side, analogous to the
intercostals. They each divide into two branches, the—

Dorsal, giving off a spinal branch.	Abdominal.

Middle Sacral (a. sacralis media) (12),—arises just at the bifurcation of the aorta; it descends along the last lumbar vertebra and the front of the sacrum to the upper part of the coccyx, giving off numerous branches on each side to anastomose with the lateral sacral arteries. It terminates in a minute branch which goes to the coccygeal gland (Luschka), and sends off branches to the rectum.

The Iliac Arteries (Arteriæ Iliacæ)

The Common Iliac Arteries (aa. iliacæ communes) extend from the bifurcation of the aorta at the 4th lumbar vertebra to the lumbo-sacral articulation, where each divides into the *External Iliac* (15) and the *Internal Iliac* (a. hypogastrica) (14); the former supplying the lower extremity, the latter going to the viscera and walls of the pelvis. The common iliac arteries are about 2 inches in length, the right being a little longer than the left, and each is crossed by the ureter, just before its bifurcation.

The Internal Iliac (arteria hypogastrica) (14) is about $1\frac{1}{2}$ inches long, extending from the lumbo-sacral articulation to the great sacro-sciatic notch, where it divides into an anterior and a posterior trunk. From the Anterior Trunk are given off, from above downward, the—

Superior Vesical (a. vesicalis superior),—the remaining previous part, of the fœtal hypogastric artery. It sends branches to the bladder the vas deferens and the ureter; and one, the Middle Vesical, to the base of the bladder.

Obturator (a. obturatoria),—through the canal in the obturator membrane to the thigh, where it divides into an internal and external branch. Within the pelvis it gives off an iliac, a vesical, and a pubic branch. In one out of every $3\frac{1}{2}$ cases this artery arises from the deep epigastric (a. epigastrica inferior), in 2 out of every 3 from the internal iliac (a. hypogastrica), in 1 out of $7\frac{1}{2}$ by two roots from both vessels and in about the same proportion from the external iliac.

Inferior Vesical (a. vesicalis inferior),—to the bladder, prostrate gland, and vesiculæ seminales. In the female this artery is called the *Vaginal* (a. vaginalis).

Middle Hemorrhoidal (a. hæmorrhoidalis medialis),—to the anus and parts outside the rectum.

Uterine (a. uterina),—in the female, anastomosing with a branch (ramus ovarii) from the ovarian. It gives off cervical branches to the cervix uteri and the azygos arteries of the vagina.

Internal Pudic (a. pudenda interna),—the smaller of the terminal branches of the anterior trunk, supplies the external generative organs. Its muscular branches in the pelvis are numerous and small; in the perineum they are the—

Inferior Hemorrhoidal (a. hæmorrhoidalis inferior).	Artery of the Bulb (a. bulbi urethræ).
Superficial Perineal (a. perinei).	Urethral (a. urethralis).
Transverse Perineal (a. transversa perinei).	Artery of the Corpus Cavernosum (a. profunda penis).
	Dorsal Artery of the Penis (a dorsalis penis).

Sciatic (a. glutæa),—the other terminal branch, supplies the muscles on the back of the pelvis. Its branches are the—

Muscular (internal), rami musculares.

Hemorrhoidal Brs.

Vesical Branches.

Coccygeal.

Cutaneous.

Comes Nervi Ischiadici, (a. comitans n. ischiadici).

Muscular (ext.), (rami musculares).

Anastomotic.

Articular.

THE POSTERIOR TRUNK gives off the following:—

Ilio-lumbar (a. ilio-lumbalis),—dividing into a lumbar and an ilica branch.

Lateral Sacral (arteriæ sacrales laterales),—superior and inferior on each side.

Gluteal (a. glutæa superior),—the continuation of the posterior trunk, divides into a superficial and a deep branch, to the glutei muscles, the skin over the sacrum, and the hip-joint. Before dividing it gives a nutrient branch to the ilium, and some muscular branches.

The External Iliac (a. iliaca externa) extends to beneath the centre of Poupart's ligament (l. inguinale), where it enters the thigh and becomes the *Femoral Artery;* lying between the femoral vein on the inside and the anterior crural nerve (n. femoralis) on the outside—V.A.N. Its branches are small muscular and glandular, and the—

Deep Epigastric (a. epigastrica inferior),—which arises a few lines above Poupart's inguinal ligament, passes between the peritoneum and the transversalis fascia, to the sheath of the rectus which it enters and ascends behind that muscle, to anastomose by numerous branches with the terminal branches of the internal mammary and inferior intercostal. It gives off the—

Cremasteric (a. spermatica in the male; a. ligamenti teres uteri in the female).

Pubic.   Muscular Branches (rami musculares).

Deep Circumflex Iliac (a. circumflexa ilium profunda),—arises opposite to the epigastric, passes along the crest of the ilium to about its middle, where it pierces the transversalis and runs backward between that muscle and the internal oblique to anastomose with the ilio-lumbar, gluteal (a. glutæa superior), lumbar and epigastric ateries.

ARTERIES OF THE LOWER EXTREMITY

The Femoral Artery (arteria femoralis) extends from Poupart's ligament (l. inguinale) to the opening in the adductor magnus, where it becomes the *popliteal artery*. Its course corresponds to a line drawn from a point midway between the anterior superior spine of the ilium and the spine of pubis, to the inner side of the inner condyle of the femur. It lies in a strong fibrous sheath with the femoral vein, but divided from the latter by a fibrous partition. It may be divided into two portions, the Common Femoral and the Superficial Femoral, for convenient description, as follows:—

The Common Femoral Artery,—about 2 inches long, is very superficial, rests on the inner margin of the psoas muscle, which separates it from the capsular ligament of the hip-joint, and is covered by the skin, superficial fascia, superficial inguinal glands, iliac portion of the fascia lata, and the anterior part of the sheath of the vessels.

The Superficial Femoral Artery,—is only superficial in Scarpa's triangle (femoral trigone), being deeper in Hunter's canal (adductor canal). It lies above on the femoral vein and the profunda artery and vein; below, on the adductor longus and adductor magnus muscles. The internal saphenous nerve crosses it from without inward.

Branches of the Femoral Artery, are as follows:—

Superficial Epigastric (a. epigastrica superficialis) *(c)*,—through the saphenous opening (fossa ovalis) to ascend on the abdomen, giving off branches to the skin, the superficial fascia and the superficial inguinal glands.

Superficial Circumflex Iliac (a. circumflexa ilium superficialis) *(j)*,—to the crest of the ilium, supplying the skin of the groin, the superficial fascia, and the superficial inguinal glands.

Superficial External Pudic (a. pudenda externa superficialis) *(d)*,—through the saphenous opening (fossa ovalis) to the skin of the abdomen, the penis and the scrotum (and the labium in the female).

Deep External Pudic (a. pudenda externa profunda) (*d*), to the skin of the scrotum and perinæum (and the labium in the female).

Muscular (rami musculares).

Profunda Femoris (Deep Femoral Artery) (*e*),—arises posteriorly about 1 or 2 inches below Poupart's (inguinal) ligament, and descends to the lower third of the back of the thigh, giving off the following branches:—

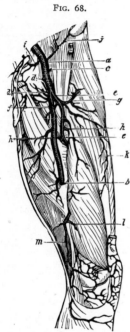

Fig. 68.

Ext. Circumflex (a. circumflexa femoris lateralis) (*g*).

Int. Circumflex (a. circumflexa femoris medialis) (*f*).

3 Perforating (aa. perforantes) (*h*).

Terminal or 4th perforating.

Muscular Branches (rami musculares) (*k*),— to the sartorius and vastus internus.

Anastomotica Magna (a. genu suprema),— arises from the femoral in Hunter's (adductor) canal and divides into a superficial and a deep branch, the latter anastomosing around the knee-joint with the superior external and internal articular arteries, and the recurrent branch of the anterior tibial.

Scarpa's Triangle (Trigonum Femorale) is a triangular space in the thigh which corresponds to the depression seen immediately below the fold of the groin. Its apex is downward, its base formed by Poupart's (inguinal) ligament, and its sides externally by the sartorious, internally by the adductor longus. Its floor is formed by the iliacus, psoas, pectineus and adductor longus muscles, from without inward. It is bisected vertically by the femoral vessels, which extend from the middle of its base to its apex. It also contains the anterior crural nerve (n. femoralis) external to the vessels, together with lymphatic vessels and glands and some fat.

Hunter's Canal (Canalis Adductorius) is the interval between the adductor magnus and the vastus internus (m. vastus medialis) in the middle third of the thigh, extending from the apex of Scarpa's triangle to the femoral opening in the adductor magnus muscle, and lying beneath the sartorius. It contains the femoral vessels in their sheath, the vein lying behind and to the outer side of the artery; also the long saphenous nerve, at first external to and then in front of the vessels.

The Popliteal Artery (a. Poplitea), the continuation of the femoral, extends from the opening in the adductor magnus, passing behind the knee-joint, to the lower border of the popliteus muscle, where it divides into the *Anterior* and *Posterior Tibial Arteries*. It is crossed by the popliteal vein and the internal popliteal nerve (n. tibialis), and gives off the following-named branches, which are distributed around the knee-joint in a free anastomosis; except the *Azygos Articular*, which pierces the posterior ligament of the joint to reach the internal ligaments and the synovial membrane. Branches are named as follows:—

Superior Muscular Branches.

Inferior Muscular, or *Sural.*

Cutaneous Branches.

Superior Articular, internal (a. genu superior medialis) and *external* (a. genu superior lateralis).

Azygos Articular (a. genu media).

Inferior Articular, internal (a. genu inferior medialis) and *external* (a. genu inferior lateralis).

The Anterior Tibial Artery (a. Tibialis anterior) extends from the bifurcation of the popliteal to the front of the ankle-joint, where it becomes the *Dorsalis Pedis*. It passes between the two heads of the tibialis posticus (m. tibialis posterior) over the upper edge of the interosseous membrane and along its anterior surface, resting on the tibia for its lower third. It is accompanied by the anterior tibial nerve (n. peronæus profundus) close to it externally, and is crossed below by the tendon of the extensor proprius hallucis. Its branches are named the—

Posterior Recurrent Tibial (a. recurrens tibialis posterior).

Superior Fibular.

Anterior Recurrent Tibial (a. recurrens tibialis anterior).

Muscular (rami musculares).

Internal Malleolar (a. malleolaris anterior medialis).

External Malleolar (a. malleolaris anterior lateralis).

The Dorsalis Pedis Artery, the continuation of the anterior tibial, extends from the front of the ankle-joint along the tibial side of the foot, to the back part of the 1st intermetatarsal space, where it terminates in the *Dorsalis Hallucis* and the *Communicating* (ramus plantaris profundus). The anterior tibial nerve lies close to its outer side. Its branches are as follows:—

Tarsal (a. tarsalis lateralis),—passing outward along the tarsus.

Metatarsal (a. arcuata),—giving off 3 Interosseous (aa. metatarseæ dorsales), and the 7 Digital branches (aa. digitales dorsales).

Dorsalis Hallucis,—to the great toe and the inner side of the second toe by its 3 digital branches.

Communicating (ramus plantaris profundus),—dips down into the sole of the foot in the 1st interosseous space of the metatarsus, to inosculate with the external plantar, completing the plantar arch. Its plantar digital branch, the *arteria magna hallucis*, supplies the inner side of the great toe and the adjacent sides of the great and second toes, on their plantar surfaces.

The Posterior Tibial Artery (A. Tibialis Posterior) is a large vessel, extending from the bifurcation of the popliteal along the back of the tibia to the fossa below the inner malleolus, where it divides into the *Internal* (medial) and *External* (lateral) *Plantar*. The posterior tibial nerve crosses it a short way below its origin and then lies near its outer side for the rest of its course. Its branches are as follows:—

Peroneal (a. peronæa),—along the fibular side, giving off the following:—
　Muscular (rami musculares).
　Nutrient of the fibula (a. nutrica fibulæ).
　Anterior Peroneal (ramus perforans).
　Communicating (ramus communicans).
　Posterior Peroneal.
　External Calcanean (ramus calcaneus lateralis).

Nutrient of the Tibia (a. nutrica tibiæ),—the largest nutrient artery of bone in the body.

Muscular Branches (rami musculares),—to the posterior muscles of the leg.

Communicating (ramus communicans),—to join a similar branch of the peroneal artery.

Internal Calcanean Branches (rami calcanei mediales),—to the heel and sole of the foot.

Internal Malleolar (a. malleolaris posterior medialis).

The Internal Plantar Artery (a. plantaris medialis), the smallest of the terminal branches of the posterior tibial, passes along the inner side of the foot and great toe.

The External Plantar Artery (a. plantaris lateralis) sweeps across the plantar aspect of the foot in a curve, the convexity of which is directed outward and forward; and at the interval between the bases of the 1st and 2d metatarsal bones it inosculates with the communicating branch from the dorsalis pedis, completing the *Plantar Arch* (arcus plantaris) or the *Stirrup Anastomosis*. It gives off numerous muscular branches, and the—

Posterior Perforating (rami perforantes posteriores),—3 small branches which ascend through the 3 outer interosseous spaces between the heads of the dorsal interossei muscles.

Digital Branches (aa. digitales plantares), 4,—supplying the sides of the 3 outer toes and the outer side of the 2d toe; its inner side, together with the great toe, being supplied by the communicating branch of the dorsalis pedis.

ARTERIAL ANASTOMOSES

The Anastomosis around the Shoulder-joint is formed by the following 8 arteries, viz.—

Posterior Scapular (ramus descendens a. transversa colli).
Subscapular (a. circumflexa scapulæ) br. of axillary.
Dorsalis Scapulæ (a. circumflexa scapulæ) br. of subscapular.
Infraspinous, br. of dorsalis scapulæ.
Suprascapular (a. transversa scapulæ), br. of thyroid axis.
Ant. Circumflex (a. circumflexa humeri anterior), br. of axillary.
Post. Circumflex (a. circumflexa humeri posterior), br. of axillary.
Acromial, br. of acromial thoracic.

The Anastomosis around the Elbow-joint is formed by the—
Superior Profunda, (a. profunda brachii), br. of brachial.
Posterior Articular, br. of superior profunda.
Radial Recurrent, br. of radial.
Interosseous Recurrent, br. of posterior interosseous.
Inferior Profunda (a. collateralis ulnaris superior), br. of brachial.
Anastomotica Magna (a. collateralis ulnaris inferior), br. of brachial.
Anterior Ulnar Recurrent, br. of ulnar.
Posterior Ulnar Recurrent, br. of ulnar.
The *Anastomotica Magna* is the vessel most engaged in this anastomosis, the only part in which it is not employed being that in front of the external condyle of the humerus.

The Anastomosis around the Hip-joint is formed by the—
Gluteal (superior gluteal), *Ilio-lumbar*, and *Circumflex Iliac*, with the *External Circumflex*.
Obturator and *Sciatic* (inferior gluteal), with the *Internal Circumflex*.
Comes Nervi Ischiadici, with the *Perforating* branches of the *Profunda*.

The Arteries Anastomosing around the Knee-joint are the—

Descending, br. of ext. circumflex.

Anastomotica Magna (a. genu suprema), br. of femoral.

Inferior Perforating, br. of profunda.

Superior Ext. Articular, br. of popliteal.

Sup. Int. Articular, br. of popliteal.

Inf. Ext. Articular, br. of popliteal.

Inf. Int. Articular, br. of popliteal.

Ant. Recurrent, br. of anterior tibial.

This anastomosis is sometimes called the *deep plexus* of the *Circum-patellar Anastomosis;* a superficial arterial plexus being situated between the fascia and skin around the patella.

The Crucial Anastomosis is formed behind the junction of the neck of the femur with the great trochanter, between the adductor magnus and quadratus femoris muscles, by the anastomosis of the following-named arteries:—

Transverse branch of *Ext. Circumflex* (from profunda), externally.

Terminal branch of *Int. Circumflex* (from profunda), internally.

First Perforating branch of the *Profunda Femoris*, below.

Anastomotic branch of the *Sciatic* (from int. iliac), above.

The Longest Anastomosis in the Body is that between the subclavian and the external iliac by the anastomosis of the *Superior Epigastric*, br. of the internal mammary, with the *Deep Epigastric*, br. of the external iliac.

[The circle of Willis has been described on page 128; the palmar and plantar arches on pages 135 and 145 respectively; and the anastomosis of the membrana tympani on page 298.]

The Collateral Circulation, after Ligature of the *Common Carotid Artery*, is established by the free communication existing between the carotid arteries of opposite sides both within and without the cranium, and by enlargement of the branches of the subclavian artery on the ligated side. Outside the skull the principal communication takes place by the following anastomoses:—

Superior Thyroid, br. of the external carotid, with the *Inferior Thyroid*, br. of the thyroid axis (from the subclavian).

Arteria Princeps Cervicis, br. of the occipital (from the external carotid), with the *Vertebral*, br. of the subclavian, and the *Profunda Cervicis*, br. of the superior intercostal (from the subclavian).

After Ligature of the Subclavian in its first part, the *Collateral Circulation* is carried on by the following anastomoses:—1, that between the *Superior* and *Inferior Thyroid* arteries (see above); 2, that between the two *Vertebrals;* 3, that between the *Internal Mammary*, the *Deep Epigastric* and the *Aortic Intercostals;* 4, the *Superior Intercostal* with the *Aortic*

Intercostals; 5, the *Profunda Cervicis* with the *Princeps Cervicis;* 6, the *Scapular* branches of the thyroid axis with branches of the *Axillary;* 7, the *Thoracic* branches of the *Axillary* with the *Aortic Intercostals.*

TABLES AND PLATES

OF THE

ARTERIAL SYSTEM

NOTE.—The arteries in the following plates should be colored red, by painting them over with ordinary crimson ink, or water-color paint, using a fine camel's-hair brush for the purpose.

Figures in parentheses in these tables refer to the number of another table, thus— *Ext. Carotid* (3) means Table No. 3 of the External Carotid Artery.

THE ARTERIAL SYSTEM

| 1. Pulmonary Artery. (Plate 1.) | { | R. PULMONARY ART. (Plate 3) | } | Numerous branches through- |
| | | L. PULMONARY ART. (Plate 3) | | out the pulmonary tissue, carrying venous blood. |

THE ARTERIAL SYSTEM.—Continued

2.
Arch of Aorta.
(Plate 1.)

R. Coronary ⎫
L. Coronary ⎬ to the muscular tissue of the heart.

Innominate

R. Common Carotid ⎧ Ext. Carotid (3).
⎨ Int. Carotid (4).

R. Subclavian
becomes *Axillary* (8)

⎧ Vertebral (5).
⎨ Thyroid Axis (6).
⎪ Int. Mammary (7).
⎩ Sup. Intercostal.

L. Common Carotid, . . Same as R. Common Carotid.
L. Subclavian, . . Same as R., continuing as *Axillary* (8).

3.
External Carotid.
(Plate 1.)

Superior Thyroid.
⎧ *Muscular* and *Glandular* branches.
⎪ *Hyoid*, along lower border of os hyoides.
⎨ *Superf. Descending*, crosses Com. Carotid.
⎪ *Sup. Laryngeal*, to larynx and epiglottis.
⎩ *Crico-thyroid*, crosses Crico-thyroid membrane.

Lingual......
⎧ *Hyoid*, along upper border of bone.
⎪ *Dorsalis Linguæ*, to tongue, tonsil, palate, etc.
⎨ *Sublingual*, to gland, mouth, gums.
⎩ *Ranine*, under surface of tongue, to tip.

Facial or *External Maxillary.*
⎧ *Inf. (Asc.) Palatine*, to soft palate and tonsil.
⎪ *Tonsillar*, to tonsil and root of tongue.
⎪ *Submandibular*, to gland, skin, muscles.
⎪ *Submental* ⎰ *Superf. Br.* anas. inf. labial.
⎪ ⎱ *Deep Br.* to the lip.
⎪ *Muscular*, to pterygoid, masseter, buccinator.
⎨ *Inf. Labial*, anas. with br. of 7th and 5th N.
⎪ *Inf. Coronary* or *labial*, anas. with br. of inf.
⎪ dental art.
⎪ *Sup. Coronary,* ⎰ *Art. of Septum Nasi.*
⎪ or *labial.* ⎱ *Br.* to ala of nose.
⎪ *Lateralis Nasi*, to ala and dorsum of nose.
⎩ *Angular*, termination of facial trunk.

Occipital.....
⎧ *Muscular*, to digastric, stylo-hyoid, etc.
⎪ *Sterno-mastoid*, to that muscle.
⎪ *Auricular*, to back part of concha.
⎨ *Inf. Meningeal*, to dura mater in post. fossa.
⎪ *Princeps Cervicis* ⎰ *Superf. Br.* anas. superf.
⎪ cervical, of trans. colli.
⎪ *Deep Br.* anas. vertebral
⎩ and deep cerv. br. of
sup. intercostal.

ARTERIES OF THE HEAD AND NECK.

Plate 1

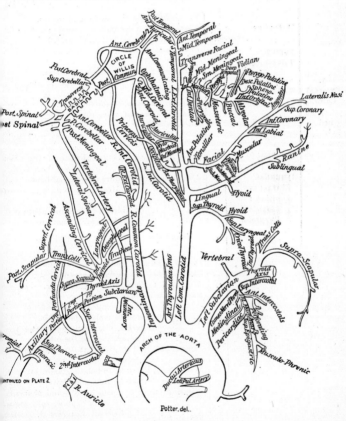

Potter. del..

CONTINUED ON PLATE 2.

149

THE ARTERIAL SYSTEM.—Continued

3. External Carotid. (Continued.)

Post. Auricular .....
- *Branches* (small), to muscles and glands.
- *Stylo-mastoid*, to tympanum, mastoid cells, etc.
- *Auricular*, to cartilage of ear.
- *Mastoid*, to scalp above ear.

Ascending Pharyngeal.
- *Prevertebral*, brs. to muscles and nerves.
- *Tympanic*, to inner wall of tympanum.
- *Meningeal Branches*, to dura mater.
- *Pharyngeal Branches*, 3 or 4 in number.

Superficial Temporal.
- *Transverse Facial*, lies on the masseter.
- *Anterior Auricular Branches*, to pinna, etc.
- *Middle Temporal*, supplies that muscle.
- *Anterior Temporal*, to the forehead.
- *Posterior Temporal*, along side of head.

INTERNAL MAXILLARY.
Divisions:
1. *Maxillary.*
2. *Pterygoid.*
3. *Spheno-maxillary.*

1.
- *Tympanic* { to memb. tympani, anas. with Stylo-mastoid and Vidian arteries.
- *Deep Auricular*, to outer surface of the membrana tympani.
- *Mid. Meningeal*, to dura and cranial bones.
- *Small* or *Accessory Meningeal*, to dura and Gasserian gang.
- *Inferior Dental* or *Mandibular*
  - *Lingual*, to m.m. of mouth.
  - *Mylo-hyoid*, in that groove.
  - *Incisor,* } Terminal Brs.
  - *Mental,* }

2.
- *Deep Temporal*, 2, under temporal muscle.
- *Pterygoid Brs.*, to pterygoid muscles.
- *Masseteric* to deep surface of masseter.
- *Buccal*, a small br. to buccinator.

3.
- *Alveolar*
  - *Dental*, to molars, bicuspids.
  - *Branches*, to antrum, gums, etc.
- *Infraorbital*
  - several brs. to the orbit.
  - *Ant. Dental*, to front teeth, antrum.
- *Post.* (*Desc.*) *Palatine*, to palate, glands, etc.
- *Vidian*, to Eustachian tube and pharynx.
- *Pterygo-palatine*, to Eustach. tube and pharynx.
- *Spheno-palatine*
  - *Artery of Septum*, to septum.
  - *External Branches* 3, to the nares, antrum, ethmoid and sphenoid cells.

THE ARTERIAL SYSTEM.—Continued

Tympanic, to tympanum by foramen in carotid canal.
Arteria Receptaculi (several), in cavernous sinus.
Ant. Meningeal, to dura mater of ant. fossa.

4. Internal Carotid. (Plate 1.)

OPHTHALMIC.
Groups:
1. *Orbital.*
2. *Ocular.*
(Plate 4. Fig. 2.)

1.
Lacrimal, to that gland, lid, etc.
Supraorbital, the largest sub-branch.
Post. Ethmoidal { *Meningeal,* to dura. *Nasal Brs.,* to nose. }
Ant. Ethmoidal, has same branches.
Sup. Palpebral, arch on margin of lid.
Inf. Palpebral, margin of lower lid.
Frontal, to muscles, skin
Nasal { *Transverse, Dorsalis Nasi,* } Terminal Branches.

2.
Art. Centralis Retinæ, to the retina.
Muscular { *Ant. Ciliary,* to the iris. *Superior,* to ocular muscles. *Inferior,* to ocular muscles. }
Short Ciliary, 6 to 12, around optic n.
Long Ciliary 2, to circles on iris.

Anterior Cerebral .... { *Ant. Communicating,* 2 lines long. *Ganglionic* and *Frontal* branches. }

Middle Cerebral ..... { *Ganglionic, Frontal, Parietal,* and *Parieto-temporal* branches. }

Posterior Communicating, { anas. with Post. Cerebral of Basilar, to form the Circle of Willis. }
Anterior Choroid, to the choroid plexus, etc.

THE CIRCLE OF WILLIS

BASILAR {
Post. Cerebral } Post. Commun. { INTERNAL CAROTID. } Ant. Cerebral
Post. Cerebral } Post. Commun. { INTERNAL CAROTID. } Ant. Cerebral
} Ant. Commun.

THE ARTERIAL SYSTEM.—Continued

5.
VERTEBRAL
(Plate 1.)

Lateral Spinal { Br. to spinal cord and membranes.
Br. to bodies of Vertebræ posteriorly.

Muscular Branches, to deep cervical muscles.

Post. Meningeal, ramify between dura mater and skull.

Anterior Spinal { joins its fellow to form Ant. Median Artery of the spinal cord.

Posterior Spinal, to spinal cord and membranes, laterally.

Post. Inf. Cerebellar { *Internal* { to cerebellum, and choroid plexus
External { of the 4th Ventricle.

Bulbar, minute branches to the medulla oblongata.

BASILAR.

Transverse { to Pons Varolii, etc.
Int. Auditory, to that canal.

Ant. Inf. Cerebellar { to the cerebellum, anas. with post. inf. cerebellar of Vertebral.

Superior Cerebellar, to pia mater, pineal gland, etc.

Posterior Cerebral { *Post. Choroid,* to choroid plexus
Ganglionic, to post. lobes.
Ant. Temporal,
Post. Temporal, } terminal
Occipital, } branches.

6.
THYROID
AXIS.
(Plate 1.)

Inferior Thyroid ... { *Inf. Laryngeal,* to post. muscles of larynx.
Tracheal Brs. to trachea, anas. Bronchial.
Œsophageal Brs. to œsophagus.
Ascending Cervical, to muscles, spinal cord.
Muscular, to muscles of hyoid bone and of the pharynx.

Transversalis Colli. { *Superficial Cervical,* beneath Trapezius.
Posterior Scapular, along post. border.

Supra-scapular .... { *Supra-acromial,* anas. Acromial Thoracic.
Supra-sternal, to skin of the chest.
Muscular, to sterno-mastoid, etc.
Nutrient, to the clavicle.

7.
INTERNAL
MAMMARY.
(Plate 1.)

Comes Nervi Phrenici (Superior Phrenic), to Diaphragm.

Mediastinal Brs. to tissue and glands, ant. mediastinum.

Pericardiac Brs. to upper part of pericardium.

Sternal Brs. to sternum and Triangularis sterni.

Anterior Intercostals, to 5 or 6 upper intercostal spaces.

Perforating, to Pectoralis major, mammary gland, etc.

Musculo-phrenic { *Ant. Intercostals,* to lower intercostal spaces.
Brs. to lower pericardium, Diaphragm, etc.

Superior Epigastric { anas. with deep Epigastric of Ext. Iliac.
supplies abdominal muscles and skin.

THE ARTERIAL SYSTEM.—Continued

**8.
Axillary.**
(Plate 2.)
1 from 1st part.
1 " 2d "
3 " 3d "

1. { *Superior Thoracic*, to Pectoral muscles and wall of thorax.
   Acromio Thoracic { *Brs.* to Pectorals and Deltoid.
     Descending, to both these muscles.
     Clavicular, to the Subclavius.

2. { *Alar Thoracic*, to glands of axilla.
   Long Thoracic, to Serratus, Pectorals and glands.

3. {
   Subscapular { *Dorsalis Scapulæ* { *Subscapular.*
       Infra-spinous.
       Median.
     Main trunk to inf. angle of the scapula.
   Anterior Circumflex { around neck of humerus, to Deltoid.
     Br. to shoulder-joint.
   Posterior Circumflex { around neck of humerus, to Deltoid
     muscle and shoulder-joint.

Becomes BRACHIAL (10), at lower margin of tendon of the Teres major muscle.

**9.
Brachial.**
(Plate 2.)

{ *Superior Profunda*,
   or
   Brachial Profunda { *Post. Articular*, to elbow-joint anastomosis
     and inner side of arm.
     Main trunk, in spiral groove of the hu-
     merus, to Deltoid, Triceps, etc.
   Nutrient, to nutrient canal of the humerus.
   Inferior Profunda (sup. uln. collat.) to the elbow-joint anastomosis.
   Anastomotica Magna (inf. uln. collat.), transversely inward on
     Brachialis anticus muscles to the elbow, where it anastomoses
     with several arteries.
   Muscular, 3 or 4, to muscles in course of artery.

Bifurcates into RADIAL (10) and ULNAR (11).

**10.
Radial.**
(Plate 2.)
1. In forearm.
2. In wrist.
3. In hand.

1. { *Radial Recurrent*, anas. branches of Sup. profunda.
   Muscular Brs. to muscles on radial side of arm.
   Ant. Carpal, to wrist-joints, anas. Ant. Carpal of Ulnar.
   Superficialis Volæ, to muscles of the thumb.

2. { *Post. Carpal* { to wrist-joints, anas. Post. Carpal of Ulnar.
     Dorsal Interosseous, for 3d and 4th spaces.
   Metacarpal, is the First Dorsal Interosseous Branch.
   Dorsales Pollicis 2, laterally on dorsum of thumb.
   Dorsalis Indicis, on radial side of index dorsum.

3. { *Princeps Pollicis*, 2 Brs. forming arch on last phalanx.
   Radialis Indicis, along radial side of index finger.
   Perforating 3 between heads of last Dorsal Interossei.
   Palmar Interosseæ { 3 or 4 along Interossei muscles, given
     off by Deep Palmar Arch.
   Palmar Recurrent, to the carpal articulations.

Forms DEEP PALMAR ARCH in the hand, completed by inosculation with the Deep Palmar (Communicating) from the Ulnar Artery.

THE ARTERIAL SYSTEM.—Continued

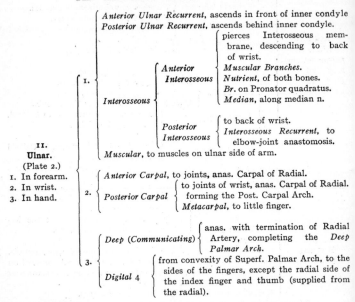

II.
Ulnar.
(Plate 2.)
1. In forearm.
2. In wrist.
3. In hand.

1.
- *Anterior Ulnar Recurrent*, ascends in front of inner condyle
- *Posterior Ulnar Recurrent*, ascends behind inner condyle.
- *Interosseous*
  - *Anterior Interosseous*
    - pierces Interosseous membrane, descending to back of wrist.
    - *Muscular Branches.*
    - *Nutrient*, of both bones.
    - *Br.* on Pronator quadratus.
    - *Median*, along median n.
  - *Posterior Interosseous*
    - to back of wrist.
    - *Interosseous Recurrent*, to elbow-joint anastomosis.
- *Muscular*, to muscles on ulnar side of arm.

2.
- *Anterior Carpal*, to joints, anas. Carpal of Radial.
- *Posterior Carpal*
  - to joints of wrist, anas. Carpal of Radial.
  - forming the Post. Carpal Arch.
  - *Metacarpal*, to little finger.

3.
- *Deep (Communicating)*
  - anas. with termination of Radial Artery, completing the *Deep Palmar Arch.*
- *Digital* 4
  - from convexity of Superf. Palmar Arch, to the sides of the fingers, except the radial side of the index finger and thumb (supplied from the radial).

Forms SUPERFICIAL PALMAR ARCH in palm of hand, by inosculating with a branch from the Radialis Indicis of the Radial Artery.

12.
Thoracic Aorta.
(Plate 3).

- *Pericardiac Branches*, distributed to the pericardium.
- *Bronchial Arteries* 3 nutrient vessels of the lungs.
- *Œsophageal*, 4 or 5, anas. brs. Inf. Thyroid, Phrenic, Gastric.
- *Posterior Mediastinal*, (several) to glands, etc., in mediastinum.
- *Intercostals.* 18.
  - *Posterior (Dorsal)*, to muscles of back.
  - *Spinal*, to the spinal cord and its membranes.
  - *Collateral Intercostal*, along upper border of the next rib below.

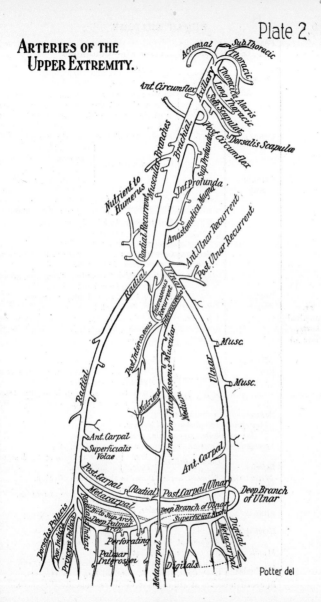

Plate 2

ARTERIES OF THE
UPPER EXTREMITY.

Potter del

THE ARTERIAL SYSTEM.—Continued

13. Abdominal Aorta. (Plate 3.)

Phrenic
- *Internal*, to front of thorax and Diaphragm.
- *External*, to side of thorax.

Cœliac Axis.

Gastric — to cardiac orifice of stomach, cardiac end, then along lesser curvature to pylorus, where it anas. with Pyloric Br. of Hepatic Art.

Hepatic
- *Pyloric*, to pylorus, anas. Gastric Art.
- *Gastro-duodenalis* { *Gastro-epiploica Dextra*. *Pancreatico-duodenalis Superior*. }
- *Right Hepatic*, { to right lobe. *Cystic*, to gall-bladder. }
- *Left Hepatic*, to left lobe of liver.

Splenic or *Lienal*
- *Pancreaticæ Parvæ* *Pancreatic Magna* } to the pancreas.
- *Gastric Vasa Brevia*, 5 to 7, to the greater curvature of stomach.
- *Gastro-epiploica Sinistra*, along the greater curvature, from left to right.
- *Terminal Brs.* enter hilum of Spleen.

Superior Mesenteric.
- *Inferior Pancreatico-duodenal*, to those organs.
- *Vasa Intestini Tenuis* 12 to 15, form arches in mesentery, in several series, from terminal arches branches ramify on intestines.
- *Ileo-colic* { *Inferior*, anas. Vasa intes. ten. *Superior*, anas. Colica dextra. }
- *Colica Dextra* { *Desc. Br.* *Asc. Br.* } Arches branching to ascending colon.
- *Colica Media* { *Right* *Left* } Arches, branching to **trans**verse colon.

Supra-renal, to supra-renal capsule.

Renal. { *Brs.* to substance of kidney. *Small Brs.* to capsule, ureter, etc. }

Spermatic (or Ovarian) to testes or ovaries, uterus, etc.

Inferior Mesenteric. (Plate 4.)
- *Colica Sinistra* { *Asc.* *Desc.* } Arches branching to descending colon.
- *Sigmoid*, across Psoas to that flexure of colon.
- *Sup. Hemorrhoidal*, { *Br.* to right *Br.* to left } side of rectum.

Lumbar 4.
- *Dorsal* { to muscles, etc., of back. *Spinal*, to canal { *Br.* *Br.* } Arches. }
- *Abdominal*, between abdominal muscles.

Middle Sacral, to coccyx, anas. Lateral Sacral.

Bifurcates { RIGHT COM. ILIAC, *R. Int. and Ext. Iliac* (14, 15). LEFT COM. ILIAC, *L. Int. and Ext. Iliac* (14, 15). }

Bifurcation occurs at 4th Lumbar Vertebra, opposite Umbilicus.

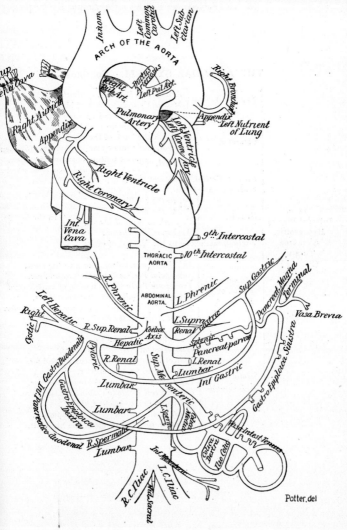

Potter. del

THE ARTERIAL SYSTEM.—Continued

14 a.
Internal Iliac or
Hypogastric.
ANTERIOR
TRUNK.
(Plate 4.)

Superior Vesical { *Art. of Vas Deferens*, to that organ.
Middle Vesical, to base of bladder.

Obturator.
  Iliac, to iliac bone and Iliacus muscle.
  Vesical, backward to the bladder.
  Pubic, on the back of the pubic bone.
  Internal, along inner margin obturator foramen.
  External, { outer margin obturator foramen.
  Br. to hip-joint by cotyloid notch.

Inferior Vesical, to base of bladder, prostate gland, etc.
Middle Hemorrhoidal, to anus, anas. other hem. arteries.

Uterine,
  Br. to the bladder.
  Br. to the ureter.
  Cervical, to neck of uterus.
  Azygos, of the vagina.   } In the female.

Vaginal, analogous to Inf. Vesical of male.

Internal Pudic, or *Pudendal*.
  Inferior Hemorrhoidal, 2 or 3 to the anus.
  Superficial Perinæal, to the scrotum, etc.
  Transverse Perinæal, to muscle of same name.
  Artery of the Bulb, large but very short.
  Artery of the Corpus Cavernosum, to that body.
  Dorsal Artery of the Penis, or *clitoris*.

Sciatic or *Inf. Gluteal*.
  Muscular Brs. within the pelvis.
  Hemorrhoidal Brs. to the rectum.
  Vesical Brs. to base and neck of bladder.
  Coccygeal, to back of coccyx.
  Inf. Gluteal 3 or 4, to Gluteus maximus.
  Comes Nervi Ischiadici, along sciatic nerve.
  Muscular Brs. to back of hip.
  Anastomotic, to the crucial anastomosis.
  Articular Brs. to capsule of the hip-joint.

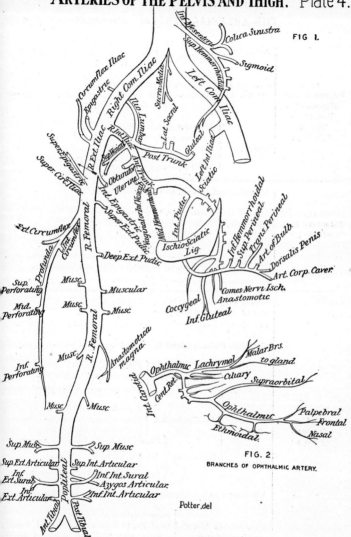

FIG 1.

Inf Mesenteric

Coluca Sinistra

Sup Hemmorhoidal

Sigmoid

Circumflex Iliac

Epigastric

Right Com Iliac

Ilio Lumbar

Sacra Media

Left Com Iliac

R.Ext.Iliac

R.Int.Iliac

Sup Sexual

Lat Sacral

Gluteal

Left Int Iliac

Post Trunk

Sciatic

Super Epigastric

Super Crt Iliac

Obturator

Ant Trunk

Uterine

Mid Hemmorhoidal

Int Epigastric

Super Ext pudic

Inf Pudic

Int Hemmorhoidal

Sup Perineal

Trans Perineal

Art of Bulb

Dorsalis Penis

Ext Circumflex

Profunda

Int Circumflex

R.Femoral

Deep Ext.Pudic

Ischio Sciatic Lig.

Art. Corp. Caver.

Sup. Perforating

Musc.

Muscular

Comes Nervi Isch.

Anastomotic

Mid. Perforating

Musc.

Musc.

Coccygeal

Inf.Gluteal

R. Femoral

Inf. Perforating

Musc.

Anastomotica magna.

Musc.

Musc.

Int Carotid

Cent Ret.

Ophthalmic Lachrymal

Malar Brs. to gland

Ciliary

Supraorbital

Ophthalmic

Palpebral

Frontal

Nasal

Ethmoidal.

Musc.

Musc.

Sup. Musc.

Sup. Musc

FIG. 2

BRANCHES OF OPHTHALMIC ARTERY.

Sup Ext Articular

Sup.Int.Articular

Inf. Ext Sural

Inf.Int.Sural

Azygos Articular.

Inf. Ext.Articular

Inf.Int.Articular

Popliteal

Potter, del

Ant Tibial

Post Tibial

THE ARTERIAL SYSTEM.—Continued

14 b.
Internal Iliac or Hypogastric.
POSTERIOR TRUNK.
(Plate 4.)

Ilio-lumbar,
- *Iliac,* to Iliacus internus and Ilium.
- *Lumbar,*
  - to Psoas and Quad. lumborum.
  - *Spinal Br.* to cord and membranes.

Superior Lateral Sacral, to dorsum of sacrum.
Inferior Lateral Sacral, to front of sacrum, and coccyx, anas. with Sacra media, etc.

Gluteal,
- *Muscular Brs.* within the pelvis.
- *Nutrient,* of the Ilium.
- *Superficial,* to Gluteus maximus, etc.
- *Deep*
  - *Superior,* to ant. sup. spine of Ilium.
  - *Inferior,* to glutei and hip-joint.

15.
External Iliac.
(Plate 4.)

Muscular Brs. several, to Psoas and glands.

Epigastric,
- *Cremasteric,* to cremaster muscle.
- *Pubic,* to inner side of femoral ring.
- *Muscular,* to abdominal muscles and skin.

Circumflex Iliac,
- between Transversalis and Int. oblique.
- *Br.* anas. with Lumbar and Epigastric.

Becomes FEMORAL (16) at Poupart's Ligament.

16.
Femoral.
(Plate 4.)

Superficial Epigastric, in superf. fascia, to umbilicus.
Superf. Circumflex Iliac, outward to iliac crest.
Superf. Ext. Pudic (pudendal), inward to skin of penis, scrotum etc.
Deep Ext. Pudic (pudendal), inward to skin of perineum, etc.

Profunda Femoris,
- *Ext. Circumflex,*
  - *Asc. Brs.* outer side of hip.
  - *Transverse,* to back of hip.
  - *Descending,* as far as knee.
- *Int. Circumflex,*
  - *Ascending,* to Adductors, etc.
  - *Descending,* to Adductors, etc.
  - *Articular,* to head of femur.
- *Perforating,*
  - *Superior,* pierces Adductor magnus.
  - *Middle,* { *Nutrient* of Femur.
  - *Inferior,* pierces Adductor magnus.

Muscular 2 to 7, along artery, to Sartorius, Vastus internus, etc.

Anastomotica Magna, or *Genu Suprema.*
- *Superficial Br.* to integument.
- *Deep Br.* to inner side of knee and joint, anas. with Sup. Articulars and Recurrent br. of Anterior Tibial.

Becomes POPLITEAL (17), at opening in Adductor magnus.

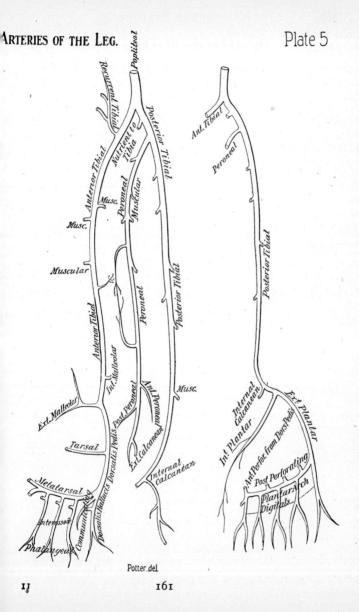

Potter.del

THE ARTERIAL SYSTEM.—Continued

**17.
Popliteal.
(Plate 4.)**

- Muscular
  - Superior Brs. to Vastus ext. and flexor muscles.
  - Inferior or Sural 2, to Gastrocnemius and Plantaris
- Cutaneous Brs. to integument of calf.
- Superior Internal Articular, to Vastus int. and joint.
- Superior External Articular, to Vastus ext. and joint.
- Azygos Articular, to synovial membrane of joint.
- Inferior Internal Articular, to head of tibia and joint.
- Inferior External Articular, to front of knee-joint.

Bifurcates into { ANTERIOR TIBIAL (18) } at lower border of Popliteus
{ POSTERIOR TIBIAL (19) } muscle.

**18.
Anterior
Tibial.
(Plate 5.)**

- Post. Recurrent Tibial, to the Popliteus muscle.
- Superior Fibular, to the Soleus and Peroneus longus.
- Ant. Recurrent Tibial, to the knee-joint anastomosis.
- Muscular Brs. numerous to muscles of leg.
- Internal Malleolar, beneath tendon of Tibialis anticus.
- External Malleolar, to outer ankle.
- Dorsalis Pedis
  - Tarsal, to tarsal joints and Ext. brev. digit.
  - Metatarsal, { 3 Interosseæ, { 7 Digital branches.
  - Dorsalis Hallucis { Brs. to great toe.
    { Br. to inner side of 2d toe
  - Communicating, { anas. Ext. Plantar (Arch)
    { 2 Digital Brs.

Ends in the PLANTAR ARCH.

**19.
Posterior
Tibial.
(Plate 5.)**

- Peroneal,
  - Anterior Peroneal, pierces interosseous membrane.
  - Posterior Peroneal, to the os calcis.
  - Nutrient Artery of the fibula.
  - Muscular, several brs. in its course.
  - Communicating { joins similar branch of the posterior Tibial.
  - Ext. Calcanean, the terminal branches.
- Muscular, to Soleus, etc., on back of leg.
- Nutrient of Tibia, the largest nutrient artery of bone.
- Communicating Br. to a similar br. of the Peroneal.
- Internal Calcanean Brs. to the heel, and sole of foot.
- Internal Plantar, along inner side of foot and great toe.
- External Plantar,
  - Brs. to muscles, fascia and skin.
  - Posterior Perforating 3 Branches.
  - 4 Digital, { Ant. Perforating Branches.

Ends as the PLANTAR ARCH, anas. with Commun. Br. of Dorsalis Pedis.

THE VEINS

Veins are vessels which return the blood from the capillaries of the body to the heart. Their walls, like those of the arteries, are composed of 3 coats—an internal serous (tunica intima), a middle muscular (tunica media), and an external one (tunica externa or adventitia) of connective tissue. Their middle coat is weaker than that of the arteries, so that they do not stand open when divided, as the arteries do. They all carry carbonized (venous) blood, except the pulmonary veins, which bring oxygenated blood to the left side of the heart. The deep veins accompany the arteries, generally in the same sheath, and are given the same names. The secondary arteries, as the radial, ulnar, brachial, etc., have each two veins, called *Venæ Comites*. The superficial veins are usually unaccompanied by arteries, and lie, as a rule, between the layers of the superficial fascia, terminating in the deep veins. Many veins are so irregular in their origin that they cannot be accurately described; they all anastomose with each other much more freely than do the arteries.

Venous Sinuses are venous channels, differing from veins in structure, but answering the same purpose. Those of the cranium are formed by the separation of the layers of the dura mater.

The Veins are divided into the *Pulmonary, Systemic,* and *Portal Systems;* the latter being an appendage of the systemic, its capillaries ramifying in the liver.

Veins having no valves are the venæ cavæ, hepatic, portal, renal, uterine, ovarian, cerebral, spinal, pulmonary, umbilical, and the very small veins.

The Pulmonary Veins alone of the veins carry arterial blood, beginning in the capillaries of the lungs, forming a single trunk for each lobule, which, uniting into a single trunk for each lobe, form two main trunks from each lung which open separately into the left auricle. Sometimes the three lobe-trunks of the right lung remain separate to their termination in the auricle, and not infrequently a common opening serves for the two left pulmonary veins.

VEINS OF THE HEAD AND NECK

Exterior Veins of the Head and Face are as follows,—

Frontal Vein,—begins on the anterior part of the skull by a venous plexus converging to a single trunk near the middle line of the forehead, which joins the supra-orbital vein at the root of the nose to form the angular vein.

Supra-orbital Vein,—begins on the forehead and joins the frontal (see above) to form the angular vein.

Angular Vein,—formed as described above, runs downward and outward on the side of the root of the nose, communicates with the ophthalmic vein, and ends in the—

Facial Vein,—a direct continuation of the angular, begins at the side of the root of the nose, descends obliquely across the masseter muscle and over the body of the lower jaw to unite with the ant. division of the temporo-maxillary to form the *common facial* vein, which enters the internal jugular.

Temporal Vein,—begins on the vertex and side of the skull, by anterior and posterior branches which unite and are joined by the middle temporal above the zygoma to form the trunk, which descends through the parotid gland and unites with the internal maxillary to form the temporo-maxillary vein.

Internal Maxillary Vein,—is formed by branches corresponding to those of the internal maxillary artery, forming the *pterygoid plexus.* The trunk passes backward behind the neck of the lower jaw and unites with the temporal to form the—

Temporo-maxillary Vein,—descends in the parotid gland and divides into an anterior branch, which joins the facial, and a posterior branch which is joined by the posterior auricular and becomes the external jugular.

Posterior Auricular Vein,—begins on the side of the head, descends behind the external ear and joins the posterior division of the temporo-maxillary, forming the external jugular.

Occipital Veins,—begin in a plexus at the back of the head and terminate in the internal jugular.

Veins of the Diploë and Interior of the Cranium,—

Veins of the Diploë,—a number of tortuous canals lying between the two tables of the skull, and divided into frontal (empties into supra-orbital) anterior temporal (empties into either the spheno-parietal sinus or anterior deep temporal), posterior temporal and occipital branches which empty into either the occipital vein or the lateral sinus (sinus transversus).

Cerebral Veins,—have no muscular coat and no valves. They are divided into superficial and deep sets. The deep cerebral are formed by the union of the *vena corporis striati* (vena terminalis) and the *choroid vein* on either side, and receive the *basilar* vein, forming the great cerebral vein (veins of Galen).

Cerebellar Veins,—on the surface of the cerebellum, are disposed in 3 sets superior, inferior and lateral.

Superior Longitudinal Sinus (sinus longitudinalis vel sinus sagittali superior),—occupies the attached margin of the falx cerebri, begins at the foramen cæcum, and ends in the *torcular Herophili* (confluens sinuum), or confluence of the sinuses.

Inferior Longitudinal Sinus (sinus sagittalis inferior),—in the free margin of the falx cerebri posteriorly, terminates in the—

Straight Sinus (sinus rectus or tentorial sinus),—at the junction of the falx cerebri with the tentorium, terminates in the lateral sinus (sinus transversus) of the opposite side.

Lateral Sinuses (sinus transversi),—in the attached margin of the tentorium cerebelli, terminate in the internal jugular vein.

Occipital Sinuses (sinus occipitales),—in the attached margin of the falx cerebri, terminate in the torcular Herophili.

Cavernous Sinuses (sinus cavernosi),—one on each side of the sella turcica, receive the ophthalmic vein and open behind into the petrosal sinuses.

Circular Sinus (sinus circularis),—is formed by two transverse vessels, the anterior and posterior *intercavernous sinuses*, connecting the two cavernous sinuses, and forming a venous circle around the pituitary body.

Superior Petrosal Sinus,—connects together the cavernous and lateral sinuses of each side.

Inferior Petrosal Sinus,—begins at the termination of the cavernous sinus, and joins the lateral sinus to form the internal jugular vein.

Transverse or *Basilar Sinus* (*plexus basilaris*),—connects the two inferior petrosal sinuses over the basilar process of the occipital bone.

Emissary Veins (emissaria),—pass through apertures in the cranial wall from the sinuses inside to the veins outside; the principal ones being 8 in number.

1. Frontal through foramen cæcum.
2. Parietal (two) through parietal foramina.
3. Occipital through foramen in occipital protuberance (occasional).
4. Post-condylar (condyloid) through foramen behind occipital condyle.
5. Emissary plexus through foramen ovale.
6. Vein of Vesalius through foramen of Vesalius.
7. Plexus through internal carotid canal.
8. Plexus through anterior condylar canal (hypoglossal canal).

Veins of the Neck, draining those above-mentioned, are the—

External Jugular (6),—terminating in the subclavian vein (4).

Posterior External Jugular,—opens into the external jugular.

Anterior Jugular (7),—enters the subclavian vein near the external jugular.

Internal Jugular (5),—formed by the junction of the two last-named sinuses at the jugular foramen, and uniting with the subclavian vein to form the innominate, at the root of the neck. In its course it receives the facial, lingual, pharyngeal, superior and middle thyroid veins, and the occipital.

Vertebral,—descends the foramina in the transverse processes of the cervical vertebræ, and empties into the innominate vein. In its course it receives the anterior and posterior vertebral and many other veins.

VEINS OF THE UPPER EXTREMITY

Veins of the Hand, Forearm, and Arm are in two sets, superficial and deep. The superficial set lies in the superficial fascia, begin in the hand by external and internal *dorsal* and superficial *palmar* veins, and are continued as follows, the *basilic* continuing as the *axillary*, which receives the *cephalic* just below the clavicle.

Dorsal.	Radial (cephalic B.N.A.)		Cephalic.	
Palmar.	Median (median cubital)	Median Cephalic		AXIL-
		Profunda		LARY
		Median Basilic		VEIN.
Dorsal.	Anat. Ulnar (basilic B.N.A.	Common Ulnar	Basilic	
	Post. Ulnar (basilic B.N.A.	(basilic B.N.A.)		
	(basilic B.N.A.			

The deep veins follow the arteries, generally as venæ comites, beginning in the hand as *Digital, Interosseous* and *Palmar* veins, they unite in the *Deep Radial* and *Deep Ulnar,* which join to form the *Venæ Comites of* the brachial artery at the bend of the elbow. The *Brachial Veins* lie one on each side of the brachial artery and join the Axillary Vein. These deep veins have numerous anastomoses, not only with each other but also with the superficial ones.

Axillary Vein (v. axillaris),—the continuation of the basilic, lies on the inside of the artery and terminates beneath the clavicle at the outer border of the 1st rib, where it becomes the—

Subclavian Vein (v. subclavia),—the continuation of the axillary, extends from the outer border of the 1st rib to the inner end of the clavicle, where it unites with the internal jugular to form the innominate vein. At the angle of junction enters the thoracic duct on the left side of the body and the right lymphatic duct on the right side. In its course it receives the external and anterior jugular veins and a branch from the cephalic.

The Innominate Vein (vena anonyma) is formed by the union of the subclavian and the internal jugular. The two innominates unite just below the 1st costal cartilage to form the superior vena cava. *The Right Innominate* (v. anonyma dextra) (3) is about 1 inch long, and receives, besides its constituent branches, the right internal mammary, right inferior thyroid, and right superior intercostal veins. *The Left Innominate* (v. anonyma sinistra) (2) is about $2\frac{1}{2}$ inches long; in its course it receives the vertebral, inferior thyroid, internal mammary, and superior intercostal veins of the left side.

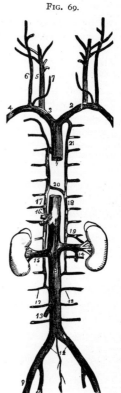

Fig. 69.

VEINS OF THE THORAX

The Veins of the Thorax include the following vessels:—

Internal Mammary, (mammaria interna),—two to each artery, unite into a single trunk which terminates in the innominate vein.

Inferior Thyroid (vv. thyreoideæ inferiores),— 2 to 4, form a plexus in front of the trachea, which gives off the left and right inferior thyroid veins, these receiving œsophageal, tracheal and inferior laryngeal veins and opening into the innominate veins.

Superior Intercostal,—the right vein (v. intercostalis suprema dextra) opens into the vena azygos major, the left vein (v. intercostalis suprema sinistra) into the left innominate.

Azygos Veins,—are described below.

Bronchial,—return the blood from the lung substance; the right one opens into the vena azygos major, the left into the left superior intercostal or the left upper azygos vein.

Spinal,—are described below.

Venæ Cavæ,—are described below; the *Superior Vena Cava* under the Veins of the Thorax, the *Inferior Vena Cava* under the Veins of the Lower Extremity.

The Azygos Veins supply the place of the venæ cavæ in the region where these trunks are deficient, being connected with the heart.

Vena Azygos Major (v. azygos) (17),—begins by a branch from the right lumbar veins usually, passes through the aortic opening in the diaphragm, and ends in the superior vena cava, having drained 10 right lower intercostals, the vena azygos minor, (v. hemiazygos), the right bronchial, œsophageal, mediastinal, and pericardial veins.

Left Lower Azygos (vena azygos minor or v. hemiazygos) (18),—begins by a branch from the left lumbar or renal, passes through the left crus of the diaphragm, crosses the vertebral column and ends in the right azygos, having drained 4 or 5 lower intercostals.

Left Upper Azygos (v. hemiazygos accessoria),—drains 3 or 4 left intercostals and empties into either of the other two. It is often wanting, its place being filled by the left superior intercostal vein (21).

The Spinal Veins may be arranged in 4 sets, as follows:—

Dorsi-spinal,—form a plexus around the spines, processes, and laminæ of all the vertebræ. They empty into the vertebral, intercostal, lumbar, and sacral veins in their respective regions.

Meningo-rachidian,—in two longitudinal plexuses, anterior and posterior, running the whole length of the spinal canal. The posterior join the dorsi-spinal veins, the anterior empty into the vertebral, intercostal, lumbar, and sacral veins in their various regions.

Venæ Basis Vertebrarum,—the veins of the bodies of the vertebræ, are contained in large, tortuous channels in the substance of the bones, and join the transverse trunk connecting the anterior longitudinal veins.

Medulli-spinale,—the veins of the spinal cord, lie in plexus form between the pia mater and arachnoid. They unite into 2 or 3 small trunks near the base of the skull, which terminate in the inferior cerebellar veins or in the inferior petrosal sinuses.

The Superior Vena Cava (1) is a short trunk about $2\frac{1}{2}$ or 3 inches in length, formed by the union of the two innominate veins, thereby receiving all the blood from the upper half of the body, and opening into the right auricle of the heart. It is half covered by the pericardium, and receives the vena azygos major and small pericardiac and mediastinal veins.

Veins of the Lower Extremity

The Veins of the Lower Extremity are in two sets, superficial and deep. The superficial are the—

Internal or Long Saphenous (saphena magna),—on the inside of the leg and thigh, enters the femoral at the saphenous opening $1\frac{1}{2}$ inch below Poupart's ligament (l. inguinale). In its course it receives:—

Cutaneous Branches.	Superficial Circumflex Iliac.
Superficial Epigastric.	Communicating Branches.

Ext. Pubic. (venæ pudendæ externæ).

External or Short Saphenous (v. saphena parva),—formed by branches from the dorsum and outer side of the foot, it ascends behind the outer malleolus, up the middle of the back of the leg, and empties into the popliteal vein, between the heads of the gastrocnemius muscle.

The deep veins are the *venæ comites* of the arteries, beginning in the foot as the external (lateral) and internal (medial) *Plantar*, which unite to form the *Posterior Tibial* (venæ tibiales posteriores). The *venæ comites* of the dorsalis pedis artery continue upward as the *Anterior Tibial* veins (venæ tibiales anteriores), which join the posterior tibial, forming the—

Popliteal,—which becomes the *Femoral*, and it the *External Iliac*, in the same manner as the respectively named arteries.

Veins of the Pelvis and Abdomen

The Veins of the Pelvis, except the middle sacral, open into the internal iliac vein. The middle sacral opens into the left common iliac.

The Internal Iliac Vein (vena hypogastrica) (10) is formed by the venæ comites of the branches of the internal iliac artery, and terminates with the external iliac, at the sacro-iliac articulation, to form the common iliac vein (v. iliaca communis). It receives the following veins:—

From the exterior of the pelvis, the—

Gluteal, (v. glutæa superior).
Sciatic (v. glutæa inferior).
Internal Pudic (vv. pudendæ internæ).
Obturator.

From the organs in the pelvic cavity the—

Hemorrhoidal Plexus.
Vesico-prostatic Plexus. } in the male.
Uterine Plexus.
Vaginal Plexus. } in the female.

The Dorsal Vein of the Penis enters the prostatic plexus.

The Veins of the Abdomen include the Portal System, the Lumbar, Spermatic, Renal, Suprarenal, Phrenic, Hepatic, External Iliac, Common Iliac and the Inferior Vena Cava.

The External Iliac Vein commences at the termination of the femoral beneath Poupart's ligament, and terminates opposite the sacro-iliac synchondrosis by uniting with the internal iliac to form the common iliac vein. It receives the *Deep Epigastric* (v. epigastrica inferior) and *Deep Circumflex Iliac*, also a small pudic vein.

The Common Iliac Veins (11) are each formed by the union of the two iliac veins as above described, and unite between the 4th and 5th lumbar vertebræ to form the inferior vena cava, the right common iliac being the shortest of the two. Each receives the *Ilio-lumbar*, sometimes the *Lateral*

Sacral, and the left one in addition the *Middle Sacral Vein,* which sometimes ends in the vena cava.

The Inferior Vena Cava (8) extends from the junction of the two
common iliac veins, passing along the front of the spine, through the tendinous centre of the diaphragm, to its termination in the right auricle of the
heart. It receives the following veins:

Lumbar (12),—4 on each side, receive dorsal and abdominal tributaries,
also veins from the spinal plexuses, and terminate in the inferior vena
cava. They are connected together by the *ascending lumbar,* which
passes in front of the transverse processes of the lumbar vertebræ.

Right Spermatic (13).—The spermatic veins arise from the testis and
epididymis, forming the *spermatic* or *pampiniform plexus,* which forms
the chief mass of the spermatic cord, and unite into 3 or 4 veins which
enter the abdomen through the internal ring, form 2 veins, then a
single one which opens on the right side into the inferior vena cava, on
the left side into the left renal vein. In the female they are called
Ovarian and terminate in the same way as in the male.

Renal (15),—are large veins, placed in front of the renal arteries, and
terminating in the inferior vena cava. The left is longer than the
right and passes in front of the aorta.

Supra-renal,—on the right side ends in the vena cava, on the left side in
the left renal or phrenic vein.

Phrenic 2,—the superior ends in the internal mammary, the inferior ends
on the right side in the vena cava, on the left side in the left renal vein.

Hepatic Veins (16),—begin in the capillary terminations of the portal
vein and hepatic artery in the substance of the liver, uniting into 3
large veins from the right and left lobes and the lobulus Spigelii, which
open into the inferior vena cava. They have no valves.

The Portal System is formed by the *Superior* and *Inferior Mesenteric,*
Splenic, and *Gastric Veins,* which collect the blood from the digestive viscera, and by their union behind the head of the pancreas form the *Portal
Vein,* which enters the transverse fissure of the liver, where it divides into 2
branches. These again subdivide, ramifying throughout the organ,
therein receiving blood also from the branches of the hepatic artery.
Its minute ramifications end in capillaries, from which the blood of the
portal system, together with that brought by the hepatic artery, is carried
by the hepatic veins to the inferior vena cava. The portal vein generally
receives the *Cystic Vein,* which sometimes terminates in the right branch
of the portal.

Veins of the Heart Itself

The Cardiac Veins return the blood from the tissue of the heart into the right auricle.   They are the—

Great Cardiac Vein.
Right or *Small Coronary Vein* (v. coronaria ventriculi).
Posterior Cardiac Vein.   *Anterior Cardiac Veins.*
Left Cardiac Veins.   *Venæ Thebesii.*
Coronary Sinus is a dilatation of the great cardiac vein, receiving the
  posterior cardiac and an oblique vein from the left auricle.

THE LYMPHATIC SYSTEM

Lymphatics are very delicate, transparent vessels; the larger having 3 coats like the arteries and veins, the smaller having 2 coats, the external and internal, but no middle muscular-elastic coat.   Lymphatics are found in nearly every texture and organ of the body which contains blood-vessels, but are absent in the non-vascular structures, as cartilage, nails, cuticle and hair.   They are nourished by blood-vessels distributed to their outer and middle coats, in which also many non-medullated nerve-fibres have been traced.   They possess valves of semilunar form, placed at much shorter intervals than are the valves in the veins.   They convey *lymph* to the blood, and possess the property of absorbing certain materials from the tissues and conveying them into the circulation; hence they are also called *absorbents*.   They discharge their contents into the blood at two points, the junctions of the subclavian and internal jugular veins, on the left side by the thoracic duct, on the right side by the right lymphatic duct.

Lacteals are the lymphatic vessels of the small intestine, conveying *chyle* to the blood during the process of digestion.

Lymphatic Glands (lymphoglandulæ) are small, solid, glandular bodies, placed in the course of the lymphatic and lacteal vessels, and found chiefly along the great blood-vessels, at the root of the lungs, in the lumbar and cœliac regions of the abdomen, in the mesentery, the mediastina, the head, neck, axilla, groin, and popliteal space.   They are named after the respective regions in which they are situated, as axillary glands, the inguinal, cœliac, bronchial, mesenteric, etc.   They consist of a fibrous *capsule*, from which *trabeculæ* are prolonged inward, dividing the gland into *alveoli* or open spaces containing *lymphoid tissue*, the proper gland-substance, which is so placed as to leave a channel (sinus), the *lymph-*

path, all around it. The glands are nourished by blood-vessels supported on the trabeculæ, and some fine nerve filaments are traced into them.

Before entering a gland the lymphatic (or lacteal) divides into several small branches, the *afferent vessels*, of which the endothelial layer only enters the gland, to form in its lymph-sinuses a plexus of vessels which unite into a single *efferent vessel*. The external coat of the afferent vessels becomes continuous with the capsule of the gland, and is received upon the efferent vessel as it emerges.

Hæmal Lymph Glands,—resemble ordinary lymph glands in all respects save that some of their sinuses contain blood.

Hæmal Glands,—all of their sinuses contain blood, otherwise they do not differ from regular lymph glands. Both Hæmal glands and Hæmal Lymph glands are more numerous in the retro-peritoneal tela along the line of the aorta.

The Thoracic Duct (ductus thoracicus) is the main channel for the lymph and chyle from the whole body except the right arm and lung, right side of the head, heart, neck, and thorax, and the convex surface of the liver. It begins in the abdomen by a triangular dilatation, the—

Receptaculum Chyli (cisterna chyli), in front of the 2d lumbar vertebra, passes through the aortic opening in the diaphragm, and opposite the 7th cervical vertebra it curves forward, outward and downward over the subclavian artery, so as to form an arch, and terminates in the left sub-clavian vein at its angle of junction with the left internal jugular vein. In the thorax it lies in the posterior mediastinum in front of the vertebral column, between the aorta on its left and the vena azygos major on its right. It has numerous valves throughout its course, and a pair of valves at its termination to prevent the passage of venous blood into its cavity.

The Right Lymphatic Duct (ductus lymphaticus dexter) is a short trunk, about $\frac{1}{2}$ inch in length and $1\frac{1}{2}$ line in diameter. It terminates in the right subclavian vein at its angle of junction with the right internal jugular, its orifice being guarded by two semilunar valves against the passage of venous blood into its cavity. It receives lymph from those parts which are not connected with the thoracic duct, namely—the right upper extremity, the right lung, the right side of the head, neck, heart and thorax, and part of the convex surface of the liver.

LYMPHATICS OF THE HEAD AND NECK

Lymphatic Glands of the Head and Neck, are as follows:—
Occipital (lymphoglandulæ occipitales), 1 or 2,—at the back of the head, close to the artery.

Posterior Auricular or *Mastoid* (lymphoglandulæ auriculares posteriores), 2,—near the mastoid process.

Anterior Auricular (lymphoglandulæ auriculares anteriores),—external to the parotid gland.

Parotid (lymphoglandulæ parotideæ),—some in and others around the parotid gland.

Buccal, 1 or more,—on the surface of the buccinator muscle.

Submandibular (lymphoglandulæ submaxillares),—beneath the ramus of the jaw.

Lingual (lymphoglandulæ linguales), 2 or 3,—on the hyo-glossus and genio-hyo-glossus muscles.

Retro-pharyngeal (lymphoglandulæ retropharyngeæ) 2,—one on each side of the middle line.

Superficial Cervical (lymphoglandulæ cervicales superficiales),—consisting of the *submaxillary,* 8 to 10, the *suprahyoid,* 1 or 2, and the *cervical* (many) in the course of the external jugular vein.

Deep Cervical (lymphoglandulæ cervicales profundæ superiores et inferiores),—forming a chain along the sheath of the carotid artery and internal jugular vein, in two sets, an upper, 10 to 20, and a lower, 10 to 15.

Lymphatic Vessels of the Head and Neck are—the *Temporal* and *Occipital,* in the scalp, respectively accompanying the temporal and occipital arteries; the *Meningeal* and *Cerebral,* in the cranium; the *Superficial* and the *Deep,* in the face; also those of the orbit, the temporal and zygomatic fossæ, the nose, tongue, pharynx, larynx and thyroid body. In the neck these vessels are continuations of those on the cranium and face.

LYMPHATICS OF THE UPPER EXTREMITY

Lymphatic Glands of the Upper Extremity (lymphoglandulæ cubitales superficiales et profundæ) are in two sets, the *Superficial,* which are few and small, and the *Deep,* in the forearm, the arm and the axilla. The *Axillary Glands,* 10 to 12, are of large size, situated around the axillary vessels, in the tissue of the axilla, and in chains along the lower border of the pectoralis major muscle and the lower margin of the posterior wall of the axilla, they are grouped as follows:—

1. Brachial or lateral.
2. Subscapular or posterior.
3. Pectoral or anterior.
4. Central.
5. Subpectoral.

6. Infraclavicular.
7. Interpectoral.
8. Deltopectoral.   (Robinson.)

Lymphatic Vessels of the Upper Extremity are the *Superficial*, beginning on the sides of the fingers and accompanying the veins; the *Deep*, occurring in 4 sets corresponding with the radial, ulnar, and anterior and posterior interosseous arteries.

Lymphatics of the Lower Extremity

Lymphatic Glands of the Lower Extremity are the—*Superficial Inguinal*, 8 to 10, in two sets, an upper oblique set (lymphoglandulæ inguinales) along Poupart's ligament (l. inguinale), and an inferior vertical set (lymphoglandulæ subinguinales), 2 to 5, around the saphenous opening in the fascia lata; *Deep Glands* are the anterior tibial popliteal (lymphoglandulæ popliteæ), deep inguinal (lymphoglandulæ subinguinales profundæ), gluteal and ischiatic.

Lymphatic Vessels of the Lower Extremity are in two sets, superficial and deep. The *Superficial* lie in the superficial fascia in two groups, an internal and an external, along the internal and external saphenous veins respectively. The *Deep* are few in number and accompany the deep blood-vessels.

Lymphatics of the Pelvis and Abdomen

Lymphatic Glands are the external iliac, internal iliac, and sacral, in the pelvis; and the lumbar and cœliac glands in the abdomen. The *Lumbar Glands* are numerous, situated in front of the lumbar vertebræ, and surround the common iliac vessels, the aorta and the vena cava. The *Cœliac Glands* 20, surround the cœliac axis and lie in front of the aorta, receiving the lymphatic vessels from a large part of the liver, the spleen, pancreas and stomach.

Lymphatic Vessels of the Pelvis and Abdomen are in 3 sets, the superficial, the deep, and those of the viscera. The *Superficial* follow the course of the superficial blood-vessels, and include the lymphatics of the gluteal region, the penis, scrotum and perinæum. The *Deep* follow the course of the principal blood-vessels. Those of the *Viscera* are the lymphatics of the various organs contained in these cavities—the bladder, rectum, uterus, kidney, liver, stomach, spleen and pancreas, and include those of the testicles.

Lymphatics of the Intestines

Lymphatic Glands of the Intestines are those of the large intestine, which are few in number, especially along the transverse colon; and those of the small intestine, 100 to 150, which lie between the layers of the mesentery and are called the *Mesenteric Glands* (lymphoglandulæ mesentericæ).

Lymphatic Vessels of the Intestines are those of the large intestine, some of which enter the mesenteric glands, others the lumbar glands; and those of the small intestine, called the *Lacteals*, from the milk-white fluid (chyle) which they usually contain. The lacteals are in two sets, superficial and deep, the latter occupying the submucous tissue and coursing transversely around the intestine.

LYMPHATICS OF THE THORAX

Lymphatic Glands of the Thorax are those of the thoracic walls (lymphoglandulæ sternales et intercostales) and those of the viscera. The former are the intercostal, the internal mammary, and the anterior and posterior mediastinal (lymphoglandulæ mediastinales anteriores et posteriores) glands; the latter are the bronchial and the superior mediastinal or cardiac glands. The—

Bronchial Glands (lymphoglandulæ bronchiales), 10 to 12,—are situated around the bifurcation of the trachea and the roots of the lungs.

Superior Mediastinal or *Cardiac Glands*,—are numerous and large, lie in front of the transverse aorta and the left innominate vein, and receive the lymph from the pericardium, the heart, and the thymus gland.

Lymphatic Vessels of the Thorax are the superficial, the deep and those of the viscera in the thoracic cavity. The *Superficial* converge to the axillary glands; the *Deep* are the intercostal, the internal mammary and the diaphragmatic; those of the *Viscera* are the lymphatic vessels of the lungs, heart, thymus gland and œsophagus.

THE NERVOUS SYSTEM

Nervous System.
- 1. Cerebro-spinal
  - 1. Central part
    - 1. Brain.
    - 2. Spinal Cord.
  - 2. Peripheral part
    - 1. Cranial Nerves.
    - 2. Spinal Nerves.
- 2. Sympathetic System
  - 1. Ganglia.
  - 2. Communicating Branches.

Nervous Tissue is formed of two different structures, viz. *Gray* or cineritious substance, in which nervous impressions and impulses originate; and *White* or fibrous substance, by which the impressions and impulses are conducted. Chemically, nervous tissue consists of proteids, neurokeratin, nuclein, protagon, lecithin, cerebrosides, cholesterin, nitrogenous extractives and salts, with some gelatin and fat, and water; the latter varying in different parts of the system, from 60 per cent. in the sciatic nerve, to 70 per cent. in the white matter of the cerebrum, and 83 per cent. in the gray matter of the same region.

Gray Nervous Substance, the essential constituent of all the ganglionic centres, is composed of *nerve-cells* or *ganglionic corpuscles*, containing nuclei

Fig. 70.

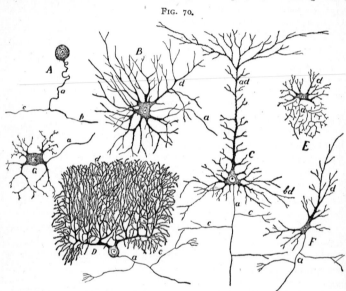

SHOWING SOME OF THE VARIETIES OF THE CELL-BODIES OF THE NEURONES OF THE HUMAN NERVOUS SYSTEM, INCLUDING THE DENDRITES AND SMALL PORTIONS OF THE AXONES. AXONE SHEATHS NOT INCLUDED. (*Morris' Anatomy.*)
A, From spinal ganglion. B. From ventral horn of spinal cord. C. Pyramidal cell from cerebral cortex. D. Purkinje cell from cerebellar cortex. E. Golgi cell of type II from spinal cord. F. Fusiform cell from cerebral cortex. G. Sympathetic. a, axone; d, dendrites; c, collateral branches; ad, apical dendrites; bd, basal dendrites; c, central process; p, peripheral process.

and nucleoli. The cells are imbedded in a ground substance, *neuroglia,* which consists of fibres and cells, and is a connective tissue in function though not in development. A neurone is a nerve-cell together with all of its processes. *Nerve-cells* vary in size and shape, and possess one or more processes, according to the number of which they are grouped into unipolar, bipolar and multipolar cells. Of these processes one is called the *axone* or *axis-cylinder process*, because it becomes the axis-cylinder of a nerve-fibre; the others are termed *dendrites* or *protoplasmic processes*.

White Nerve Substance or **Nerve-fibre,** contains two kinds of fibres, the medullated or white and the non-medullated or gray. *Medullated Fibres* contain a central core or *axis-cylinder*, the essential part of the nerve-fibre, and regarded as a direct prolongation of a nerve-cell. This is surrounded by the *medullary sheath,* or *white substance of Schwann,* composed of fatty matter in a fluid state, which insulates and protects the axis-cylinder. These are enclosed in the primitive sheath or *neurilemma,* sometimes called the tubular membrane or sheath of Schwann, which is absent in the fibres found in the brain and spinal cord. A bundle or *funiculus,* of such fibres, held together by *endoneurium,* is surrounded by *perineurium,* both formed of delicate connective tissue; and several funiculi are collected into larger bundles, *fasciculi,* which are bound together by a common membrane, the *epineurium,* and then are called a *Nerve.* The whole arrangement is precisely analogous to that of a submarine telegraph cable. The nerve is nourished by a minute system of capillary blood-vessels, and has certain medullated fibres in the epineurium, termed the *nervi nervorum,* or nerves of the nerves.

The *Non-medullated Fibres,* also called *gray* or *gelatinous* nerve-fibres, or fibres of Remak, consist of a central core- or *axis-cylinder* enclosed in a nucleated sheath. They constitute most of the sympathetic nerves and include some of the cerebro-spinal.

Terminations of Nerves. Their *origin* or central termination occurs from the nerve centre by one or two roots, in the latter case sometimes widely apart from each other. The efferent nerve-fibres originate in the cells of the gray substance, the afferent fibres branch among the cells without uniting with them. The *peripheral termination* of sensory nerves seems to be in minute primitive *fibrillæ* or networks thereof; that of motor nerves in special *terminal organs,* variously named, as the end-bulbs of Krause, the tactile corpuscles of Wagner, the Pacinian corpuscles, the neuro-tendinous and neuro-muscular spindles, and the motorial end-plates of the striped or voluntary muscular fibre.

Ganglia are separate small aggregations of nerve-cells, connected with each other, with the cerebro-spinal axis, and with nerves in various situations. They consist of a collection of nerve-cells and nerve-fibres, invested by a membranous envelope, which is continuous with the perineurium of the nerves, and sends processes into the interior of the ganglion to support the blood-vessels supplying its substance. They are found on the posterior roots of all the spinal nerves, on the posterior (sensory) root of the 5th cranial nerve; on the facial, auditory, glosso-pharyngeal and pneumogastric nerves; also in a connected series along each side of the vertebral column anteriorly, forming the trunk of the sympathetic, and on the branches of that nerve.

THE BRAIN

Development of the Brain. At an early period of embryonic life the cerebro-spinal axis consists of a thin-walled tube, the *neural tube*, which, while still open at its caudal end, becomes enlarged at its cephalic end, where constrictions appear, dividing this end into 3 primary *vesicles*, the anterior, middle and posterior. From these vesicles are developed the ventricles of the brain, the rest of the neural tube forming the central cavity of the spinal cord. Thickenings of the wall of the neural tube form the substance of the brain and spinal cord. The—

> *Anterior Primary Vesicle, Prosencephalon,*—divides into an anterior (*telencephalon*) and a posterior (*diencephalon*) secondary vesicles. From the telencephalon are developed the cerebral hemispheres; corpora striata; corpus callosum; fornix; lateral ventricles; olfactory lobe; front part of the third ventricle; front part of the tuber cinereum; infundibulum; and the posterior lobe of the pituitary body (hypophysis). From the diencephalon are developed, the optic thalami (thalamus); corpora geniculata (metathalamus); pineal body, the posterior part of the tuber cinereum; posterior part of the third ventricle; corpora mammillaria; optic nerve and optic tracts.
>
> *Middle Primary Vesicle, Mesencephalon,*—its cavity becomes the aqueduct of Sylvius, and with the parts developed around it constitutes the *mesencephalon* or mid-brain. From the mesencephalon are developed, corpora quadrigemina; pedunculi (crura) cerebri; and aquæductus cerebri (aquæduct of Sylvius).
>
> The constricted communication between the middle primary vesicle and the posterior primary vesicle is known as the *isthmus rhombencephali*, from it are developed the superior cerebellar peduncles (brachia conjunctiva) and the valve of Vieussens (anterior medullary velum).
>
> *Posterior Primary Vesicle, Rhombencephalon,*—by constriction forms an anterior secondary vesicle, *metencephalon;* and a posterior secondary vesicle, *myelencephalon.*
>
> From the metencephalon are developed the cerebellum; pons varolii (pons); and front part of the fourth ventricle.

From the myelencephalon are developed the medulla oblongata and the posterior portion of the fourth ventricle.

Structure of the Cerebrum. The cerebrum is composed of gray and white matter, the former disposed in two great groups,—that of the cerebral cortex and that in the basal ganglia.

The Gray Matter of the Cortex is composed of 6 alternating white and gray layers. The cortex is made up of nerve-cells and nerve-fibres. The *Nerve-cells* are arranged in 5 layers, named, from the surface inward, as follows: the *molecular* layer, the outer layer of *polymorphous cells*, the layer of *small pyramidal cells*, the layer of *large pyramidal cells*, the inner layer of *polymorphous cells*. In certain parts of the cortex this arrangement is variously departed from, as many as 9 layers being described in the cuneus. The *Nerve-fibres* are either medullated fibres or naked axis-cylinders embedded in a matrix of neuroglia.

The Basal Ganglia are a series of ganglionic masses in the base of each cerebral hemisphere, subjacent to the island of Reil, they and it constituting the oldest part of the hemisphere, the first to appear in the order of development. They are semi-detached local thickenings of the gray cortex, and are named as follows:—

Corpus Striatum,—composed of two nuclei, the caudate and the lenticular (lentiform) (described on page 191). Closely associated with it are certain fasciculi of white matter, the—

    Internal Capsule (page 192).
    External Capsule (page 192).
    Anterior Commissure (page 192).
    Tænia Semicircularis (stria terminalis) (page 190).

Claustrum,—a thin band of gray matter, described under the corpus striatum on page 191.

Nucleus Amygdalæ,—a thickening of the cortex of the apex of the temporal lobe, producing a bulge, the *amygdaloid tubercle,* in the roof of the extremity of the descending cornu of the lateral ventricle.

The Optic Thalamus, though in close proximity to the corpus striatum, is not placed among the basal ganglia of the hemispheres, being considered part of the diencephalon or inter-brain.

The White Matter consists of medullated fibres in bundles, arranged in the following 3 systems:—

PROJECTION FIBRES (peduncular),—connecting the hemispheres with the medulla oblongata and the cord. They originate in the cells of the cerebral cortex from whence they proceed, forming the corona radiata as they converge to enter the internal capsule when they are collected into the several bundles which are continued as the crusta (basis) of the crura (pedunculi) cerebri.

TRANSVERSE OR COMMISSURAL FIBRES,—connect the two hemispheres. They are the transverse fibres of the corpus callosum, and the anterior and posterior commissures of the 3d ventricle.

ASSOCIATION FIBRES,—connect different structures in the same hemisphere; the *short* connecting adjacent convolutions; and the *long*, connecting distant structures, as follows: the—

Uncinate Fasciculus,—from the frontal to the temporal lobe, across the bottom of the fissure of Sylvius, (fissura cerebri lateralis).

Cingulum,—antero-posteriorly in the convolution of the corpus callosum, from the anterior perforated substance to the hook of the uncinate gyrus (anterior end of the sup. occipito-temporal gyrus).

Superior Longitudinal Fasciculus,—connects the frontal lobe with the occipital and temporal lobes.

Inferior Longitudinal Fasciculus,—connects the temporal with the occipital lobe. It runs the entire length of both lobes and connects their convolutions.

Perpendicular Fasciculus,—connects the inferior parietal lobule with the inferior occipito-temporal convolution (gyrus fusiformis).

Fornix,—connects the hippocampal convolution (superior occipito-temporal) with the corpora albicantia (corpora mammillaria) and the optic thalamus.

THE MENINGES

Membranes of the Brain are the dura mater, the arachnoid membrane, and the pia mater.

The Dura Mater is a dense fibrous membrane lining the interior of the skull. It consists of two layers which are coalesced throughout the greater part of their extent. The inner layer which is produced into the intervals between parts of the brain forming partitions, and the outer layer which is strongly attached at the base of the cranial cavity and along the cranial sutures into which it sends processes. The outer layer forms the internal periosteum of the cranial bones. It is continuous with the dura mater of the spinal cord, with the pericranium, and the periosteum of the orbit; being prolonged to the outer surface of the skull through the various foramina at its base. It sends 4 processes into the cavity of the skull for the support of the different parts of the brain, also several tubular processes and prolongations through orifices and foramina in the skull for the protection of nerve trunks and vessels. The Cerebral dura mater derives its nerve supply from the 4th and 5th cranial nerves, and from the sympathetic (Whitaker). It presents the following points for examination—

The Meningeal Arteries,—are on, or close to, the outer surface, whereas the veins are deeply placed between the two layers and form sinuses (see page 164).

Falx Cerebri,—an arched process into the longitudinal fissure of the brain vertically; contains in its upper and lower margins the superior and inferior longitudinal sinuses.

Tentorium Cerebelli,—a lamina of dura mater supporting the posterior lobes of the brain, and covering the upper surface of the cerebellum. It incloses the lateral and superior petrosal sinuses.

Falx Cerebelli,—projects between the lateral lobes of the cerebellum, from the tentorium to the foramen magnum.

Diaphragma Sellæ,—a horizontal process forming a small circular fold which almost covers the pituitary body and constitutes a roof for the sella turcica.

Pacchionian Bodies (granulationes arachnoideales),—clusters of white granulations situated on both the outer and inner surface of the dura mater near the larger sinuses, and in the interior of the larger sinuses (see page 182).

The Arachnoid Membrane is a delicate single-layer envelope which covers the brain, lying between the dura mater and the pia mater, although throughout a large part of its extent it is not distinct from the pia mater. It is separated from the dura mater by the superficial cerebral veins. It dips into the great longitudinal fissure of the brain and into the interval between the cerebrum and cerebellum but it does not enter the fissures between the convolutions of the brain. Processes of it are prolonged around the cranial nerves as far as their points of exit from the skull. It is supplied probably by the 5th, 7th and 11th cranial nerves (Whitaker).

Subdural Space (cavum subdurale),—is the space between the arachnoid and the dura mater. It contains a small amount of fluid of the nature of lymph.

Subarachnoid Space (cavum subarachnoidalis),—is the interval between the arachnoid and pia mater, forming the two large spaces, mentioned below, at the base of the brain, but small on the surface of the hemispheres. It is occupied by a spongy connective tissue, in the meshes of which the cerebro-spinal fluid is contained. It communicates with the general ventricular cavity of the brain by 3 openings, one of which, the *foramen of Magendie* (metapore), is in the middle line at the lower end of the roof of the 4th ventricle.

Anterior Subarachnoidean Space (cisterna interpeduncularis),—is the interval between the arachnoid and the pia mater at the base of the brain, where the former membrane extends across between the two temporal lobes.

Posterior Subarachnoidean Space (cisterna cerebellomedullaris),—is a similar interval between the hemispheres of the cerebellum and the medulla oblongata. These two spaces communicate with each other across the inferior cerebellar peduncles (corpores restiformes).

Cerebro-spinal Fluid,—occupies the subarachnoid space of the brain and spinal cord, and also the ventricular cavities of the brain. Its average quantity is about 2 oz., being most abundant in old persons. It forms a water-bed for the protection of the nervous centres from the effects of concussions.

Granulationes Arachnoideales or Pacchionian bodies,—are numerous, small, granulations, which are not glandular in structure but enlarged normal villi of the arachnoid; found on the outer and inner surfaces of the dura mater, in the superior longitudinal sinus, and on the pia mater. They are not usually found until after the 7th year of age, and are occasionally wanting.

The Pia Mater is a vascular membrane, supplied by branches of the internal carotid and vertebral arteries. It covers the surface of the brain, dipping down into all the sulci, and forms the velum interpositum (tela chorioidea ventriculi tertii) and choroid plexus (plexus chorioideus ventriculi lateralis) of the lateral and 4th ventricles. It consists of a minute plexus of blood-vessels, held together by a very fine areolar tissue; and contains numerous lymphatic vessels and nerves, the latter being derived from both the cerebro-spinal and sympathetic systems. Its nerve supply is derived from 3d, 5th, 6th, 7th and 8th cranial nerves and from the sympathetic (Whitaker).

Weight of the Brain. Its average weight in the male adult is from 1360 (Smith) to 1400 (Spitzka) grammes; in the female 1250 grammes (Spitzka), of which the cerebrum is about seven-eighths.

Divisions of the Brain. The Brain may be divided into the *Cerebrum,* the *Cerebellum,* the *Pons Varolii* (pons) and the *Medulla Oblongata;* but for the descriptive purposes it is best considered under the following 5 divisions, viz. the—

Cerebral Hemispheres or *Telencephalon,*—comprising the various lobes, the lateral and 5th ventricles, and the basal ganglia.

Inter-brain or *Diencephalon,*—the region of the 3d ventricle, including also the optic thalami and the pineal gland.

Mid-brain or *Mesen-cephalon,*—comprising the crura cerebri, the corpora quadrigemina, the corpora geniculata, and the aqueduct of Sylvius (aquæductus cerebri).

Hind-brain or *Metencephalon,*—comprising the pons Varolii, the cerebellum, and the upper half of the 4th ventricle.

Medulla Oblongata or *Myelencephalon,*—including the lower half of the 4th ventricle.

The Cerebrum or Telencephalon. The cerebrum presents an external surface of gray matter called the cortex, the large upper part of which is called the *Pallium* or *Mantle;* the smaller lower or basilar part is called the *Rhinencephalon.* The surface of the brain presents numerous clefts; some of these clefts cause a corresponding projection into the cavities of the interior of the brain and are called *Fissures* (fissuræ) in order to distinguish them from the others called *Sulci,* which are those clefts which separate lobes (or lobules) from each other. Clefts that separate the lobes from each other are called inter-lobular sulci, while those that divide lobes into convolutions or gyri are known as intra-lobular sulci. The cerebrum is divided into two hemispheres by the Great Longitudinal fissure (fissura longitudinalis cerebri).

The Cerebral Hemispheres

Lobes in each Hemisphere, are as follows:—

Frontal Lobe,—bounded internally by the longitudinal fissure, below by the fissure of Sylvius (fissura cerebri lateralis), and posteriorly by the fissure of Rolando (sulcus cerebri centralis).

Parietal Lobe,—extending down to the fissure of Sylvius (fissura cerebri lateralis), and antero-posteriorly from the fissure of Rolando (sulcus cerebri centralis) to the external parieto-occipital fissure.

Occipital Lobe,—behind the parieto-occipital fissure.

Temporal Lobe,—lying in the middle fossa of the skull, and bounded in front by the fissure of Sylvius (fissura cerebri lateralis).

Central Lobe, or Island of Reil (Insula),—lies in the fissure of Sylvius (fissura cerebri lateralis) covered by the frontal and temporal lobes.

Limbic Lobe,—arches around the corpus callosum and the hippocampal fissure; is well developed in animals having a keen sense of smell.

Olfactory Lobe,—situated on the under surface of the frontal lobe, and divided into the olfactory bulb, the olfactory tract, the trigonum, and the posterior olfactory lobule (ant. perforated space or substantia perforata anterior).

Fissures of the Cerebrum are as follows:—

Longitudinal Fissure (fissura longitudinalis cerebri),—extends from the front of the cerebrum to the back, separating it into two hemispheres, which are connected in the middle portion by the central commissure, the *corpus callosum* (10), forming the floor of the fissure in this part of its length.

Sylvian Fissure, or *Fissure of Sylvius* (fissura cerebri lateralis),—on each side at the base and lateral side of the brain. Starting at the anterior perforated substance it passes outward to the external surface of the hemisphere, where it divides into a short anterior limb (ramus anterior horizontalis), a short ascending limb (ramus anterior ascendens), and a horizontal limb (ramus posterior). It lodges the middle cerebral artery.

Fissure of Rolando (sulcus cerebri centralis) (1),—on the superior surface of each hemisphere, extending from the longitudinal fissure about its centre, downward and forward toward the fissure of Sylvius, separating the frontal and parietal lobes. This fissure is said to be found only in man and the higher primates.

Parieto-occipital Fissure,—extends from the longitudinal fissure outward for about an inch between the parietal and occipital lobes.

Calloso-marginal Fissure (sulcus cinguli),—above the gyrus fornicatus (gyrus cinguli) on the inner surface of each hemisphere.

Internal Parieto-occipital Fissure,—extends downward and forward to join the calcarine fissure, on a level with the hinder end of the corpus callosum.

Calcarine Fissure (fissura calcarina),—begins close to the posterior extremity of the hemisphere, runs horizontally forward, joined by the parieto-occipital fissure, and terminates a little below the posterior end of the corpus callosum (11).

Collateral Fissure,—below and external to the preceding, runs forward from the posterior extremity of the brain nearly as far as the tip of the temporal lobe.

Dentate or *Hippocampal Fissure*,—commences behind the posterior end of the corpus callosum (11) and runs forward to the recurved part (uncinate gyrus) of the hippocampal gyrus (posterior horizontal part of the sup. occipito-temporal convolution).

Transverse Fissure,—a horse-shoe shaped gap or cleft at the base of the brain, extending from the foramen of Munro on each side to the termination of the descending cornu of the lateral ventricle. One-half the fissure is in each hemisphere, and it admits an invagination of the pia mater, which forms the *choroid plexus* in the lateral ventricle and the *velum interpositum* (tela chorioidea ventriculi tertii) in the 3d ventricle. It gives exit to the venæ Galeni.

Parallel Fissure, formerly called the *first temporo-sphenoidal fissure*,—on the lateral surface of the hemisphere below the fissure of Sylvius (fissura cerebri lateralis).

Cerebral Convolutions. The superior and inner surfaces of each hemisphere are formed of convolutions (*gyri*) with intervening fissures and depressions (*sulci*) of various depths, the gyri and sulci being both formed of gray matter thus arranged to enable it to present a great extent of surface. The convolutions are not uniform in all brains as to arrangement, nor are they symmetrical in the two hemispheres. The principal convolutions are the following-named:—

FIG. 71.

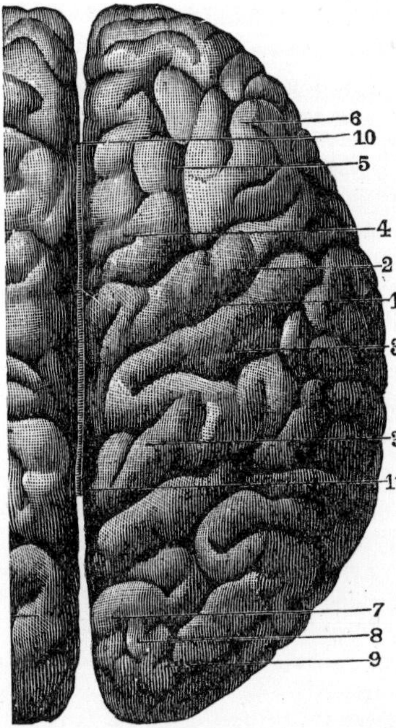

On the Frontal Lobe are 8, externally — the ascending (gyrus centralis anterior) (2), superior (4), middle (5) and inferior (6) frontal; inferiorly the internal, anterior and posterior orbital. The *inferior frontal* on the left side is named the *convolution of Broca* and is the *language centre.*

On the Parietal Lobe are 4, externally—the ascending (gyrus centralis posterior) (3), superior and inferior parietal, and the quadrate or *precuneus*, internally. The inferior parietal is subdivided into the supramarginal, the angular, and postparietal gyri, the latter (2) lying around the posterior end of the superior temporal sulcus (parallel fissure) (see above).

The Occipital Lobe has 4, externally—the superior (7), middle (8) and inferior (9) occipital; and internally the cuneate lobule or *cuneus*.

Temporal Lobe has 5 gyri,—externally, the superior, middle, and inferior temporal gyri; below on the tentorial surface, the superior occipito-temporal (gyrus lingualis or subcalcarine), and the inferior occipito-temporal (gyrus fusiformis). Part of the inferior temporal gyrus also shows on this surface. On the upper surface, two or three indefinite gyri can be seen. The superior occipito-temporal lobe is by some considered to be two lobes, in which case, its anterior, upwardly hooked portion is called the uncinate gyrus, the posterior horizontal portion being called the hippocampal gyrus.

The Central Lobe or *Island of Reil* (insula), is subdivided by the sulcus centralis into the precentral lobe (pars frontalis) and the postcentral lobe (pars occipitalis). The insula is pyramidal in shape and consists of 5 or 6 convolutions called gyri operti.

Under Surface of the Base of the Brain, from before backward, excluding the vessels and the cranial nerves, shows the following points for examination. In the middle line are the—

Longitudinal Fissure,—its anterior portion separating the frontal lobes, and its posterior portion between the occipital lobes.

Corpus Callosum,—the great transverse commissure, seen in the longitudinal fissure, and showing its *peduncles*, one on each side, to meet the corresponding outer root of the olfactory tract.

Lamina Cinerea,—a thin, triangular, gray layer, continuous with the anterior perforated space (locus perforatus anterior). In the midline it is divided into a right and a left portion by a very thin almost transparent portion—the *lamina terminalis*, which forms the anterior and inferior boundary of the 3d ventricle.

Optic Commissure,—formed by the junction of the optic tracts.

Tuber Cinereum (17)—a gray lamina behind the optic commissure, forming part of the floor of the third ventricle. From it projects the—

Infundibulum,—a hollow process, its canal connecting the pituitary cavity with the 3d ventricle in the fœtus.

Eminentia Saccularis,—between the corpora albacantia or mammillària and the tuber cinereum, it is a trefoil-shaped eminence homologous with the *saccus vasculosus* of the lower vertebrates.

The Pituitary Body or *Gland* (*Hypophysis Cerebri*),—is a small oval body depending by the *infundibulum* from the *tuber cinereum* in the floor of the third ventricle. It occupies the pituitary fossa (fossa hypophyseos) in the sella turcica of the sphenoid bone. It consists of two

FIG. 72.

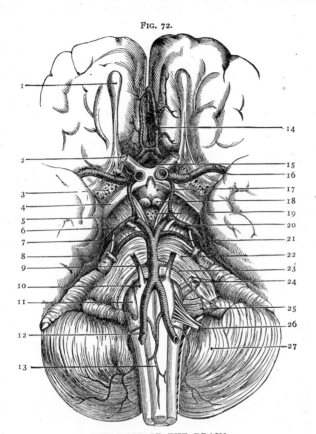

THE BASE OF THE BRAIN

1. Olfactory Bulb. 2. Second, or Optic Nerves. 3. Anterior Perforated Space. 4. Optic Tract. 5. Crus Cerebri. 6. 3d Nerve. 7. 4th Nerve. 8. 5th Nerve. 9. 6th Nerve. 10. Pyramid. 11. Olivary Body. 12. Vertebral Artery. 13. Anterior Spinal Artery. 14. Anterior Cerebral Artery. 15. Lamina Cinerea. 16. Middle Cerebral Artery. 17. Tuber Cinereum. 18. Corpora Albicantia. 19. Posterior Perforated Space. 20. Posterior Cerebral Artery. 21. Superior Cerebral Artery. 22. Pons Varolii. 23. Inferior Cerebellar Artery. 24. 7th and 8th Nerves. 25. 9th, 10th and 11th Nerves. 26. 12th Nerve. 27. Cerebellum.

lobes. Anterior (buccal or glandular) lobe is the larger, it secretes a colloid substance much like that of the thyroid gland (glandula thyreoidea). Its structure is much like that of the para-thyreoid bodies. It consists of compartments which are lined with cuboidal cells of two varieties. The *principal* cells are the more numerous, they are small cells with very granular cytoplasm. The large cells are *chromophile cells*. The anterior lobe is derived from the *primitive buccal cavity* (stomatodæum). Posterior or cerebral lobe is the smaller and is connected by the *infundibulum* to the *tuber* cinereum, but is not known to be functional. It is composed chiefly of neurogliar connective tissue and blood-vessels, throughout which are interspersed numerous branched cells. It has no organized structure. It is derived from the hypophyseal diverticulum of the diencephalon. The hypophysis gets its blood supply from the hypophyseal branches of the internal carotid artery, it is classed as one of the *ductless glands*.

Corpora Albicantia (corpora mammillaria) (18),—two round, white eminences, united together; they are the anterior crura of the fornix folded on themselves.

Posterior Perforated Space (*Pons Tarini* or *Substantia Perforata Posterior*) (19),—perforated for vessels to the optic thalami; forms part of the floor of the 3d ventricle.

Pons Varolii (pons) (22),—a broad band of white fibres, passing from one cerebellar hemisphere to the other described on page 203.

Medulla Oblongata (13),—pyramidal in form, emerges from the posterior border of the pons Varolii. It is described on page 208.

On each side of the middle line are seen the—

Frontal Lobe,—its under surface (see *ante*, page 185); lying thereon is the—

Olfactory Lobe,—consisting of the olfactory bulb (1), the olfactory tract, the trigonum olfactorium, and the posterior olfactory lobule or anterior perforated space (3).

Anterior Perforated Space (substantia perforata anterior), (3) or posterior olfactory lobule,—at the commencement of the fissure of Sylvius (fissura cerebri lateralis); is perforated for small arteries going to the corpus striatum.

Fissure of Sylvius (fissura cerebri lateralis),—is described on page 184.

Optic Tract (4),—runs obliquely across the crus cerebri as a flat band, and enters into the optic commissure.

Crus Cerebri or *Cerebral Peduncle* (5),—a thick bundle of white matter in front of the anterior border of the pons, passing forward and outward to enter the under surface of the hemisphere. The two crura connect the cerebrum with the cerebellum, medulla oblongata and spinal cord. With the optic tracts they form the boundaries of the *inter-peduncular space*.

Temporal Lobe,—its under surface (see page 186).

Cerebellum (27),—covering the occipital lobe of the cerebrum. It is described separately on page 206.

Ventricles of the Brain are 5 in number, of which the two lateral and the 5th belong to the cerebral hemispheres, the 3d is the cavity of the interbrain, and the 4th belongs to the cerebellum and the medulla oblongata. They are situated as follows:—

Two Lateral Ventricles, (ventriculi laterales),—within the substance of the hemisphere, one in each; they are connected with the 3d ventricle and indirectly with each other by the *foramina of Munro* (foramina interventricularia) and the 3d ventricle.

Third Ventricle (ventriculus tertius),—a narrow crevice between the optic thalami, lying below the lateral ventricles and communicating with them by the *foramina of Munro* (foramina interventricularia). It is connected with the 4th ventricle by the *iter a tertio ad quartum ventriculum* or aqueduct of Sylvius (aquæductus cerebri).

Fourth Ventricle (ventriculus quartus),—between the cerebellum and the medulla oblongata.

Fifth Ventricle (cavum septi pellucidi),—between the two laminæ of the septum lucidum (septum pellucidum), between the two lateral ventricles. It is not a true ventricle.

The Lateral Ventricles are two irregular cavities in the cerebral hemispheres, separated from each other by a partition, the *septum lucidum,* (or pellucidum), and each having a central cavity and 3 prolongations or cornua, the anterior in the frontal lobe, the middle in the temporal lobe and the posterior in the occipital lobe. They communicate with each other and with the 3d ventricle by the *foramina of Munro* (foramina interventricularia). The central cavity (pars centralis) is situated in the parietal lobe and is bounded as follows:—

Roof,—the under surface of the corpus callosum.

Floor,—from before backward, the caudate nucleus of the corpus striatum, tænia semicircularis (stria terminalis), optic thalamus, choroid plexus, the thin sharp free edge of the lateral half of the fornix and its posterior pillar.

Internally,—the septum lucidum (septum pellucidum), separating it from the opposite ventricle.

Externally, in front and *behind,*—brain-substance.

Structures named above are briefly described as follows:—

> *Corpus Callosum*,—the great transverse commissure, arching backward to become continuous with the fornix, reflected below, forming *the peduncles* at the entrance of the fissure (lateral cerebral) of Sylvius; and marked above by a depression, *the Raphé*, and longitudinal elevations, the *striæ longitudinales*, mediales and laterales, or *nerves of Lancisi*.

> *Septum Lucidum* (septum pellucidum),—consists of 2 layers of white and gray matter, lined by epithelium; is placed vertically between the lateral ventricles, from the raphé of the corpus callosum above to the fornix below. The cavity in its centre is the 5th ventricle (or cavum septi pellucidi).

> *Fornix*,—is a commissure situated beneath the corpus callosum, but continuous with it posteriorly, the *septum lucidum* (s. pellucidum) separating them in front. It is composed of association fibres which are axis-cylinder processes connecting different parts of the same hemisphere. It is of triangular form with the apex in front. Its *anterior pillars* curve downward to the base of the brain, are there reflected, forming the *corpora albicantia* (corpora mammillaria), and end in the optic thalami. Its *posterior pillars* (crura fornicis) pass down the descending horns of the lateral ventricles, along the concavities of the hippocampi majores, and are each continued as the *corpus fimbriatum* or *tænia hippocampi*, into the *uncus* or hook of the hippocampal convolution. The *Lyra* (psalterium) is a series of markings on its under surface.

> *Foramina of Munro* (foramina interventricularia),—together form a Y-shaped opening situated between the anterior pillars of the fornix in front and above and the anterior extremities of the optic thalami below and behind. Each is crescentic in outline and by it the lateral ventricles communicate with the 3d ventricle and with each other.

> *Tænia Semicircularis* (Stria Terminalis),—consists of commissural fibres passing between the corpus striatum and the optic thalamus.

> *Choroid Plexus of Veins*,—is the margin of a fold of pia mater which enters at the transverse fissure, passes up the descending cornu, through the foramen of Munro, and as the *Velum Interpositum* (tela chorioidea ventriculi tertii) spreads out over the roof of the 3d ventricle.

> *Corpus Striatum*,—is described on page 191.

> *Optic Thalamus*,—is described on page 193.

Cornua of the Lateral Ventricles. The *Anterior Cornu* (cornu anterius) curves over the anterior end of the corpus striatum into the frontal lobe.

The *Posterior Cornu* (cornu posterius) curves downward and inward in the occipital lobe, and contains a smooth eminence, the *Hippocampus Minor*, which is caused by the calcarine fissure; below this is a slight elevation called the *calcar avis*. As the calcar avis and the hippocampus diverge from each other they leave a triangular interval called the *trigonum collaterale*. The *Middle Cornu* (cornu inferius) descends into the temporal lobe to the transverse fissure at the base of the brain, curving backward, outward, downward, forward, and inward (initials of the directions form the mnemonic word BODFI). On its floor are the following:—

Hippocampus Major,—a white eminence, about 2 inches long, formed by the infolding of the cerebral cortex to produce the dentate or hippocampal fissure.

Pes Hippocampi,—the scolloped end of the hippocampus.

Pes Accessorius (Eminentia Collateralis),—between the hippocampi, at the junction of the middle and posterior cornua, it is caused by the collateral fissure.

Corpus Fimbriatum,—a continuation of the posterior pillar of the fornix (crus fornicis).

Choroid Plexus of Veins,—a process of pia mater (see page 190).

Dentate Convolution (fascia dentata),—a band of gray matter, just below the fimbria, its free border is notched by the branches of the choroid artery.

Transverse Fissure (fissura chorioidea),—at the extremity of the cornu, extending to the foramena of Munro (foramena interventricularia). It is described on page 184.

The Fifth Ventricle (cavum septi pellucidi) is a narrow chink situated between the layers of the *septum lucidum* (septum pellucidum), and therefore lies between the lateral ventricles. In the *fœtus* it communicates with the 3d ventricle by an opening between the anterior pillars of the fornix (columnæ fornicis). Originally it was part of the longitudinal fissure and was shut off by the union of the hemispheres in the formation of the corpus callosum above and the fornix below. It usually contains fluid, of the nature of lymph.

The Corpus Striatum is a body of gray matter imbedded in the white substance of each hemisphere, and is partly seen in the lateral ventricle and its anterior cornu, this part being the—

Nucleus Caudatus (caudate nucleus),—the intra-ventricular portion; a pear-shaped mass having its narrow end on the outer side of the optic thalamus.

Nucleus Lentiformis (lenticular nucleus),—the extra-ventricular portion, only seen in sections of the hemisphere. It is divided by the
white external and internal laminæ into three portions, the two medial
portions together constitute the globus pallidus, the remaining part
is much the larger and is called the putamen.

Internal Capsule,—a curved lamina of white matter separating the
caudate nucleus from the lenticular (lentiform) posteriorly. It is
formed by projection fibres from the crus cerebri, the corpus striatum and the optic thalamus. [Projection fibres are axis-cylinder
processes connecting cells in the gray matter of the hemispheres
with other cells at lower levels in the cerebro-spinal axis.] Its
anterior limb (pars frontalis) is the portion in front of the curve
or *genu*, its *posterior limb* (pars occipitalis) lying behind the genu.

External Capsule,—a lamina of white matter bounding the putamen of
the lenticular (lentiform) nucleus externally, and made up of association fibres from the anterior commissure and the subthalamic
region.

Claustrum,—a thin layer of gray matter on the outer surface of the
external capsule, regarded as a detached portion of the gray matter
of the island of Reil (insula).

THE INTER-BRAIN

The Inter-brain or **Thalamen-cephalon** (Diencephalon) is the region
of the 3d ventricle, and is connected in front and above with the cerebral
hemispheres, behind with the mid-brain or mesencephalon. Its upper
surface is covered by the *fornix;* inferiorly it reaches the base of the brain,
it comprises the following structures,—optic thalami, corpora geniculata
(metathalamus), pineal body (corpus pineale), posterior part of the
tuber cinereum, posterior part of the third ventricle, corpora albicantia
(corpora mammillaria), optic nerve, and optic tract.

The Third Ventricle (ventriculus tertius) is a mere fissure, situated
in the mid-line, between the optic thalami. It communicates with the
lateral ventricles above by the *foramina of Munro* (foramina interventricularia) and with the 4th ventricle behind by the *iter a terio ad
quartum ventriculum* (aquæductus cerebri). It is crossed by 3 bands,
the anterior, middle, and posterior commissures, the middle one being of
gray matter, the others of white.

Anterior Commissure,—is composed of commissural fibres, it appears to
connect together the corpora striata; its fibres are traced into the
temporal lobes, and include fibres from the olfactory tract of the

opposite side. Commissural fibres are axis-cylinder processes which connect identical parts of the two hemispheres.

Middle Commissure (massa intermedia),—is composed of gray matter and connects the two optic thalami.

Posterior Commissure,—is composed of commissural fibres (see above); it stretches across from one optic thalamus to the other, and contains fibres connecting the two thalami, besides decussating fibres from various parts of the mid-brain.

Boundaries of the Third Ventricle are as follows:—

Roof,—the velum interpositum (tela chorioidea ventriculi tertii), and above it the fornix.

Floor,—the parts comprised in the interpeduncular space at the base of the brain, viz.—the tuber cinereum, with its infundibulum and pituitary body, corpora albicantia (corpora mammilaria), posterior perforated space (substantia perforata posterior). Eminentia saccularis, and chiasma optica.

Anteriorly,—the anterior pillars of the fornix (columnæ fornicis), and the lamina terminalis which joins the right and left half of the lamina ceneria.

Posteriorly,—the pineal gland (corpus pineale), posterior commissure and the iter a terio ad quartum ventriculum (cerebral aqueduct).

Laterally,—the optic thalami and the peduncles of the pineal body.

The Optic Thalami are two large, oblong masses, composed mainly of gray matter and situated on either side of the 3d ventricle, between the diverging portions of the corpora striata. Their outer and inferior surfaces are blended with contiguous parts of the brain; their upper, inner and posterior surfaces are free. They are intimately connected, by communicating fibres, with the tegmenta of the crura cerebri, the optic tract, the cerebral cortex, the corpora striata and the corpora albicantia (corpora mammillaria). Each optic thalamus terminates anteriorly as a rounded point,—

Anterior Tubercle,—containing the *anterior nucleus.*

As they pass backwards the optic thalami diverge outwards from each other and each terminates as a rounded swelling, the

Posterior Tubercle or *Pulvinar* to which is attached laterally the external geniculate body (corpus geniculatum laterale).

Corpora Geniculata (metathalamus) four oval eminences, a pair of which is situated below and external to the pulvinar of the thalamus on each side of the brain.

External Geniculate Body (corpus geniculatum laterale) the larger of the pair, is at a higher level and is slightly anterior as well as external or lateral to the internal geniculate body (corpus geniculatum mediale). The external geniculate body (corpus geniculatum laterale) belongs to and is properly a part of the optic thalamus, it receives the outer or lateral limb of the optic tract.

Internal Geniculate Body (corpus geniculatum mediale) receives the outer part of the inner or medial limb of the optic tract. These fibres do not however enter the eye, they originate in one of the inferior corpora quadrigemina (colliculus inferior) on one side of the brain, run forwards, cross by way of the optic chiasm, and then run backwards to the internal (lateral) geniculate body and inferior colliculus of the side opposite to that of their origin, this constitute what is known as the *commissure* of Gudden.

Pineal Body (corpus pineale), or epiphysis cerebri, is a small oval reddish vascular body (or gland), situated in front of the anterior corpora quadrigemina (colliculi superiores) in the mid-line, just over the opening of the aquæductus cerebri (Sylvius) into the third ventricle. It derives its blood supply from the velum interpositum (tela chorioidea ventriculi tertii) to which it is firmly attached. It has two peduncles which run forwards, one on each side of the third ventricle, on the inner or medial surfaces of the optic thalami, to join the anterior pillars of the fornix (columnæ fornicis).

The pineal body, classed as one of the ductless glands, is not composed of nervous elements but consists of numerous follicles which are lined by epithelium. Some of the follicles are filled with a very viscid liquid containing many epithelial cells constituting what are known as *corpora amylacea*, some contain sabulous concretions of lime, magnesia and ammonia salts (brain sand) constituting what is known as the *acervulus cerebri*. The pineal body is homologous to the so-called "pineal eye" of some reptiles and some of the other lower vertebrates.

Trigonum Habenulæ, a small triangular space with the apex pointing forward, and its base corresponding to one of the anterior corpora quadrigemina (colliculus superior). It is the interval between one of the crura or peduncles of the pineal body and the optic thalamus of the same side. In this triangle is a cluster of nerve cells forming the *ganglion habenulæ.*

The Mesencephalon or **Mid-brain** is the so-called *isthmus cerebri.* It is the constricted portion which connects the pons (varolii) with the diencephalon (inter-brain or thalamen-cephalon) and the cerebral hemispheres. Comprised in it, on its ventral surface are the two *crura (pedun-*

uli) cerebri, and on its dorsal surface are the four *corpora quadrigemina colliculi*). It is traversed by the *aquæductus cerebri* (Sylvius). Above and in front, it is continuous with the diencephalon or inter-brain, and below with the pons Varolii.

The Crura Cerebri (pedunculi cerebri), two thick conical stalks which constitute the stems of the cerebral hemispheres, are the upward continuation of the medulla oblongata. Their parallel portions are blended and held together by a mesial raphé which is indicated in front or ventrally by a longitudinal groove. This portion is covered in front or ventrally by the pons Varolii. The crura (peduncles) as they emerge above the upper border of the pons Varolii, diverge laterally from each other, enlarging as they ascend.

Each crus (pedunculus) then passes beneath the optic thalamus and enters a cerebral hemisphere and continues to the internal capsule. As seen from in front or ventrally, the interval between the divergent crura (pedunculi) cerebri is called the inter-peduncular space.

In this space are the corpora albicantia (corpora mammillaria). The floor of the space is formed by the substantia perforata posterior also called the posterior perforated space. The inner or medial sides of the crura (pedunculi) cerebri are grooved by the superficial origin of third or oculo-motor nerves. Winding forward around the outer or lateral sides of the crura (pedunculi) cerebri are the optic tracts and below them, the fourth or trochlear nerves. On the dorsal surface of the crura (pedunculi) cerebri are the corpora quadrigemina (colliculi) supported by the lamina quadrigemina covering in the aquæductus cerebri (Sylvius).

Upon cross section, each crus (peduncle) will be found to consist of two portions which are separated from each other by a darker colored portion called the substantia nigra, the portion that is in front of or ventral to the substantia nigra is the Crusta or Pes (Basis Pedunculi) Cerebri; the portion that is behind or dorsal to the substantia nigra is the Tegmentum.

The Crusta (Basis Pedunculi) **Cerebri** constitutes the anterior or ventral part of the crura (pedunculi) cerebri. It is composed entirely of longitudinal fibres which descend from the cerebral hemisphere (corticifugal fibres) most of which are continuous with the pyramidal tracts of the medulla. Three principal tracts or bundles are recognized: 1st, *pyramidal tracts* in the middle and inner portions of the crusta, the inner part being the geniculate fasciculus and the outer the pyramidal tracts proper; 2d, *cortico-pontine;* and 3d, *caudate-cerebellar tracts.*

The *pyramidal* (cerebro-spinal) *tracts* are *direct motor* strands composed of descending cortico-spinal projection fibres which originate in the following way. As the axis-cylinder processes descend from cells in the precentral cerebral cortex, they form the *corona radiata* by converging as they approach the internal capsule. They then proceed through the *genu* and the anterior two-thirds of the posterior limb (*pars occipitalis*) of the internal capsule to be continued as the pyramidal tracts in the crusta (basis) of the crus (pedunculus) cerebri. Here they are differentiated into an inner and an outer portion.

The *inner portion* is the part of the pyramidal tract that came down through the *genu* of the internal capsule, it is continued as the *geniculate fasciculus*, the fibres of which terminate in the nuclei of the 5th, 7th, and 12th cranial nerves.

The *outer portion* of the pyramidal tract is the part that traversed the anterior two-thirds of the *pars occipitalis* (posterior limb) of the internal capsule, it is continued as the,—

1. *Pyramidal Tract Proper* through the pons Varolii into the anterior pyramid (ventral area) of the medulla where its fibres are differentiated into three strands, the crossed, the direct, and the uncrossed.

Crossed Pyramidal Tract (fasciculus cerebro-spinalis lateralis). Most of the fibres of the pyramidal tract proper decussate in the medulla (inferior pyramidal motor decussation) and are then continued downwards as the crossed pyramidal tract (lateral cerebrospinal fasciculus) in the lateral column (funiculus lateralis) of the spinal cord (medulla spinalis), *on the side opposite to that of their origin*, to ultimately become connected with the anterior roots of the spinal nerves.

Direct Pyramidal Tract (fasciculus cerebro-spinalis anterior) or fasciculus of Türck, is composed of fibres of the pyramidal tract proper which do not decussate in the medulla but continue downwards in anterior column (funiculus anterior) of the spinal cord (medulla spinalis), *on the same side as that of their origin*, where at various levels its fibres cross through the gray matter of the cord to become connected with anterior nerve roots *of the opposite side*.

Uncrossed Pyramidal Tract comprises those fibres of the pyramidal tract proper which do not decussate either in the medulla or in the cord but continue downwards in the lateral column (funiculus lateralis) of the spinal cord (medulla spinalis), *on the same side as that of their origin*, where they mingle with the fibres of the crossed pyramidal tract (fasciculus cerebro-spinalis lateralis) and become connected with anterior nerve roots *on the same side as that of their origin*.

2. The *Cortico-pontine Tracts* are the first link of the neurone chain constituting the *indirect motor tract*, the complete series being cerebral cortex; cortico-pontine tract; nucleus points; cerebellar cortex; dentate nucleus; superior peduncle (brachium conjunctevum) of cerebellum; red nucleus (nucleus ruber); rubro-spinal tract; spinal gray matter; spinal nerve to muscle. There are two groups of cortico-pontine fibres,—

Fronto-pontine tract, during its passage through the cerebral peduncle lies medial to the geniculate fasciculus of the *pyramidal tract*. Originating in the mid-frontal cortex, its fibres pass through the back part of the anterior limb (pars frontalis) of the internal capsule continuing by way of the crusta (basis) pedunculi cerebri to the nucleus pontis.

Temporo-pontine tract which lies posterior and lateral to the principal portion of the *pyramidal* tract during its course through the crus (pedunculus) cerebri. Originating in the cortex of the two lowermost temporal gyri, its fibres pass inwards under the lenticular (lentiform) nucleus, traverse the postero-inferior part of the posterior limb (pars occipitalis) of the internal capsule, continuing by way of the crusta (basis) of the crus (pedunculus) cerebri to the nucleus pontis.

3. *Caudate-cerebellar Tract* (stratum intermedium) occupies the interval between the *substantia nigra* which is posterior, and the *pyramidal* and *cortico-pontine* tracts which surround it in front and laterally. It is made up of fibres running from the caudate nucleus to the cerebellum.

Substantia Nigra,—is a dark band of pigmented gray matter, semilunar in cross section. It divides the basilar (crusta) portion of the cerebral peduncle (crus) from the tegmental portion.

Tegmentum,—of the cerebral peduncle (crus) consists of network of transverse and longitudinal fibres among which are enmeshed many scattered nerve cells and two well-defined clusters of nerve cells. The gray matter (substantia grisea) of the tegmentum is continuous with the *formatio reticularis* of the pons and medulla, the principal nuclear clusters are,—

1. *Stratum Griseum Centrale*,—which is the gray matter surrounding the aquæductus cerebri (Sylvius).

2. *Red Nucleus* (nucleus tegmenti ruber),—consists of multi-polar cells, it is situated beneath the anterior corpus quadrigeminum (colliculus superior).

It is the termination of the superior cerebellar peduncles (brachia

conjunctiva). Some of the fibres originating in it run up to th
ventro-lateral nucleus of the thalamus, others descend in the rubr
spinal tract.

White Matter (substantia alba),—of the tegmentum consists both
transverse and longitudinal fibres. Its *transverse fibres* most
enter into the formation of *oculo-motor* and *trochlear* nerves, q.
Its *longitudinal fibres* are mostly sensory and ascend towards th
brain cortex (corticipital). They are differentiated into the follow
ing main bundles.

1. *Medial Lemniscus* (medial fillet). The tegmental and ponti
   portion consists of ascending (corticipital) sensory nerve fibres aft
   they have emerged from the *superior pyramidal sensory decussati*
   which is just above the nucleus gracilis and nucleus cuneatus in th
   back part of the medulla oblongata. They convey sensory impuls
   from muscles, bones, and joints. The medial lemniscus is formed k
   the combination of fibres arising from the nuclei of the fascicul
   gracilis and fasciculus cuneatus. They originate in the followi
   way,—The sense-organs in muscles, bones, and joints are connect
   by the peripheral processes (dendrites) to the ganglion cells (*
   neurones of the chain*) in the ganglia on the posterior roots of the spi
   nerves, by way of which, the central processes (axones) of those ce
   enter and then run upwards in the posterior column (funicul
   posterior) of the spinal cord (medulla spinalis) *on the same side*
   that of their origin. All those coming from spinal nerves below t
   8th thoracic, are combined to form the *Fasciculus Gracilis* (colun
   of Goll) occupying the medial portion of the posterior column (funic
   lus posterior) of the cord, in which position it continues as it ru
   upwards to the medulla where it terminates in an expansion enclosi
   the *nucleus gracilis*, this upper portion being known as the *clav*
   The *Fasciculus Cuneatus* (column of Burdach) originates in exac
   the same way from all of the spinal nerves above the 9th thorac
   It runs upwards, laterally to the fasciculus gracilis, in the poster
   column (funiculus posterior) of the cord until it reaches the medu
   in which it terminates as an expansion enclosing the *nucleus cuneat*
   The *2d neurones of the chain* after leaving the nucleus gracilis
   nucleus cuneatus, may go by way of the inferior cerebellar pedun
   (corpus restiforme) to the cerebellar cortex of the *opposite side,*
   they may decussate in the medulla (*superior pyramidal sens*
   decussation) and then proceed as *medial lemniscus or fillet* by way
   the pons through the tegmentum of the crus (pediculus) cerebri
   the *side opposite* to that of their origin; then through the thalam

or through the posterior limb (pars occipitalis) of the internal capsule, to the cerebral cortex.

2. *Lateral Lemniscus* (lateral fillet), is the upward continuation of the *cochlear division* of the central auditory tract. Its fibres are derived in the following way,—The cochlear nerve arises from the central processes of the T-shaped cells (1st neurone of the chain) in the *spiral ganglion* of the cochlea, it then passes backwards and enters the medulla, beneath the lower border of the pons on the outer side of the restiform body. Its fibres then divide into ascending and descending branches. The fibres of the ascending branch terminate in the cells of the *ventral cochlear nucleus*, which lies in front of the restiform body in the interval between the cochlear and vestibular divisions of the auditory nerve (n. acusticus). The fibres of the descending branch terminate in the cells of the *dorsal cochlear nucleus*, which lies beneath the trigonum acusticum, behind the restiform body and between it and the flocculus of the cerebellum. The axones of the cells (2d neurone) in the dorsal and ventral cochlear nuclei form two bundles, of which the dorsal bundle or striæ medullares cross the floor of the 4th ventricle to the medial plane in which they penetrate the tegmentum and decussate, some of the fibres entering the lateral lemniscus of the opposite side, others entering the trapezoid body (corpus trapezoideum).

The axones in the ventral bundle (*trapezial*) enter the trapezoid body where some of them terminate in the large cells (3d neurone) constituting the *nucleus trapezoideus*. Most of these trapezial axones decussate before terminating in the superior olive. The axones leaving the superior olive (4th neurone) are joined by the axones of the dorsal bundle (striæ medullares) so constituting the lateral lemniscus (lateral fillet) which bends upwards and is again interrupted by the *nucleus lemnisci lateralis* (5th neurone) whence it proceeds by way of the tegmentum to the nucleus of the posterior quadrigeminal body (colliculus inferior) (6th neurone) and to the medial geniculate body (7th neurone) from which arise axones that pass through the sub-lenticular portion of the internal capsule, then by way of the temporal portion of the corona radiata to the auditory area in the cortex of the superior and transverse temporal gyri. A few fibres reach the posterior corpora quadrigemina (colliculi inferiores) without having decussated.

3. *Ventral Longitudinal Fasciculus* (tecto-spinal or mesencephalospinal tract, or sulco-marginal fasciculus),—is composed of axones descending from the anterior corpora quadrigemina (colliculi superiores). These fibres immediately commence to decussate ("optic

acoustic reflex path") and as they descend, continue to decussate through the medial raphé on each side of which they lie. During the course of this tract through the pons and medulla many of its fibres terminate in the nuclei of all of the motor cranial nerves, the tract it self enters the anterior column (funiculus anterior medullæ spinalis) of the cord *on the side opposite to that of its origin.* Continuing downwards, between the direct pyramidal tract (ventral cerebro-spinal fasciculus) and the anterior medial fissure, its fibres terminate in cells of the anterior horn (columna anterior).

4. *Medial Longitudinal Fasciculus* (posterior longitudinal bundle),—is composed mostly of short association fibres. It originates in a special nucleus of its own that is situated in that part of the floor of the 3d ventricle which is immediately behind, or above, the corpora albicantia (corpora mammillaria); it passes downwards, close to the mid-line between the medial lemniscus (medial fillet) and the gray matter (substantia griesea centralis) of the aquæductus cerebri (Sylvius) where it becomes intimately connected with the nuclei of the 3d 4th, and 6th cranial nerves, and the cells of the anterior corpus quadrigeminum (colliculus superior). It continues downwards close to the mid-line immediately in front of the gray matter forming the floor of the 4th ventricle where it becomes connected with the nuclei of the 7th and vestibular portion of the 8th cranial nerves. It gives off and receives many collaterals in the formatio (substantia) reticularis as it traverses the pons and medulla in order to enter the anterior column (funiculus anterior medullæ spinalis) of the cord where its fibres terminate in the cells of the anterior horn (columnæ anterior). This tract seems to be made up mostly of fibres which have decussated. Throughout its entire course it always lies close to the mid-line immediately in front of the central gray matter, of whatever structure it traverses.

5. *Spino-thalamic Tract,*—is composed of direct ascending fibres which transmit sensation of pain, heat and cold, pressure and touch, from the skin on one side of the body to the opposite side of the brain. The sensory end-organs of the skin are connected with the peripheral processes (dendrites) of cells in the ganglia of the posterior roots of the spinal nerves. The central processes (axones) of these cells are connected with cells in the gray matter of the posterior horn (columna posterior) of the cord (medulla spinalis) from which axones pass forwards and cross by way of the *anterior white commissure* to the opposite side of the cord (medulla spinalis) where they ascend, at first loosely scattered, in the antero-lateral funiculus, they ultimately

become condensed into a distinct tract or fasciculus which ascends in the lateral side of the medulla, continues upwards through the pons, medial to the *olivo-cerebellar* and *rubro-spinal* tracts, then, along with the *medial lemniscus*, it traverses the tegmentum and the posterior limb (pars occipitalis) of the internal capsule to terminate in the thalamus.

6. *Superior Peduncles* (*brachia conjunctiva*) *of the Cerebellum,*—consists of fibres originating in the dentate nuclei of the cerebellum. They are two white bands, a right and a left, which emerge, widely apart, from the front of the cerebellum. As they run upwards and for-wards they converge forming the lateral boundaries and a small por-tion of the roof of the front or upper half of the 4th ventricle. They join each other in the mid-line, decussate and then pass upwards under cover of the posterior pair of corpora quadrigemina (colliculi inferiores) each one terminating in the red nucleus (nucleus tegmenti ruber) *of the side opposite to that of its origin.*

7. *Rubro-spinal tract* (pre-pyramidal or Monakow's tract),—is a descending crossed motor strand which seems to be the downward continuation of some of the fibres of the superior peduncles (brachia conjunctiva) of the cerebellum which having come from the dentate nucleus and crossed to the red nucleus *of the opposite side,* are by means of the rubro-spinal tract connected *to their original side* of the spinal cord. The fibres of the rubro-spinal tract originate in the red nucleus (nucleus tegmenti ruber) just beneath the anterior corpus quadrigeminum (colliculus superior) they cross the medial plane to the opposite side, descend close to the lateral lemniscus behind the trapezium in the pons, becoming superficial in the medulla, where they lie in the furrow of the lateral area or pyramid between the olive and the spinal tract of the trigeminal nerve, they enter the lateral column (funiculus lateralis) of the spinal cord (medulla spinalis) where they continue downwards immediately in front of the crossed pyramidal tract (fasciculus cerebro-spinalis lateralis) which is in-vaded by some of the fibres, the others terminating in the cells of the anterior horn (columna anterior).

8. *Descending* (*Mesencephalic*) *Root of the Trigeminal Nerve,*—enters into the composition of the *Masticator Nerve* (motor portion of the fifth). Its fibres originate in the giant pyramidal cells in the lower part of the somæsthetic (sensory-motor) area of the cerebral cortex. These pyramidal fibres traverse the genu of the internal capsule, continue through the tegmentum, medial to the superior peduncle (brachium conjunctivum) of the cerebellum, then decussate before

terminating in accessory motor nucleus of the fifth nerve. This nucleus is also known as the Mesencephalic Nucleus of the Masticator Nerve, it is a column of gray matter lateral to the gray matter (stratum griseum centrale) surrounding the cerebral aqueduct (Sylvius).

9. *Olivary Fasciculus* (thalamo-olivary or central tegmental tract),— is composed of fibres that originate both in the lenticular (lentiform) nucleus and the thalamus, traverse the central portion of the tegmentum and continue in the pons, behind the medial lemniscus in the formatio reticularis to the inferior olivary nucleus, being continued from the olive *to the opposite* cerebellar hemisphere by way of the cerebello-olivary fibres.

Corpora Quadrigemina (colliculi) are 4 rounded eminences placed in pairs, 2 in front and 2 behind, on the dorsal surface of the mid-brain (mesencephalon) immediately behind the 3d ventricle and beneath the posterior border of the corpus callosum. All 4 collectively are often called the Tectum or Tectum Mesencephali, *e.g.*, in names such as "*tecto-spinal.*" The upper or anterior pair were called the *nates* (colliculi superiores), the lower pair the *testes* (colliculi inferiores). They are connected by 4 bands the *brachia*, with the corpora geniculata, those of the anterior corpora quadrigemina (colliculi superiores) being continued directly into the optic tract. They are composed of white matter externally and gray matter internally. The anterior pair contain the—

Stratum Zonale,—a thin stratum of white matter on the surface.

Stratum Cinereum (stratum griseum colliculi superioris),—next below a layer of gray matter.

Stratum Opticum,—the upper gray-white layer, having many fine nerve fibres intersecting the gray matter.

Stratum Lemnisci,—the deep gray-white layer, consisting of nerve fibres and nerve-cells of large size.

Aqueduct of Sylvius, or *Iter a tertio ad quartum ventriculum* (aquæduct cerebri) is a narrow canal, about ½ inch long, connecting the 3d ventricle with the 4th, and situated between the corpora quadrigemina (colliculi and the tegmentum. It is surrounded by a layer of gray matter (stratum griseum centrale) which is continuous with the gray matter of the 3d and 4th ventricles, and contains groups of cells which are connected with the roots of the 3d, 4th and 5th cranial nerves.

The Hypo-thalamic Region (right or left),—is the forward prolongation of the tegmentum becoming blended with the under surface of the thalamus, it consists mainly of the upward and forward production of the *nucleus* (nucleus tegmenti ruber), *medial lemniscus* (fillet), and the s *antia nigra* which is here expanded laterally by an additional cluster of nerve cells forming the Nucleus Hypothalamicus.

The Rhombencephalon morphologically comprises: 1. isthmus rhombencephali, 2. metencephalon, and 3. myelencephalon.

Isthmus Rhombencephali (isthmus of the hind-brain) comprises:

a. Superior Peduncles (brachia conjunctiva) of the cerebellum (see page 201).

b. Superior Medullary Velum (valve of Vieussens) is triangular in shape with the apex pointing forwards. It forms the roof of the anterior or upper half of the 4th ventricle by filling up the interval between the two superior peduncles (brachia conjunctiva) of the cerebellum. It consists of a lamina of white matter which is crossed on its upper surface by several transverse bands of gray matter which collectively are known as the *lingula cerebelli*.

The Metencephalon or the Hind-brain, —comprises the pons Varolii, the Cerebellum, and the upper half of the 4th Ventricle. The latter is described with its lower half, under the Medulla Oblongata, in the next section.

FIG. 73.

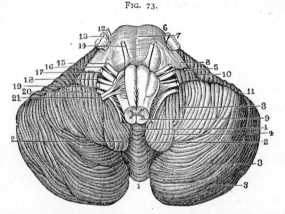

The Pons Varolii (6), is the bond of union of the various parts of the brain, connecting the cerebrum with the cerebellum (3) and the medulla oblongata (9). It is about 1½ inch wide and 1 inch long and thick, and is situated between the hemispheres of the cerebellum above the medulla oblongata and below the crura (pedunculi) cerebri. It consists of—a *central* or anterior portion (*pars ventralis*) (7), containing layers of transverse and longitudinal fibres, also a small quantity of gray matter, *tegmental*, dorsal, or posterior portion (pars dorsalis), which is a continuation of the reticular formation of the medulla, most of its constituent being continued into the tegmentum of the crura (pedunculi) cerebri.

The Gray Matter of the Pons consists of the following important collections of nerve-cells:—

Superior Olivary Nucleus (nucleus olivarius superior),—an isolated mass of gray matter situated on the dorsal surface immediately above the inferior olivary nucleus (nucleus olivarius inferior) of the medulla

Nuclei of the 5th Nerve 2,—one for the motor (12) and one for the sensory root (13), the latter external to the former.

Nucleus of the 6th Nerve,—beneath the floor of the 4th ventricle, close to the root of the facial nerve; its fibres pass through the pons and emerge at its lower margin (14).

Nucleus of the Facial (7th) Nerve,—situated deeply below the floor of the 4th ventricle; its roots follow a tortuous course in the pons, emerging at its lower border (15), external to those of the abducent nerve.

Nuclei of the Auditory (8th) Nerve 2,—are dorsal and ventral, both lying chiefly in the medulla but prolonged into the pons; the roots emerging at its lower border (17), in the groove between the olivary body (oliva and the restiform body (corpus restiforme).

Nuclei Pontis,—small masses of gray matter in the ventral or anterior portion of the pons.

Substantia Gelatinosa (of Rolando),—which is continuous with that of the spinal cord and medulla.

Locus Cœruleus, a slate-colored bluish spot on the upper part of the floor of the 4th ventricle.

The White Matter of the Pons consists of 4 sets of medullated nerve fibres, superficial transverse, superficial longitudinal, deep transverse and deep longitudinal.

The Superficial Transverse Fibres,—are on the ventral surface of the pons, they continue laterally into the middle peduncles (brachia pontis) of the cerebellum.

The Superficial Longitudinal Fibres of the pons comprise,—

1. Upward continuation of the anterior pyramids (ventral area) of the medulla (see page 209).
2. Cortico-pontine Tracts (see page 197).
3. Stratum Intermedium or Caudate-cerebellar Tract (see page 197)

The Deep Transverse Fibres,—form the trapezium (corpus trapezoideum) and then pass laterally into the middle peduncles (brachia pontis.

of the cerebellum (see lateral lemniscus, page 199, and acoustic nerve, page 220).

The *Deep Longitudinal Fibres*,—of the pons constitute a portion of the reticular formation in which the following distinct bundles can be traced,—

1. Olivary Fasciculus, Thalamo-olivary or Central Tegmental Tract (see page 202), lies in the reticular formation dorsal to the medial lemniscus.

2. Descending or Mesencephalic Root of the Trigeminal Nerve (see page 201).

3. Fasciculus Teres, is composed of fibres of the facial nerve which, by looping upwards behind the nucleus of the abducens nerve and then running forwards and upwards, forms the eminentia teres or medialis (colliculus facialis) which lies in the floor of the anterior or upper half of the 4th ventricle, immediately lateral to the mid-line.

4. Medial Lemniscus or Fillet (see page 198), which comprises the *fasciculus gracilis* (column of Goll) and the *fasciculus cuneatus* (column of Burdach).

5. Lateral Lemniscus or Fillet (see page 199), composed of the cochlear fibres of the central auditory path.

6. Ventral Longitudinal or Sulco-marginal Fasciculus (Tecto-spinal or Mesencephalo-spinal Tract) (see page 199).

7. Medial Longitudinal Fasciculus (Posterior Longitudinal Tract) (see page 200).

8. Rubro-spinal Fasciculus (Pre-pyramidal or Monakow's Tract) (see page 201).

9. Ascending Antero-lateral Tract of Gowers, comprises a direct and an indirect path through which sensation of pain, temperature, pressure, and touch reaches the brain.

   a. Spino-thalamic Tract is the direct path (see page 200).

   b. Ventral Spino-cerebellar Tract (Superficial Ventro-lateral Spino-cerebellar Fasciculus) is the indirect path. The term "Gowers' Tract" is limited by some to this tract only. It originates in the following way, the sensory end organs are connected with the peripheral processes (dendrites) of cells in the ganglia of the posterior roots of spinal nerves, the central processes (axones) of these cells are connected with cells in the base of the lateral horn (columna lateralis), known as "Stillings' Nucleus," and with cells in the lateral horn (columna lateralis) of the spinal cord (medulla spinalis). The axones of these cells, *both of the same and the opposite side*, are agminated into a bundle, the Ventral Spino-cerebellar Tract (Superficial Ventro-lateral Spino-cerebellar Fasciculus) which travels upwards in the lateral column (funiculus lateralis) of the spinal cord (medulla spinalis). It maintains this position as it traverses the medulla until it reaches the pons where it runs forwards and upwards as high as the level of the trigeminal nerve, it then runs backwards and downwards, enters the superior peduncle (brachium conjunctivum) of the cerebellum, and terminates in the lingula of the superior vermis cerebelli *of its own side.*

The Cerebellum consists of gray matter (*substantia corticalis*) on the surface and white matter (*corpus medullare*) in the interior. Its surface is not convoluted like that of the cerebrum, but is traversed by curved fissures and furrows (*sulci*), the latter separating the laminæ (folia or gyri) of which it is composed. It lies in the inferior occipital fossæ of the skull, beneath the occipital lobes of the cerebrum, from which it is separated by a process of dura mater, the *tentorium cerebelli.* It is divided into a central portion or lobe, the *Vermis Cerebelli* or *Vermiform Process* (1), and two lateral *Hemispheres;* all continuous with each other and substantially the same in structure. It presents the following primary fissures:—

Great Horizontal Fissure (10),—horizontally round the free margin, from the pons in front to the median line behind, giving origin to the secondary fissures.

Incisura Cerebelli Anterior, or Anterior Cerebellar Notch,—a broad, shallow, vertical notch, separating the hemispheres in front.

Incisura Marsupialis (2), or Posterior Cerebellar Notch,—a deep notch, separating the hemispheres from each other behind.

Vallecula,—a deep depression on the inferior surface, containing the lower extremity of the vermis (vermis inferior).

Secondary Fissures of the Cerebellum are 8 in number, 4 superiorly and 4 inferiorly. They pass in a curved direction from side to side across the cerebellum, beginning (except one) and ending in the great horizontal fissure. They are named from before backward as follows:

On the upper surface of the cerebellum, the—

Pre-central. *Post-central.* *Anterior Semilunar* or *Pre-clival.*
Posterior Semilunar or *Post-clival.*

On the lower surface of the cerebellum, the—
Post-nodular. *Retro-tonsillar* or *Pre-pyramidal.*
Anterior Inferior or *Post-pyramidal.* *Posterior Inferior* or *Post-gracile.*
The *post-gracile* is a branch of the post-pyramidal, and ends in the great horizontal fissure.

Lobes of the Cerebellum. The 3 primary lobes, the *Vermis* or *Worm* and the *Hemispheres*, are divided by the above-named secondary fissures into 19 lobes, named as follows:—

On the upper surface of the Worm (vermis superior), from before backward 5, the—

Lingula.   *Lobulus Centralis.*   *Culmen Monticuli.*
Diclive or *Clivus Monticuli.*   *Folium Cacuminis* or *Commissura Simplex.*

On the upper surface of the Hemispheres, from before backward 5, the—
Vinculum Lingualæ or *Frænulum.*   *Ala Lobuli Centralis.*
Anterior Semilunar or *Crescentic Lobe.* *Posterior Semilunar* or *Crescentic Lobe.*
Superior Semilunar or *Posterior Superior Lobe.*

On the lower surface of the Worm, from before backward 4, the—
Nodule.   *Uvula.*   *Pyramid.*   *Tuber Valvulæ.*

On the lower surface of the Hemispheres, from within outward 5, the—
Flocculus (5).   *Tonsil* or *Amygdala* (4).   *Biventral Lobe* (3).
Gracile or *Slender Lobe* (3).   *Inferior Semilunar Lobe* (3).

White Matter (Corpus Medullare) of the Cerebellum includes the *peduncular fibres* and the *fibres proper.* The former are projection fibres and are arranged in 3 peduncles on each side, which arise from the anterior part of the hemispheres, and connect the cerebellum with itself and with the rest of the brain, as follows:—

Superior Peduncles (brachia conjunctiva),—in part form the roof of the 4th ventricle; they pass from the corpus dentatum under the corpora quadrigemina, below which their fibres decussate, going to the red nucleus of the tegmentum, and by a relay through the optic thalamus to the cerebral cortex. Stretching from one peduncle to the other is the—

Valve of Vieussens, or Superior Medullary Velum (see page 203),—a thin lamina of white matter, which with the superior peduncles forms part of the roof of the 4th ventricle (see page 211).

Middle Peduncles (brachia pontis) (8),—comprise most of the transverse fibres of the pons, and are chiefly commissural fibres connecting the cerebellar hemispheres with each other. All are connected with the nucleus pontis of the same or the opposite side, those that are not commissural are the continuation of the cortico-pontine tracts (see page 197).

Inferior Peduncles (corpora restiformes),—connect the cerebellum with the medulla oblongata.

Fibræ Propriæ, the proper fibres of the cerebellum,—are of 2 kinds; the *commissural,* connecting the hemispheres, and the *association* or *arcuate fibres,* connecting adjacent laminæ.

Cortical Gray Matter (Substantia Corticalis) of the Cerebellum is situated on the surface, forming the cortex, a section of which presents a characteristic foliated appearance, named the *Arbor Vitæ,* due to the branching of the laminæ given off from the central white matter to the cortical portion. The gray matter of the cortex consists of three layers, as follows:

Molecular or *External Gray Layer,*—consists of fibres and cells.

Middle Layer Containing the Cells of Purkinje, (the characteristic cells of the cerebellum), an incomplete stratum of flask-shaped cells, their bases resting on the granular layer, their necks giving off numerous dendrites to the molecular layer.

Granular or *Internal rust-colored Layer of Turner,*—contains numerous small nerve-cells or granules of reddish-brown color, also many nerve-fibrils, among which are the axones of the Purkinje cells. This layer also contains larger cells, known as the *Golgi cells,* situated in its outer part.

Central Gray Matter of the Cerebellum is disposed on each side in 4 centres, one of which, the dentate nucleus is large; the others being of small size. They are situated in the middle of the white matter of the organ, and are as follows: the—

Dentate Nucleus, or Ganglion of the Cerebellum,—an irregularly folded lamina of gray matter, having an opening anteriorly, the *hilum,* from which emerge most of the fibres of the superior peduncle (brachium conjunctivum.)

Nucleus Emboliformis,—lies to the inner side of the dentate nucleus, partly covering its hilum. It is probably part of the dentate nucleus.

Nucleus Globosus,—an elongated mass on the inner side of the preceding.

Nucleus Fastigii, or Roof Nucleus of Stilling,—is close to the middle line at the anterior end of the vermiform process (vermis) and immediately over the roof of the 4th ventricle. The fibres of the vestibular nerve terminate in this nucleus after having decussated in the vermis.

THE MEDULLA OBLONGATA

The Medulla Oblongata, or *Myelencephalon,* formerly called the *Spinal Bulb,* is the lowermost division of the brain and is continuous with the spinal cord. It extends from the lower margin of the pons Varolii (5) to the *inferior pyramidal* (motor) *decussation* (12) corresponding to the lower margin of the foramen magnum. Its ventral surface rests on the basilar groove of the occipital bone, its dorsal surface is in the fossa between the cerebellar hemispheres.   It is 1 inch long, ¾ inch broad above, and ½ inch thick; and of pyramidal form, its broad end upward.   On its surface are the *anterior and posterior median fissures;* the former terminating just below the pons in a cul-de-sac, the *foramen cæcum;* the latter expanding into the 4th ventricle about the middle of the medulla.   On each side the medulla presents the following parts:—

Pyramid (7),—a bundle of white matter alongside the anterior median fissure, formed by the upward continuation of the direct tract (fasciculus cerebro-spinalis anterior) of the anterior column (funiculus anterior) and the crossed tract (fasciculus cerebro-spinalis lateralis) of the lateral column (funiculus lateralis) of the spinal cord.   As the latter tract ascends it decussates with its fellow of the opposite side across the fissure, forming the inferior *decussation of the pyramids* (8).   Each pyramid is bounded by the antero-lateral sulcus which is continuous with that of the cord. ·

Olive (*Olivary Body*)(9),—an ovoid projection on the outer side of the pyramid and immediately below the pons.   In the groove between the olive and pyramid, the hypoglossal nerve fibres (27) emerge; in that between the olive and restiform body (inferior cerebellar peduncle) emerge the glosso-pharyngeal (24), pneumogastric (n. vagus) (25) and spinal accessory (n. accessorius) (26) nerves.   The *Inferior Olivary Nucleus* or *corpus dentatum* is a thin, wavy lamina of gray matter, open at its upper and inner part.   Three *accessory nuclei* (dorsal, medial and lateral) are also situated in the olive.

FIG. 74

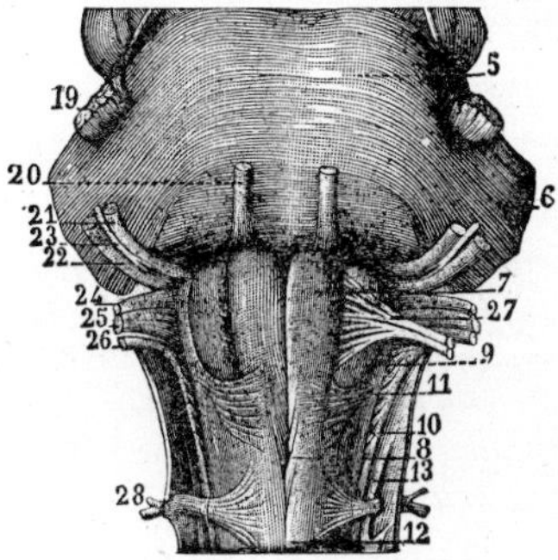

Fasciculus of Rolando (10),—a slight, longitudinal prominence on the outer side of the olivary body.   It corresponds to a mass of gray matter, *substantia gelatinosa*, continuous with the posterior horn of the gray matter of the cord.

Lateral Column,—hidden above by the olivary body but showing below it; is the continuation of the lateral column (funiculus lateralis) of the cord in part.

Restiform Body (inferior cerebellar peduncle),—between the lateral

14

column and the fasciculus cuneatus; contains the *arcuate fibres* external and internal, and the *dorsal spino-cerebellar fasciculus* (direct cerebellar tract). The two restiform bodies diverge as they ascend assist in forming the lateral walls of the 4th ventricle, and enter the cerebellar hemispheres as the inferior peduncles of the cerebellum.

Dorsal Spino-cerebellar Fasciculus (direct cerebellar tract of Flechsig) —arises from cells in the *dorsal nucleus* (Clark's column) which occupies the base (cervix) of the posterior horn (columna posterior) of the cord from the level of the 3d lumbar to that of the 7th cervical nerve. The axones arising in these cells pass to the dorso-lateral periphery of the lateral column (funiculus lateralis) up which they continue until they reach the medulla, then they run up behind the origins of the 9th, 10th and 11th cranial nerves, and then bend outwards and forwards, entering the restiform body (inferior cerebellar peduncle) in which they continue to the cells in the cortex of the cerebellar hemisphere *of the same side as that of their origin.*

External or *Superficial Arcuate Fibres,* are in two sets. *The anterior* set of fibres are the more numerous, they arise from cells in the *nucleus gracilis* and *nucleus cuneatus,* run forwards, and decussate in the medial raphé, emerge in the anterior medial fissure and run outwards across the surface of the pyramid and lower part of the olive, then turn upwards and enter the restiform body (inferior cerebellar peduncle) *of the side opposite to that of their origin.*

The posterior set of fibres also arise from the cells in the cuneate and gracile nuclei; they run outwards, forwards, and upwards directly into the restiform body (inferior cerebellar peduncle) *of the same side as that of their origin.*

Internal or *Deep Arcuate Fibres* form an intricate network situated between the olives and behind the pyramids. Some of these fibres, the *olivo-cerebellar* and *cerebello-olivary,* enter the restiform body (inferior cerebellar peduncle). The remaining fibres are association or commissural fibres connected with the nuclear cells in the *formatio reticularis* of the tegmentum and the nuclei of the sensory cranial nerves.

Fasciculus Cuneatus,—between the restiform body and the funiculus gracilis; is the continuation of the postero-lateral column of the cord (see lateral lemniscus, page 198).

Fasciculus Gracilis (posterior pyramid),—a narrow, white band, parallel to and alongside the posterior fissure; is the continuation of the postero-median column of the cord. Its enlarged upper extremity is club-shaped and called the *clava* (see lateral lemniscus, page 198).

Other Structures in the Medulla. Internally the medulla is composed of longitudinal bundles of nerve-fibres, masses of gray matter constituting nerve nuclei, and nerve-fibres originating from the nuclei.   The—

Independent Nuclei,—are those of the 5th, 8th, 9th, 10th, 11th and 12th cranial nerves, which arise in or near the floor of the 4th ventricle; also the nucleus of the *fasciculus teres* (eminentia medialis or teres), that of the *olivary body*, the *accessory olivary* nuclei, and the *tractus solitarius* or trineural tract, the ascending root of the 9th nerve.

Raphé or *Medial Septum,*—is situated in the middle line of the medulla above the decussation of the pyramids, and consists of fibres having different directions and of multipolar nerve-cells.

Formatio Reticularis,—is a coarse network, situated within the anterior and lateral regions of the medulla, and is formed by the breaking up of the anterior gray matter by the white fibres of the crossed pyramidal (cerebro-spinal) tracts.

The Fourth Ventricle, or Ventricle of the Cerebellum, is a diamond-shaped cavity lying between the cerebellum and the posterior surface of the pons Varolii and medulla oblongata.   Its upper angle is on a level with the upper border of the pons, it corresponds with the lower opening of the *cerebral aqueduct of Sylvius,* by which this ventricle communicates with the 3d ventricle.   Its lower angle is on a level with the lower border of the olivary body (oliva), it is continuous with the central canal of the spinal cord, and is called the *calamus scriptorius,* from its resemblance to the point of a pen.   The ventricle is closed posteriorly by a layer of pia mater, the *tela choroidea inferior,* with its choroid plexuses, in which layer are 3 openings; the *foramen of Magendie* (metapore), just above the calamus scriptorius in the median line, and the *foramina of Key and Retzius* at the extremities of the lateral angles.   Through these foramina the ventricles of the brain communicate with the subarachnoid space of the brain and spinal cord.   The fourth ventricle is bounded as follows:—

Roof,—is tent-shaped and formed by superior peduncles of the cere-bellum, the superior medullary velum or valve of Vieussens, the tela choroidea inferior (see above) and its choroid plexus, the obex, and the inferior medullary velum.

Floor,—is formed by the posterior surface of the pons above and the medulla below.   It contains the median furrow, on each side of which are—the fasciculus teres (eminentia medialis or colliculus facialis), striæ acusticæ (striæ medullares), conductor sonorus (striæ obliquæ), fovea superior, fovea inferior, ala cinerea, tuberculum acusticum, locus cæruleus, tænia violacea, and the eminences of origin of certain nerves (see pages 212 and 213).

Laterally,—in the upper part are the superior peduncles of the cerebellum; in the lower part, the inferior peduncles (restiform bodies) fringed by the funiculi graciles, their clavæ and the ligulæ.

Parts named above, and heretofore undescribed, are the—

Sulcus Longitudinalis Medianus,—the vertical median fissure; from the centre of which on each side emerge the—

Striæ Medullares or *Striæ Acusticæ,*—white fibres crossing the floor of the ventricle transversely, dividing it into two triangles, and passing outward to the auditory nerve. They are the axons of the nerve-cells of the tuberculum acusticum.

Conductor Sonorus (striæ obliquæ),—a whitish band of fibres in no way differing from the striæ medullares except that they run from the midline obliquely outward and forward instead of transversely. They are not constant.

Inferior Medullary Velum,—a thin layer of white matter, stretching over the ventricle toward its lateral angles.

Obex and *Lingula,*—are respectively the inferior and superior parts of a little irregular ridge, which runs from the clava of the funiculus gracilis to its fellow of the opposite side.

Eminentia Teres (colliculus facialis),—the prominent centre of a spindle-shaped eminence made by an underlying bundle of white fibres, the *fasciculus teres*, formed in part by the fibres of the facial nerve.

Fovea Superior,—an angular depression, external to the fasciculus teres and above the striæ medullares.

Locus Cæruleus,—a bluish depressed area above the fovea superior.

Fovea Inferior,—an angular groove, its apex at the striæ, its limbs diverging below, enclosing the—

Ala Cinerea or *Trigonum Vagi,*—a triangular area, corresponding with the nuclei of the vagus and glosso-pharyngeal nerves.

Eminentia Cinerea,—a prominent elevation of the ala cinerea.

Trigonum Hypoglossi,—a triangular area, internal to the inner limb of the fovea inferior, and corresponding to the tract of nerve-cells from which the hypoglossal nerve originates.

Trigonum Acustici,—a triangular area, external to the outer side of the fovea inferior, having at its base a prominence, the *tuberculum acusticum*.

Nuclei of Origin, in the floor of the 4th Ventricle, comprise the nuclei of the cranial nerves from the 5th to the 12th inclusive, also vaso-motor, cardiac and respiratory centres. Near the ventricle, in the anterior wall of the aqueduct of Sylvius, are the nuclei for the 3d and 4th nerves. Those in the floor itself are as follows:—

5th Nerve (trigeminus),—two groups of cells, extending the length of the medulla and alongside the aqueduct of Sylvius, the nuclei lying close to the lateral recesses of the ventricle.

6th Nerve (abducens),—in the upper part, close to the median line.

7th Nerve (facial),—below and external to the 6th.

8th Nerve (auditory), 2 nuclei, one beneath the striæ, the other just outside the ventricle.

9th Nerve (glosso-pharyngeal) and *10th Nerve* (vagus),—in the upper part of the ala cinerea, near the inferior angle of the ventricle.

11th Nerve (spinal accessory),—below the preceding, in the lower part of the ala cinerea, and running down into the cord as low as the 6th cervical vertebra.

12th Nerve (hypoglossal),—internal to the 9th and 10th beneath the fasciculus teres, and in the trigonum hypoglossi.

THE SPINAL CORD (MEDULLA SPINALIS)

The Spinal Cord is that part of the cerebro-spinal axis which is situated in the spinal canal. Its length is about 17 or 18 inches, terminating at the lower border of the 1st lumbar vertebra in the *filum terminale* (16). It is cylindrical in general form, with 2 enlargements, one in the cervical region, the other in the lumbar. It is composed of gray and white matter, the gray being inside (instead of outside, as in the cerebrum), and arranged so as to present a crescentic appearance in horizontal section, joined by a transverse commissure, and the extremities forming the *Anterior and Posterior Horns* (columnæ), from which regions respectively the anterior and posterior roots of the spinal nerves have their apparent origin. The—

Membranes,—of the cord are 3, as in the brain: the dura mater, arachnoid, and pia mater. The *Dura Mater* represents only the meningeal or supporting layer of the cranial dura mater. It is not adherent to the spinal column, but is connected thereto by fibrous tissue. The *Arachnoid* is arranged as on the brain, its sub-arachnoid space being filled with its fluid, for the protection of the cord. The *Pia Mater* has a fibrous band on each side, the *ligamentum denticulatum* (9), connecting it to the dura mater by 21 serrations.

Fissures,—number 6, the anterior and posterior median, and on each side the postero-lateral (11) and the posterior intermediate.

Columns (funiculi),—are 4 in number, 2 on each side of the cord; a small *posterior column*, and a large *antero-lateral column*, separated from each other by the postero-lateral fissure. The posterior column is further divided in its upper part, into a *postero-median* and a *postero-lateral* column, which are separated from each other by the posterior intermediate septum.

Central Canal,—a minute canal, barely visible to the naked eye, extends the whole length of the cord, originating above in the lower angle of the 4th ventricle (1) and terminating below in a somewhat dilated extremity.

FIG. 75.

White Substance of the Cord consists of medullated fibres, mostly disposed longitudinally, but some obliquely and transversely, also blood-vessels and neuroglia. The *Neuroglia* supports the fibres and cells of the gray substance as well as the fibres of the white, and is accumulated in three situations; on the surface of the cord, beneath the pia mater; around the central canal, as the *substantia gelatinosa centralis;* as a cap over the posterior horn of gray matter, forming the *substantia cinerea gelatinosa.*

Nerve-tracts in the white substance of the cord, shown by investigation of pathological lesions, as extending along various portions of the cord and into or from the brain, are 8 in number, as follows:—

In the antero-lateral column (funiculus antero-lateralis) are 6, the—

Direct Pyramidal Tract (fasciculus cerebro-spinalis anterior),—next to the median fissure and in the upper part of the cord; consists of descending fibres from the motor area of the cerebral cortex of the same side, passing through the pyramid of the medulla, crossing in the anterior white commissure of the cord, and disappearing about the middle of its thoracic region (see page 196).

Crossed Pyramidal Tract (fasciculus cerebro-spinalis lateralis),—in the hinder part of the column; consists of descending fibres from the motor area of the cortex on the opposite side, through the pyramid of the medulla, crossing in the decussation of the pyramids (see page 196).

Antero-lateral Ascending (Gower's) *Tract* (anterior spino-cerebellar fasciculus),—in the anterior part of the column; consists of ascending fibres arising from cells in the posterior horn, crossing in the anterior gray commissure, and passing upward through the medulla and pons to the cerebellum through its superior peduncles (brachia conjunctiva) (see page 205).

Direct Cerebellar Tract (dorsal spino-cerebellar fasciculus),—behind the preceding, commencing in the lumbar region; consists of fibres from cells in the posterior gray matter, ascending through the restiform body to the cerebellum (see page 210).

Tract of Lissauer (fasciculus postero-lateralis)—a small tract, formed by some of the fibres of the posterior roots of the spinal nerves, running upward for a short distance and entering the posterior horn of gray matter.

Antero-lateral Ground Bundle (fasciculus proprius anterior et fasciculus proprius posterior),—is the remaining part of the column, situated next to the gray matter of the cord; contains—longitudinal association fibres, uniting cell-groups of the gray matter with each other; fibres crossing the anterior commissure from the gray matter of the opposite side; horizontal fibres belonging to the anterior roots of the spinal nerves.

In the Posterior Column (funiculus posterior) are 2 tracts, the—

Tract of Goll (fasciculus gracilis),—next to the posterior fissure; consists of fibres from the posterior roots of the spinal nerves, ascending to the medulla where they end in the nucleus gracilis (see page 198).

Tract of Burdach (fasciculus cuneatus),—between the preceding and the gray matter; consists of fibres from the posterior roots of the spinal nerves, some ascending a short distance and entering the gray matter, others entering Goll's tract and passing to the medulla (see page 198).

Gray Substance of the Cord occupies the central portion, a transverse section showing it in the form of two crescents joined by the gray commissure (commissura grisea). Each crescent has an *anterior* and a *posterior cornu* or horn (columna); a *lateral* horn being also seen in the upper thoracic region. The gray substance consists of nerve-fibres, nerve-cells, blood-vessels and connective tissue. The—

Nerve-fibres,—are found as a dense interlacement of minute fibrils, formed of the axons and dendrons of the nerve-cells and nerves of larger size.

Nerve-cells.—some form columns of cells placed longitudinally, and some are scattered throughout the gray matter.

Clarke's Posterior Vesicular Column (nucleus dorsalis),—is a group of nerve-cells at the base of the posterior horn on its inner side, extending from the 7th cervical nerve to the 3d lumbar.

FIG. 76.

The Spinal Nerves are transmitted from each side of the spinal cord through the intervertebral foramina of the spinal column, in 31 pairs, of which the cervical number 8, the thoracic 12, the lumbar 5, the sacral 5, and the coccygeal 1. Each nerve arises by two roots; an *anterior* (13) or motor root, and a *posterior* (10) or sensory root, the latter being distinguished by a ganglion, the *spinal ganglion* (12). These nerves are described separately *infra*, after the description of the cranial nerves. The—

Cauda Equina (17) (horse's tail),—is a sheaf of nerves composed of the elongated roots of the 4 upper sacral nerves, passing downward to reach their respective foramina of exit from the spinal canal.

THE CRANIAL NERVES (NERVI CEREBRALES)

The Cranial Nerves number 12 pairs, those from the 5th to the 12th inclusive having their deep origin wholly or in part from the floor of the 4th ventricle, and all, except the first two, originating in or near that situation. Their *superficial or apparent origin* is their connection with the surface of the brain, their *deep or real origin* lies in some special nucleus of gray matter deeply situated in the brain. After emerging from the surface the nerves pass through tubular prolongations of the dura mater in various foramina at the base of the skull, to their final distribution.

1st Nerve, Olfactory (n. olfactorius) (Plate 6), nerves of smell (fila), about 20 in number, composed of non-medullated fibres,—*arise* from the under surface of the olfactory bulb (see page 188); *deeply* by 2 white roots, the *medial root* from the area of Broca and the callosal and sub-callosal gyrus; the *lateral root* from the anterior perforated space (substantia perforata anterior) and from the union of the temporal and uncinate gyri, and by the middle gray root (trigonum olfactorium) from the optic thalamus; *exit* by numerous foramina in the cribriform plate of the ethmoid bone; *to* form a plexiform network over the upper third of the nasal septum, the superior turbinal process and the adjacent surface of the ethmoid bone, from which branches are distributed to the Schneiderian membrane of the nose.

2d Nerve, Optic (n. opticus) nerve of sight (Plate 6),—*arises* from the optic commissure (chiasma opticum) (16) and tracts (15); *deeply* from the external geniculate body (corpus geniculatum laterale), the pulvinar of the optic thalamus, and the upper quadrigeminal body (colliculus superior) these being the lower visual centres; also from the cuneate and lingual lobules of the occipital lobe (cortical visual centres); *exit* by the optic foramen; *to* the retina of the eye. [This nerve and the optic tract are more fully described under the sub-title Nerves of the Eye.]

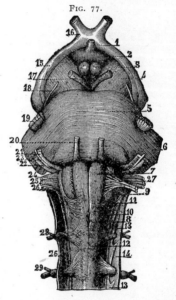

Fig. 77.

3d Nerve, Motor Oculi (n. oculomotorius) (Plate 6), motor nerve of the eye-ball,—*arises* from the inner side of the crus (peduncle) cerebri (17), in front of the pons (5); *deeply* from a nucleus in the floor of the aqueduct of Sylvius (aquæductus cerebri); *exit* by the sphenoidal (superior orbital) fissure; *to* all the muscles of the orbit except the superior oblique and external rectus, also through the ciliary ganglion to the sphincter of the iris and the ciliary muscle.

4th Nerve, Trochlear or **Pathetic** (n. trochlearis) (Plate 6), motor of the eye-ball,—*arises* from the outer side of the crus (peduncle) cerebri (18), in front of the pons; *deeply* from a nucleus in the floor of the aqueduct of Sylvius, below that of the 3d nerve decussates in the superior medullary velum with its companion nerve; *exit* by the sphenoidal (superior orbital) fissure; *to* the superior oblique (trochlear) muscle of the eye-ball of the side opposite to that of its origin.

5th Nerve, Trifacial or (n. trigeminus) (Plate 7), nerve of sensation and motion,—*arises* by 2 roots (19) from the side of the pons Varolii; *deeply* from a nerve-tract in the medulla oblongata and the locus cæruleus (sensory root), the floor of the 4th ventricle and the wall of the cerebral aque-

FIG. 78.

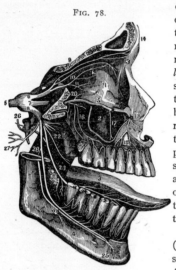

duct of Sylvius (motor root or masticator nerve); *exit* in 3 divisions by the sphenoidal fissure, the foramen rotundum and the foramen ovale respectively. The *Gasserian* or *semilunar ganglion* (5) is situated on its sensory root at the origin of the three divisions. This nerve resembles a spinal nerve in arising by two roots, in having a ganglion on its posterior (sensory) root, and in its compound function. It is the great sensory nerve of the head and face, and the motor nerve of the muscles of mastication. Its *divisions* are the ophthalmic, the maxillary and the mandibular as follows:—

OPHTHALMIC (n. ophthalmicus) (6), a sensory nerve,—*exit* by the sphenoidal (superior orbital) fissure; *to* the eye-ball, lacrimal gland, mucous lining of the eye and nasal fossæ, and the skin of the forehead, eyebrow and nose. Its branches are the—

Frontal (9) { Supra-orbital.
Supra-trochlear.   *Lacrimal* (10) { Branches to the gland, the conjunctiva, and the eyelid.

Nasal (11) or nasociliary { Ganglionic, to the ciliary ganglion.
Ciliary, to the ciliary muscles, iris and cornea.
Infra-trochlear, to the skin of the eyelids and side of the nose, the conjunctiva, lacrimal sac and caruncula lacrimalis.

MAXILLARY (7), a sensory nerve,—*exit* by the foramen rotundum; *to* the temple, cheek, lower eyelid, nose, lip, upper teeth and the spheno-palatine ganglion, thence to the palate. Its branches are the—

Meningeal (n. meningeus medius).

Orbital (n. zygomaticus) (20) { Temporal (ramus zygomaticotemporalis). Malar (ramus zygomaticofacialis). }

2 *Spheno-palatine* (nn. sphenopalatini).
2 *Posterior Sup. Dental* (16) (rami alveolares superiores posteriores).
Middle Superior Dental (ramus alveolaris superior medius).
Anterior Sup. Dental (18) (ramus alveolaris superior anterior).
Palpebral (rami palpebrales inferiores).
Nasal (rami nasales interni).
Labial (rami labiales superiores).

MANDIBULAR (8), includes the *masticator nerve* or motor root of the 5th, and is a nerve of motion, common sensation and special sense (taste). Its *exit* is by the foramen ovale. Its *recurrent branch* goes to the dura mater and the lining of the mastoid cells; its *motor* filaments to the muscles of mastication; its *sensory* ones to the teeth and gums of the lower jaw, the skin of the temple and external ear, the lower face and lip, and the anterior ⅔ of the tongue. Its branches are the—

Recurrent or meningeal (n. spinosus).
Internal Pterygoid (masticator).
Masseteric (masticator).   *Auriculo-tem-*
Deep Temporal 2 (masticator). *poral* (26)
Buccal (n. buccinatorius).
External Pterygoid (masticator).

{ Br. to the facial nerve. Br. to otic ganglion. Ant. Auricular 2. Brs. to meatus auditorius 2 Articular. Parotid. Superior Temporal. }

Lingual or *Gustatory* (23),—to the tongue, mouth, gums and sub-lingual gland: communicates with the facial, inferior dental and hypoglossal nerves and the sub-mandibular ganglion.

Inferior alveolar or *Dental* (24) { Mylo-hyoid (masticator) (28), to that muscle and digastric. Dental Brs. to the molar and bicuspid teeth. Incisive, to the canine and incisor teeth. Mental (25), to the chin and lower lip. }

6th Nerve, Abducent (n. abducens) (Plate 10), motor of the eyeball,— *arises* from the pyramid of the medulla oblongata, close to the pons (20, Fig. 76); *deeply* from the floor of the 4th ventricle, beneath the eminentia teres; *exit* by the sphenoidal (superior orbital) fissure; *to* the external rectus muscle of the eyeball.

7th Nerve, Facial, *Portio Dura* (n. facialis) (Plate 8), is the motor nerve of the face, the stapedius, the muscles of the external ear and other muscles. The *Pars intermedia* (glosso-palatine nerve) is a sensory nerve to the palate and its *chorda tympani* branch is the nerve of taste for the anterior ⅔ of the tongue, and the vaso-dilator of the sub-mandibular and sublingual glands. It *arises* from the upper part of the medulla oblongata, in the groove between the olivary and restiform bodies (21, Fig. 76); *deeply* in the floor of the 4th ventricle, from a nucleus in the lower part of the pons near that of the 6th nerve; the Pars Intermedia takes its deep origin from the Solitary Tract; *exit* by the internal auditory meatus, through the aquæductus (canalis facialis) Fallopii and the stylo-mastoid foramen; to the muscles of expression of the face, those of the ear, etc., and to the tongue. Behind the ramus of the jaw its diverging branches form the *pes anserinus* or goose's foot. It *communicates* with the meningeal sympathetic plexus by the external superficial petrosal nerve; with the spheno-palatine and otic ganglia, by the large and small superficial petrosal nerves; with the auditory, great auricular, auriculo-temporal, pneumogastric (n. vagus), glosso-pharyngeal, small occipital, and superficial cervical nerves, the three divisions of the 5th nerve, and the carotid plexus. The *petrosal nerves* mentioned above are given off by the *geniculate ganglion*, a swelling on the 7th nerve in the aquæductus (canalis facialis) Fallopii (described separately). Its *branches of distribution* are the—

Tympanic,—to the stapedius muscle.

Chorda Tympani,—nerve of taste, etc. (see above).

Posterior Auricular,—dividing into Auricular and Occipital.

Digastric,—to that muscle.

Stylo-hyoid,—to that muscle.

Temporo-facial
- Temporal Brs. to the temporal region.
- Malar Brs. to the occip.-frontalis and the lower eyelid.
- Infra-orbital
  - Superficial Brs.
  - Deep Brs.

Cervico-facial
- Buccal Brs. to the mouth and cheek muscles.
- Mandibular Brs.
- Cervical Brs.

8th Nerve, Auditory, *Portio Mollis* (n. acusticus) (Plate 10), the special nerve of the sense of hearing, is soft in texture and destitute of neurilemma, —*arises* from the groove between the pons and medulla, between the restiform body and the 7th nerve (22, Fig. 76); *deeply* from the floor of the 4th ventricle by 2 roots, one from the trigonum acustici, the other from the accessory nucleus and the tuberculum acusticum. *Goes* by the internal auditory meatus; *to* the internal ear. It is the only cranial nerve which does not leave the cranium. Its branches are two, the—

Vestibular, to the vestibule. *Cochlear*, to the cochlea (see page 309).

9th Nerve, Glosso-pharyngeal (n. glosso-pharyngeus) (Plate 9), sensory nerve and nerve of taste,—*arises* by 3 or 4 filaments from the medulla oblongata in the groove between the olivary and restiform bodies (24, Fig. 76); *deeply* from a nucleus in the floor of the 4th ventricle and the tractus or fasciculus solitarius in the lower part of the medulla; *exit* by the jugular foramen; *to* the mucous membrane of the fauces and base of the tongue, and the mucous glands of the mouth and tonsil. It *communicates* with the facial, pneumogastric (vagus) and sympathetic nerves. Its branches of distribution are the—

Tympanic or *Jacobson's Nerve*,—described under Ear (see page 302).
Carotid Branches,—along the internal carotid artery.
Pharyngeal,—to the pharyngeal plexus.
Muscular,—to the stylo-pharyngeus muscle.
Tonsillar Branches,—forming the tonsillar plexus, thence to the soft palate and fauces.
Lingual 2,—one to the base, the other to the posterior half of the tongue, being distributed to the mucous membrane, the papillæ and the follicular glands.

10th Nerve, Pneumogastric (n. vagus) (Plate 9),—the auriculo-laryngo-pharyngo-œsophago-tracheo-pulmono-cardio-gastro-hepatic nerve (Pancoast), is composed of both motor and sensory fibres. It *arises* by 8 or 10 filaments from the medulla oblongata (25, Fig. 76), between the olivary and restiform bodies; *deeply* from the nucleus vagi in the floor of the 4th ventricle, the tractus or fasciculus solitarius and the nucleus ambiguus in the medulla; *exit* by the jugular foramen; and is distributed *to* the parts and organs named in the above euphonious appellation; *supplying* sensory and motor fibres to the organs of voice and respiration, and motor fibres alone to the pharynx, œsophagus, stomach and heart. It has a *ganglion* on its root and another on its trunk, thereby *communicating* with the 7th, 9th, 11th and 12th cranial nerves, the 1st and 2nd cervical nerves and the sympathetic. Its branches of distribution are the—

Meningeal (ramus meningeus),—a recurrent filament to the dura mater.
Auricular (ramus auricularis) or *Arnold's Nerve*,—to the external ear.
Pharyngeal (ramus pharyngeus),—to the pharyngeal plexus.
Superior Laryngeal (n. laryngeus superior),—a nerve of sensation to the larynx, dividing into the External (ramus externus) and Internal (ramus internus) Laryngeal.

Recurrent Laryngeal (n. laryngeus inferior),—the motor nerve of the larynx; gives off œsophageal, tracheal and pharyngeal branches.

Cervical Cardiac Branches (rami cardiaci superiores),—to the cardiac plexuses.

Thoracic Cardiac Branches (rami cardiaci inferiores),—to the deep cardiac plexus.

Anterior Pulmonary Branches,—to that plexus.

Posterior Pulmonary Branches,—to that plexus.

Œsophageal Branches (rami œsophagei),—to the œsophageal plexus.

Gastric (rami gastric),—on the left side to the anterior surface of the stomach, on the right side to the posterior surface; some filaments going to the hepatic plexus.

11th Nerve, Spinal Accessory (n. accessorious) (Plate 9), a motor nerve; consists of the two parts, the accessory (ramus internus) to the vagus and the spinal portion (ramus externus). The *Accessory or Bulbar* portion (ramus internus) *arises* by 4 or 5 filaments from the medulla below the vagus (26, Fig. 76); *deeply* from the nucleus ambiguus and the column of cells underneath the *ala* cineria in the floor of the 4th ventricle; *exit* by the jugular foramen; *to* the pharyngeal and superior laryngeal branches of the vagus and through the former probably supplying the muscles of the soft palate. The *Spinal* portion (ramus externus) *arises* by several filaments from the lateral tract of the cord behind the anterior roots of the upper five cervical spinal nerves; *deeply* from the dorso-lateral gray tract of the cord from the olive down to the level of the 5th cervical nerve; *exit* by the jugular foramen, having first entered the skull by the foramen magnum; *to* the sterno-mastoid and trapezius muscles, forming plexuses with the 2d, 3d and 4th cervical nerves.

12th Nerve, Hypoglossal (n. hypoglossus), *Nonus or Ninth of Willis* (Plate 10), the motor nerve of the tongue,—*arises* by 10 to 15 filaments from the medulla oblongata in the groove between the pyramid and the olivary body (27, Fig. 76); *deeply* from the trigonum hypoglossi in the floor of the 4th ventricle; *exit* by the anterior condylar foramen (canalis hypoglossi) in two bundles; *to* certain muscles of the tongue and other muscles; *communicating* with the vagus, sympathetic, 1st and 2d cervical and the lingual. Its branches of distribution are the—

Meningeal Branches,—to the dura mater.

Descendens Hypoglossi (ramus descendens),—to the sterno-hyoid, sterno-thyroid and omohyoid muscles; joins the communicans hypoglossi branch of the cervical plexus.

Thyro-hyoid (ramus thyreohyoideus),—to the thyro-hyoid muscle.

Muscular Branches,—to the stylo-glossus, hyo-glossus, genio-hyoid and genio-hyo-glossus muscles, and to the intrinsic muscles of the tongue (rami linguales).

Nerves entering the Cranium before passing out of it, are the spinal portion (ramus externus) of the spinal Accessory (n. accessorius), and the Nasal branch (n. nasociliaris) of the Ophthalmic division of the 5th nerve. The first enters by the foramen magnum, and leaves by the jugular foramen. The second enters from the orbit by the anterior ethmoidal foramen (canalis ethmoidale anterius), and leaves by the nasal slit at the side of the crista galli.

GANGLIA OF THE CRANIAL NERVES

Ganglia are on and connected with several of the cranial nerves. Those connected with the 5th nerve have each motor, sensory and sympathetic roots. The various ganglia are named and connected as follows:—

With the 3d Nerve,—the ophthalmic, lenticular, or ciliary ganglion (ganglion ciliare).

On the Fifth Nerve,—the Gasserian or semilunar ganglion.

With the 5th Nerve,—the ophthalmic (ganglion ciliare), the spheno-palatine (Meckel's), the otic, and the sub-mandibular or sub-maxillary ganglia.

On the 7th Nerve,—the geniculate ganglion (ganglion geniculi) or intumescentia ganglioformis.

With the 7th Nerve,—the spheno-palatine (Meckel's) ganglion, and the otic ganglion.

With the Cochlear portion (radix cochlearis) of the 8th Nerve,—the spiral ganglion.

With the Vestibular portion (radix vestibularis) of the 8th Nerve,—the vestibular ganglion (Scarpa's).

On the 9th Nerve,—the jugular (ganglion superius) and petrous (ganglion inferius) ganglia.

On the 10th Nerve,—the jugular or ganglion of the root (ganglion jugulare), and the inferior or ganglion of the trunk (ganglion nodosum).

With the 11th Nerve,—the jugular ganglion (ganglion jugulare) of the 10th nerve is connected with the accessory portion (ramus internus) of the 11th.

Gasserian or **Semilunar Ganglion** (Plate 7), on the sensory root of the 5th nerve, is situated near the apex of the petrous portion of the temporal bone. It *communicates* with the carotid plexus of the sympathetic by filaments on its inner side. Its *branches* are the 3 divisions of the 5th nerve, the ophthalmic, maxillary, and mandibular, the latter trunk being joined by the motor root (*masticator nerve*) of the nerve outside the cranium. The ganglion also gives off minute branches to the tentorium cerebelli and the dura mater in the middle cranial fossa.

Ophthalmic, Ciliary, or **Lenticular Ganglion** (ganglion ciliare) (Plate 6), is about the size of a pin's head, and is situated at the back of the orbit. Its *roots* are 3 in number,—a sensory (radix longa ganglii ciliaris), from the nasal branch (n. nasociliaris) of the ophthalmic; a motor root (radix brevis ganglii ciliaris), from the 3d nerve; and a sympathetic root (radix sympathetica ganglii ciliaris), from the cavernous plexus. Its *branches* are the short ciliary nerves (nn. ciliares breves), to the ciliary muscle, the iris and the cornea.

Spheno-palatine or **Meckel's Ganglion** (Plate 7), the largest of the cranial ganglia, is situated in the spheno-palatine or pterygo-maxillary fossa, close to the spheno-palatine foramen. Its *roots* are—a sensory, from the maxillary nerve; a motor, from the facial, through the large superficial petrosal (n. petrosus superficialis major); and a sympathetic root, from the carotid plexus, through the large deep petrosal (n. petrosus profundus); the two last-named joining to form the Vidian nerve (n. canalis pterygoidei) before entering the ganglion. Its *branches* are the—

Ascending Branches (rami orbitales),—to the orbit.

Anterior or *Large Palatine* (n. palatinus anterior),—to the gums and hard palate.

Middle or *External Palatine* (n. palatinus medius),—to the uvula, tonsil and soft palate.

Posterior or *Small Palatine* (n. palatinus posterior),—to the levator palati and azygos uvulæ muscles, the soft palate, tonsil and uvula.

Superior Nasal Branches (rami nasales posteriores superiores),—to the mucous membrane of the superior and middle turbinal processes and that lining the posterior ethmoidal cells.

Naso-palatine (n. nasopalatinus),—to the mucous membrane behind the incisor teeth, and that of the septum of the nose.

Pharyngeal or *Pterygo-palatine*,—to the mucous membrane of the upper part of the pharynx.

Posterior Nasal Branches (rami nasales posteriores inferiores),—to the mucous membrane at the back of the roof of the mouth, and that of the septum and superior meatus of the nose.

Otic Ganglion (ganglion oticum), *Arnold's* (Plate 7), is situated on the inner surface of the mandibular nerve, immediately below the foramen ovale. Its *roots* are—a sensory, from probably the glosso-pharyngeal;

motor, from probably the facial; both through the small superficial petrosal (n. petrosus superficialis minor) continued from the tympanic plexus; and a sympathetic root from the middle meningeal plexus. It *communicates* also with the internal pterygoid branch of the mandibular, and with the auriculo-temporal. Its *branches* are—a filament (n. tensoris tympani) to the tensor tympani muscle, one (n. tensoris veli palatini) to the tensor palati, and one to the chorda tympani nerve.

Sub-mandibular or Sub-maxillary Ganglion (Plate 7) is situated above the sub-maxillary gland. Its *roots* are—a sensory (rami communicantes cum n. linguali), from the lingual branch of the mandibular; a motor, from the facial by the chorda tympani; and a sympathetic root from the facial plexus. Its *branches* (rami sub-maxillares) are 5 or 6 in number, distributed to the mucous membrane of the mouth, Wharton's duct (ductus sub-maxillaris), and the sub-mandibular or sub-maxillary gland.

Geniculate Ganglion (ganglion geniculi) (2) or *Intumescentia Gangliformis* (Plate 8), is a reddish, gangliform swelling on the 7th or facial nerve, situated in the aquæductus Fallopii (canalis facialis), above the tympanum and near the Gasserian ganglion (ganglion semilunare). It *communicates* with the spheno-palatine ganglion, the otic ganglion and the meningeal plexus of the sympathetic, by the 3 *superficial petrosal nerves*, which are seen on removing the Gasserian ganglion (ganglion semilunare) (7), as follows:—

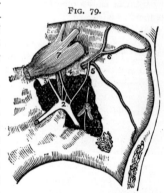

FIG. 79.

Large Superficial Petrosal (3),—passes through the hiatus Fallopii (hiatus canalis facialis), thence across the foramen lacerum medium to the Vidian canal (canalis pterygoidei) where it joins the large deep petrosal from the carotid plexus, to form the Vidian nerve (n. canalis pterygoidei), as which it goes to Meckel's ganglion (ganglion spheno-palatinum) (page 224), forming its motor root.

Small Superficial Petrosal (4),—immediately external to the preceding, going from the geniculate ganglion of the 7th to the otic ganglion, lying directly over the tensor tympani muscle.

External Superficial Petrosal (5),—going from the 7th nerve to the sympathetic plexus on the middle meningeal artery (6).

15

The Vidian Nerve (n. canalis pterygoidei) (Plate 8), is a short ner‑
of communication, between the facial and sympathetic on the one han‑
and the spheno-palatine ganglion on the other, supplying that gangli‑
with its motor and vaso-motor roots. It is formed by the junction ‑
the—

Large Superficial Petrosal, br. of the facial (p. 220), with the—

Large Deep Petrosal, br. of the carotid plexus (p. 237), which tunnels t‑
cartilage filling in the foramen lacerum medium (p. 41). It then e‑
ters the Vidian canal (canalis pterygoidei) (p. 25) in the pterygo‑
process of the sphenoid bone, passing through which it finally joi‑
the posterior part of the spheno-palatine ganglion (p. 224).

Ganglia of the 9th Nerve (Plate 9). The *Jugular Ganglion* (gangli‑
superius) is regarded as a segmentation from the petrous ganglion (ga‑
glion inferius) below. The *Petrous Ganglion* (ganglion inferius) is situat‑
in a depression on the lower border of the petrous portion of the tempor‑
bone. From it arise the filaments which connect the 9th nerve with t‑
10th and the sympathetic; and it communicates also with the 7th nerv‑
Its *branches* of distribution are the tympanic, carotid, pharyngeal, musc‑
lar, tonsillar, and lingual branches of the 9th nerve (see page 221).

Ganglia of the 10th Nerve (Plate 9). The *Ganglion of the Root* (ga‑
glion jugulare) is connected by filaments with the accessory porti‑
(ramus internus) of the 11th nerve, with the petrous (inferior) gangli‑
of the 9th, with the 7th, and with the sympathetic. The *Ganglion of t*‑
Trunk (ganglion nodosum) involves all the fibres of the nerve, as also t‑
accessory portion (ramus internus) of the 11th, which passes through ‑
It is connected with the 12th nerve, the superior cervical ganglion of t‑
sympathetic, and the loop between the 1st and 2d cervical nerves.

THE SPINAL NERVES (NERVI SPINALES)

The Spinal Nerves number 31 pairs, of which the cervical number‑
the thoracic 12, the lumbar 5, the sacral 5, and the coccygeal 1. All t‑
cervical nerves escape above the corresponding vertebræ except the 8‑
which emerges between the 7th cervical and 1st thoracic vertebræ, ea‑
of the others below the corresponding vertebræ, through the intervertebr‑
foramina. Each nerve arises by 2 *roots*,—an anterior motor root (effe‑
ent), and a posterior sensory one (afferent), the latter having a gangli‑
on it, the *spinal ganglion*, situated in the intervertebral foramen. T‑
roots unite, and the *spinal nerve* thus formed divides into 2 *divisions* (ram‑
each having motor and sensory fibres. Just before this division tak‑

place, each nerve gives off a minute *gray ramus communicans*, which after being joined by a branch of the sympathetic, re-enters the spinal canal and is distributed to the spinal cord (medulla spinalis) and its meninges, these are called *recurrent meningeal* nerves. The *posterior divisions* (rami) are small and generally unimportant; they supply the muscles and integument of the back. The *anterior divisions* (rami) supply the neck, front, and sides of the trunk, and the extremities; uniting in various regions to form plexuses, from which important nerve-trunks originate. Each anterior division (ramus), from 2d thoracic to 2d lumbar inclusive, is connected by a slender filament with the sympathetic. These are called *splanchnic* branches or *white rami communicantes;* there 's a second set of them given by the 2d and 3d or by the 3d and 4th sacral nerves.

THE CERVICAL NERVES

The Cervical Nerves (Plate 11), are 8 in number. The anterior divisions of the 4 upper form the cervical plexus; the anterior divisions of the lower 4, together with the 1st thoracic, form the brachial plexus. The posterior division (ramus) of the 1st cervical, the *suboccipital nerve,* differs from the others in not dividing into internal and external branches. It gives off a communicating branch, to the second cervical, and 5 muscular branches. The posterior division (ramus) of the 2d cervical is much larger than the anterior, it is called the Great Occipital (n. occipitalis magnus), a cutaneous nerve.

The Cervical Plexus (plexus cervicalis) (Plate 11), is formed by the anterior divisions of the upper 4 cervical nerves. It is situated opposite the upper 4 cervical vertebræ, resting on the levator anguli scapulæ (m. levator scapulæ) and scalenus medius muscles and covered in by the sterno-mastoid. Its branches number 10, of which the first 4 are superficial and the last 6 are deep, as follows:

Occipitalis Minor (n. occipitalis minimus),—ascending to the back of the side of the head.

Auricularis Magnus
{
Facial, to the skin over the parotid gland.
Auricular, to the skin of the pinna, concha, etc.
Mastoid, to the integument behind the ear.
}

Superficial Cervical (n. cutaneous colli),—by 2 branches to the skin of the neck.

	Suprasternal (nn. supraclaviculares anteriores),—t(the skin of that region.
Supraclavicular	Supraclavicular (nn. supraclaviculares medii),—t(the skin over the pectoral and deltoid.
	Supra-acromial (nn. supraclaviculares posteriores),— to the skin of the shoulder.

Communicating,—brs. to the 10th (vagus), 12th (hypoglossal) and sympathetic nerves.

Muscular,—to the anterior recti and rectus lateralis muscles.

Communicantes Hypoglossi 2, join the descendens hypoglossi nerve.

Phrenic,—is described below.

Deep Communicating,—to the spinal accessory nerve.

Deep Muscular,—to the sterno-mastoid, trapezius, levator angul scapulæ (m. levator scapulæ) and scalenus medius muscles.

The Phrenic Nerve (nervus phrenicus), or *Internal Respiratory of Bell* arises by 3 heads from the 3d, 4th, and 5th cervical, descends across th(front of the scalenus anticus (m. scalenus anterior), crossing the sub clavian and internal mammary arteries in the middle mediastinum, and i distributed to the inferior surface of the diaphragm. It sends filament to the pericardium and pleura, and communicates with the solar an(phrenic plexuses of the sympathetic in the abdomen. On the right sid(of the body it is situated more deeply, and is shorter and more vertical ir direction than on the left side. In the thorax each phrenic nerve i accompanied by the comes nervi phrenici artery, a branch of the interna mammary.

The Brachial Plexus (plexus brachialis) (Plate 12), is formed by th(union of the anterior division of the four lower cervical nerves and the firs thoracic. The 5th, 6th and 7th cervical unite into one trunk externally to the scalenus medius, as also do the 8th cervical and 1st thoracic behin(the same muscle. Below the line of the clavicle both these trunks bifur cate; the two adjacent branches unite behind the axillary artery makin(the *Posterior Cord,* and the remaining 2 form the *Outer* (lateral) and *Inne* (medial) *Cords, as referred to the artery.* Each of these cords bifurcates but the 2 adjacent branches of the outer and inner cords unite over th(artery, to form the *Median Nerve,* leaving 4 other branches,—the *Ulnar* derived from the inner cord, the *Musculo-cutaneous* (n. musculocutaneus) from the outer cord, and the *Musculo-spiral* (n. radialis) and *Circumflex* (n. axillaris) from the posterior cord. (See Plate 12.)

THE BRANCHES of the brachial plexus are as follows:—

Above the clavicle are given off 4, the—

Communicating,—completing the phrenic nerve.

Muscular, to the longus colli, scaleni, rhomboidei, and subclavius muscles. The branch actuating the rhomboidei and levator anguli scapulæ (n. levator scapulæ) is sometimes called the *posterior scapular* (n. dorsalis scapulæ).

Posterior, or Long Thoracic (n. thoracalis longus), external respiratory nerve of Bell,—to the serratus magnus, arising from the 5th, 6th and 7th cervical.

Suprascapular,—from the 1st trunk of the plexus, to the supra- and infra-spinatus muscles and the shoulder-joint.

elow the clavicle are 12, namely, the—

Anterior Thoracic 2,—*external* (lateral) and *internal* (medial) from the outer (lateral) and inner (medial) cords, to the pectoral muscles.

Subscapular 3,—from the posterior cord, to the subscapularis, teres major and latissimus dorsi muscles. The *long sub*scapular is also called *nervus thoracodorsalis.*

Circumflex (n. axillaris),—from the posterior cord, to the muscles and integument of the shoulder, and the shoulder-joint.

Musculo-cutaneous (n. musculocutaneus),—from the outer cord, to the forearm externally, piercing the coraco-brachialis muscle. Its cutaneous branch is also called nervus cutaneus antibrachii lateralis.

Internal Cutaneous (n. cutaneus antibrachii medialis),—from the inner cord, to the arm and forearm.

Lesser Internal Cutaneous (n. cutaneus brachii medialis) nerve of Wrisberg,—from the inner cord, to the back of the arm. Is sometimes wanting, sometimes connected with the intercosto-humeral.

Median (n. medianus),—from outer (lateral) and inner (medial) cords, passes between the two heads of the pronator radii teres (m. pronator teres), supplying the pronators, flexors, first 2 lumbricales, and the integument of the thumb, $2\frac{1}{2}$ fingers, and the radial side of the palm. Its branches are all in the forearm, except its terminals in the palm of the hand, and are named the—

Muscular.

Anterior Interosseous (n. interosseus antibrachii volaris).

Palmar Cutaneous (n. ramus cutaneus palmaris n. mediani).

External { Br. to thumb muscles.
{ Digital, (nn. digitales volares communes) to thumb and index.

Internal { Digital (nn. digitales volares proprii) to thumb, and $2\frac{1}{2}$
{ fingers.

Ulnar,—from the inner (medial) cord, passes between the two heads of

the flexor carpi ulnaris at the inner condyle of the humerus, supplyir
the elbow- and wrist-joints, several muscles, and the palmar and dors
integument of the little finger and half of the ring finger. Branch
are the—

Articular (elbow).	Dorsal Cutaneous.	Superficial Palmar.
Muscular.	Articular (wrist).	Deep Palmar.
Cutaneous.		

Musculo-spiral (n. radialis),—from the posterior cord, accompanies t
superior profunda artery and vein in the spiral groove of the humeru
and in front of the outer (lateral) condyle it divides into the radi
(ramus superficialis n. radialis) and posterior interosseous (ram
profundus n. radialis) nerves. Its branches are—

Muscular (rami musculares n. radialis) divided into internal (media
posterior, and external (lateral).

Cutaneous (rami collaterales n. radialis) one internal (n. cutane
brachii posterior) and two external (n. cutaneous brachii posteri
ramus proximalis et ramus distalis).

Radial (ramus superficialis n. radialis) divides into an external and
internal branch, the latter giving off 4 digital, to the ulnar side of t
thumb and the adjacent sides of $2\frac{1}{2}$ fingers. Communicating bran
to ulnar (ramus anastomoticus ulnaris).

Posterior Interosseous (ramus profundus n. radialis), supplies all t
muscles of the radial side and back of the arm, except 3, also the lig
ments and articulations of the carpus.

TABLE OF THE CORDS OF THE BRACHIAL PLEXUS

Outer or Lateral Cord (superior)

Musculo-cutaneous (n. musculotaneus) . derivation 5, 6, *C*.
External (lateral) Anterior Thoracic. . . . derivation 5, 6, 7, *C*.
Outer (lateral) head of Median. . . . . . . derivation 6, 7, *C*.

Inner or Medial Cord (inferior)

Inner (medial) head of median. . . . . derivation 8, *C*. 1, *T*.
Internal (medial) Anterior Thoracic. . . . derivation 8, *C*. 1, *T*.
Internal Cutaneous (n. cutaneus anti-
    brachii medialis). . . . . derivation 8, *C*. 1, *T*.
Lesser Internal Cutaneous (n. cutaneus
    brachii medialis). . . . . derivation 1, *T*.
Ulnar. . . . . derivation 8, *C*. 1, *T*.

Posterior Cord

Upper Subscapular	derivation	5, 6, C.	
Long Subscapular (n. thoraco-dorsalis)	derivation	5, 6, 7, C.	
Lower Subscapular	derivation	5, 6, C.	
Circumflex (n. axillaris)	derivation	5, 6, C.	
Musculo-Spiral (n. radialis)	derivation	5, 6, 7, 8, C. (1, T.).	

THE THORACIC NERVES (NERVI THORACALES)

The Thoracic Nerves (Plate 12) are 12 in number on each side. Their *posterior divisions* pass backward beneath the transverse processes, and divide into internal and external branches, supplying the muscles and integument of the back. Their *anterior divisions*, the *intercostal nerves*, are distributed to the walls of the thorax and abdomen, separately from each other, without plexiform arrangement. The upper 6, except the 1st and the intercosto-humeral (intercosto-brachial) branch of the 2d, are limited in their distribution to the parietes of the chest. The lower 6 supply the walls of the chest and abdomen, the last one sending a cutaneous filament to the buttock. The *Lateral Cutaneous* nerves are derived from the intercostals, midway between the vertebræ and the sternum; they pierce the external intercostal and serratus magnus (m. serratus anterior) muscles, and divide into anterior and posterior branches. Peculiar among the thoracic nerves and their branches are the—

First Thoracic,—divides into 2 branches, one entering into the brachial plexus, the other forming the 1st intercostal nerve.

Intercosto-humeral (n. Intercostobrachialis),—is the lateral cutaneous branch of the 2d intercostal (anterior division of the 2d thoracic); it pierces the external intercostal muscle and crosses the axilla, joining with a filament from the lesser internal cutaneous (n. cutaneus brachii medialis) (nerve of Wrisberg), supplying the skin of the upper half of the inside and back of the arm, and communicating with the internal cutaneous (n. cutaneus brachii posterior) branch of the musculo-spiral nerve (n. radialis).

Last Thoracic,—is larger than the other thoracic nerves. Its anterior division runs along the lower border of the last rib, and communicates with the first lumbar nerve by the thoraco-lumbar branch, also with the ilio-hypogastric branch of the lumbar plexus. One of its branches, the—

Lateral Cutaneous of the 12th Thoracic,—is also of large size, and is distributed to the integument over the front part of the gluteal region, some of its filaments extending as low as the trochanter major of the femur.

THE LUMBAR NERVES

The Lumbar Nerves are 5 in number on each side. Their roots are large and descend vertically in the spinal canal to reach their respective inter-vertebral foramina of exit. Their *posterior divisions* pass backward between the transverse processes, and divide into internal (medial) branches, supplying the deep muscles of the back; and external (lateral) branches are mostly cutaneous. Their *anterior divisions* pass outward behind the psoas magnus muscle or between its fasciculi. The anterior divisions of the upper 4 nerves are connected by anastomotic loops, form-ing the *lumbar plexus;* that of the 5th with a branch of the 4th forms the *lumbo-sacral cord* (truncus lumbosacralis), which joins with the anterior divisions of the upper 3 sacral nerves and part of the 4th to form the *sacral plexus.* (See Plate 14.)

The Lumbar Plexus (plexus lumbalis) (Plate 14), is formed by loops from the 12th thoracic and the upper 4 lumbar nerves. It is situated in the substance of the psoas magnus muscle in front of the transverse processes of the lumbar vertebræ. Its branches are given off by the connecting loops, and are as follows:—

Ilio-hypogastric,—from the 1st lumbar nerve, to the integument of the gluteal and hypogastric regions.

Ilio-inguinal,—from the 1st lumbar nerve, gives off muscular branches to the internal oblique as it pierces it. It then accompanies the spermatic cord, or round ligament, divides into anterior scrotal or anterior labial to the integument of the upper and inner thigh and the scrotum or labium majus.

Genito-crural (genito-femoral),—from the 1st and 2d lumbar nerves, gives off genital branch (n. spermaticus externus), to the cremaster muscle or round ligament, and a femoral branch (n. lumbo-inguinalis), to the integument over the anterior superior part of the thigh.

External Cutaneous (n. cutaneus femoris lateralis),—from the 2nd and 3rd lumbar nerves, to the integument of the anterior, outer and pos-terior parts of the thigh.

Obturator (n. obturatorius),—from the 2nd, 3rd, and 4th lumbar nerves, through the obturator foramen, to the obturator externus and adduc-tor muscles of the thigh, the hip- and knee-joints, and occasionally the integument of the thigh and leg.

Accessory Obturator (n. obturatorius accessorius) (often absent),—from the 3rd and 4th lumbar nerves, to the pectineus muscle and the hip-joint.

Anterior Crural (n. femoralis),—from the 2nd, 3rd, and 4th lumbar
nerves, to the iliacus and pectineus muscles, all the muscles on the
front of the thigh except the tensor fasciæ femoris, the hip- and knee-
joints, and the integument on the front and inner side of the thigh.   It
descends through the psoas magnus muscle, passing beneath Poupart's inguinal ligament to the thigh, where it divides into an interior
and a posterior division.   Its branches are—

Muscular, within the abdomen, to the iliacus muscle.

Arterial, within the abdomen, to the femoral artery.

Middle Cutaneous, to the skin on the front of the thigh.

Internal Cutaneous, to the skin on the knee and leg.

Muscular, to the pectineus and sartorius muscles.

Long Saphenous (n. saphenus), to the skin over the patella and that on
the front and inner side of the leg.

Muscular, to the quadriceps extensor muscle.

Articular Branches, to the hip- and knee-joints.

The Sacral and Coccygeal Nerves

The Sacral Nerves number 5, the Coccygeal 1, on each side.   Their roots
re long and descend vertically in the spinal canal as the *cauda equina* or
orse's tail, to reach their respective foramina of exit.   Their *posterior divi-
ions* are small; they supply the multifidus spinæ muscles and the skin of
he gluteal region; those of the lower 2 sacral and the coccygeal supplying
he extensor coccygis and the skin over the coccyx.   Their *anterior divisions*
ommunicate with the sacral ganglia of the sympathetic; those of the 3
pper sacral, with the lumbo-sacral cord (truncus lumbo-sacralis) and a
ranch from the 4th sacral, unite to form the *sacral plexus*.   The anterior
ivision of the 4th sacral divides into visceral and muscular branches, the
ormer supplying the pelvic viscera, the latter the levator ani, sphincter
ni, and coccygeus muscles.   The anterior division of the 5th sacral and
he coccygeal supply the coccygeus muscle and the skin over the coccyx.

The Sacral Plexus (Plexus Sacralis) (Plate 14),—is formed by the union
f the anterior divisions of the upper 3 and part of the 4th sacral nerves (*c*),
ith the lumbo-sacral cord (truncus lumbo-sacralis) (*a*) derived from the
th and 5th lumbar nerves.   The plexus lies upon the pyriformis muscle, is
vered by the pelvic fascia, communicates with the sympathetic, and
ves off 2 great nerve-trunks or cords, the *upper cord* being prolonged as the
reat sciatic nerve, the *lower cord* becoming the pudic nerve, both passing
it of the pelvis by the great sacro-sciatic foramen.   The branches of the
cral plexus are as follows:—

Muscular Branches,—to the pyriformis, obturator internus, the 2 gemelli and the quadratus femoris.

Superior Gluteal (n. glutæus superior) (*b*),—from the lumbo-sacral cord to the gluteus medius and minimus muscles and the tensor fasciæ femoris.

FIG. 80.

Inferior Gluteal (n. glutæus inferior),—from the lumbo-sacral cord and the 1st and 2d sacral nerves, to the gluteus (glutæus) maximus muscle.

Small Sciatic (n. cutaneus femoris posterior) (*f*),—from the 2d and 3d sacral nerves, to the integument of the perineum and back part of the thigh and leg, by gluteal, perineal and femoral cutaneous branches.

Perforating Cutaneous (n. clunium inferior medialis), sometimes classed as a branch of the "pudendal plexus,"—from the 2d and 3d sacral nerves, perforating the great sacro-sciatic (sacro-tuberous) ligament, to the skin over the gluteus maximus muscle.

Pudic (n. pudendus), sometimes classed as a branch of the "pudendal plexus" (*e*),—from the 3d and 4th sacral nerves, escapes by the great sacro-sciatic foramen, crosses the spine of the ischium and re-enters the pelvis through the lesser sacro-sciatic foramen, to supply the perineum, anus and genitalia. Its branches are the—

Inf. Hemorrhoidal (n. hæmorrhoidalis inferior).

Perineal (n. perinei), dividing into 2 superficial perineal cutaneous branches and muscular branches to all of the perineal muscles.

Dorsal Nerve of the Penis (n. dorsalis penis vel clitoridis).

Great Sciatic (n. ischiadicus) (*g*),—the largest nervous cord in the body, and the continuation of the upper cord of the sacral plexus, arises from the lumbo-sacral cord and the upper 4 sacral nerves, and escapes by the great sacro-sciatic foramen to the back of the thigh, giving off—

Articular Branches (rami articulares), to the hip-joint.

Muscular Branches (rami musculares), to the flexor muscles of the

leg, viz.—the biceps, semitendinosus and semimembranosus, also
to the adductor magnus.

External (n. peronæus communis) (*h*) and Internal (n. tibialis) (*i*)
Popliteal, the terminal branches, generally arising at the lower
third of the thigh.

The Internal Popliteal Nerve (n. tibialis) (*i*), the larger of the two terminal branches of the great sciatic, descends along the back of the lower
thigh and the middle of the popliteal space, to the lower part of the
popliteus muscle, where it becomes the Posterior Tibial Nerve (*k*). Its
branches are the—

Articular (rami articulares) 3,—supplying the knee-joint.

Muscular (rami musculares) (*j*), 4 or 5,—to the gastrocnemius, plantaris,
soleus and popliteal muscles.

Communicans Tibialis (ramus anastomoticus tibialis),—joins the communicans peronei from the external popliteal nerve to form the—

External or *Short Saphenous* (n. cutaneus suræ medialis) (*p*),—descends
to the outer malleolus and is distributed to the skin of the outer side of
the foot and the little toe.

The Posterior Tibial Nerve (*k*), the continuation of the internal popliteal
descends along the back of the leg to behind the inner malleolus, where it
divides into the External (lateral) and Internal (medial) Plantar nerves (*l*).
Its branches are the—

Muscular (rami musculares),—to the soleus, tibialis posticus, flexor
longus digitorum and flexor longus hallucis.

Calcaneo-plantar or *Internal Calcaneal* (rami calcanei mediales),—to the
skin of the heel and inner side of the sole of the foot.

Articular (ramus articularis ad articulationem talocrualem),—to the
ankle-joint.

Internal Plantar (n. plantaris medialis),—to the inner plantar muscles,
sole of the foot, and the plantar integument of the inner $3\frac{1}{2}$ toes (nn.
digitales plantares communes).

External Plantar (n. plantaris lateralis),—to the external plantar muscles, and the plantar integument of the outer $1\frac{1}{2}$ toes (nn. digitales
plantares communes).

The External Popliteal or **Peroneal Nerve** (n. peronæus communis) (*h*),
the smaller of the two terminal branches of the great sciatic (n. ischiadicus),
descends from the bifurcation of the latter nerve, obliquely along the outer
side of the popliteal space, winds around the neck of the fibula, and about
an inch below the head of that bone it divides into the Anterior Tibial
or Deep Peroneal (n. peronæus profundus) (*m*) and Musculo-cutaneous or

Superficial Peroneal (n. peronæus superficialis) (*n*) nerves. Its branches are—

Articular (rami articulares), 3,—to the front and outer side of the knee.

Cutaneous (n. cutaneus suræ lateralis), 2 or 3,—to the integument along the back and outer side of the leg. One of these branches, the—

Communicans Peronei (ramus anastomoticus peronæus),—joins with the communicans tibialis (ramus anastomoticus tibialis) (see above) to form the external saphenous nerve (n. cutaneus suræ medialis).

Anterior Tibial or *Deep Peroneal* (n. peronæus profundus) (*m*),—supplying the extensor muscles, the ankle-joint, and the integument of the adjacent sides of the great and 2d toes.

Musculo-cutaneous or *Superficial Peroneal* (n. peronæus superficialis) (*n*),—by 2 branches (*o*) (internal and external) to the peroneal muscles, the integument of the ankles, and the dorsal integument (n. cutaneous dorsalis medialis) and sides of all the toes, except the outer side of the little toe and the adjoining sides of the great and 2d toes, the former being supplied by the external saphenous (n. cutaneus suræ medialis), and the latter by the internal (medial) branch of the anterior tibial.

THE SYMPATHETIC SYSTEM

The Sympathetic Nervous System consists of—a series of ganglia, connected together by intervening cords, one series on each side of the median line of the body, partly in front and partly on each side of the vertebral column, beginning in the *ganglion of Ribes* on the anterior communicating artery and ending in the *ganglion impar* in front of the coccyx; three great gangliated plexuses, situated in the thoracic, abdominal, and pelvic cavities respectively; smaller ganglia, in relation with the abdominal viscera; and numerous communicating and distributing nerve fibres. (See Plate 16.)

Ganglia in the Cranium. Besides the ganglia of the cranial nerves (described on page 223), all of which are connected with the sympathetic, there are in the cranium or in its immediate vicinity certain ganglia belonging to the sympathetic system, as follows:—

Carotid Ganglion,—on the internal carotid artery.

Ganglion of Bochdalek,—above the canine tooth at the junction of a branch from the spheno-palatine ganglion with the middle superior alveolar and anterior superior alveolar nerves.

Ganglion of Valentine,—situated at the juncture of the middle superior alveolar and the posterior superior alveolar nerves.

The Carotid Plexus is situated on the outer side of the internal carotid artery, as it lies by the side of the body of the sphenoid bone, and is formed by filaments from the outer branch of the superior cervical ganglion. It *communicates* with the Gasserian ganglion (ganglion semilunare) and the 6th nerve; also with the tympanic branch of the 9th by two branches, the *small deep petrosal* and the *carotico-tympanic;* and with the spheno-palatine ganglion by the *large deep petrosal*, which joins the great superficial petrosal to form the Vidian nerve (n. canalis pterygoidei) before entering the ganglion (see page 226).

The Cavernous Plexus is situated in the upper portion of the cavernous sinus, below the last bend of the internal carotid artery, and is formed chiefly by the internal division of the ascending branch from the superior cervical ganglion. It *communicates* with the 3rd, 4th, ophthalmic division of the 5th, and the 6th nerves, also with the ophthalmic ganglion. It sends filaments to the wall of the internal carotid artery, which are prolonged into plexuses around the cerebral and ophthalmic arteries. The filaments on the anterior communicating artery form the *ganglion of Ribes*, which here connects the sympathetic of the two sides of the body.

The Gangliated Cord (Truncus Sympatheticus)

The Cervical Ganglia are 3 in number on each side of the neck, the superior, middle and inferior cervical; of which the superior is the largest and is probably formed by the coalescence of four ganglia corresponding to the upper four cervical nerves. They are as follows:—

Superior Cervical Ganglion,—of fusiform shape, situated behind the carotid sheath opposite the transverse processes of the 2d and 3d cervical vertebræ. Its branches form the carotid, cavernous, and pharyngeal plexuses; one of its internal branches unites with the superior laryngeal nerve, and another is the *superior cervical cardiac nerve* going to the cardiac plexuses.

Middle Cervical Ganglion,—on the inferior thyroid artery, opposite the 6th cervical vertebra gives off the *middle cardiac nerve* to the deep cardiac plexus, also many communicating branches.

Inferior Cervical Ganglion,—on the superior intercostal artery, between the neck of the 1st rib and the transverse process of the 7th cervical vertebra. It gives off several communicating branches and the *inferior cardiac nerve* to the deep cardiac plexus.

The Thoracic Ganglia are 11 or 12 in number on each side of the spine, resting against the heads of the ribs and covered by the pleura costalis, except the last two, which are placed on the side of the bodies of the 11th and 12th thoracic vertebræ. Occasionally two ganglia coalesce into one, and the first is frequently blended with the last cervical ganglion. They are connected together by cords prolonged from their substance. They receive branches (white rami communicantes) from the thoracic nerves. They give off *central branches* (gray rami communicantes) connecting with the thoracic spinal nerves; and *peripheral branches* from the upper 5 or 6 ganglia to the thoracic aorta, etc., from the 3rd and 4th ganglia to the posterior pulmonary plexus, and from the lower 6 or 7 ganglia to form by their union the three splanchnic nerves, as follows:—

   Great Splanchnic,—from branches of the 5th to the 10th inclusive, connecting with the upper 5, passes through the posterior mediastinum, perforates the crus of the diaphragm, to the semilunar (cœliac) ganglion of the solar (cœliac) plexus.

   Lesser Splanchnic,—from the 10th and 11th, passes through the diaphragm with the great splanchnic, to the renal and solar (cœliac) plexuses.

   Least or Renal Splanchnic,—from the last thoracic ganglion, also perforates the diaphragm, and ends in the renal plexus; it is not always present.

The Lumbar Ganglia consist usually of 4 small ganglia on each side, connected together by intervening cords, and situated in front of the vertebral column. Their *central branches* (gray rami communicantes) communicate with the lumbar spinal nerves. Of their *peripheral branches* some help to form the aortic plexus, others go to the hypogastric plexus, and all give off numerous filaments to the bodies of the lumbar vertebræ and the ligaments connecting them. The lumbar ganglia receive branches (white rami communicantes) from the 1st, 2d and sometimes 3d lumbar nerves.

The Pelvic Ganglia are 4 or 5 small ganglia on each side, connected together by intervening cords, and situated in front of the sacrum. The lower cords of each side converge below and unite on the front of the coccyx in the coccygeal ganglion or *ganglion coccygeum impar*. Their *central branches* (gray rami communicantes), 2 from each ganglion, communicate with the sacral nerves. Of the *peripheral branches*, some pass to the pelvic plexus, others go to a plexus on the middle sacral artery and all communicate on the front of the sacrum with the corresponding branches of the other side. The sacral portion of the sympathetic trunk receives one with rami communicantes.

The Great Plexuses (Plate 16)

The Great Plexuses of the Sympathetic are large aggregations of nerves and ganglia, situated in the thoracic, abdominal, and pelvic cavities, and named the *Cardiac Plexus*, the *Cœliac* or *Solar Plexus*, and the *Hypogastric Plexus*. Their branches form secondary plexuses which supply the viscera of the cavities, as described below.

The Cardiac Plexus is situated at the base of the heart, and is divided into a superficial portion and a deep portion, both of which are closely connected with each other. They form by their branches the anterior and posterior coronary plexuses and the anterior pulmonary plexus.

The Superficial Cardiac Plexus is formed by the left superior cardiac nerve, the left inferior cervical cardiac branches of the pneumogastric, and filaments from the deep cardiac plexus. At the junction of these nerves a small ganglion, the *cardiac ganglion of Wrisberg*, is occasionally found, situated immediately beneath the arch of the aorta on the right side of the ductus arteriosus (ligamentum arteriosum). This plexus lies in the concavity of the arch of the aorta, and in front of the right pulmonary artery. Branches from it pass to the—

Right Anterior Coronary Plexus,—formed chiefly from the preceding, also from the deep cardiac plexus. It passes forward between the aorta and the pulmonary artery. It follows the ramifications of the right coronary artery on the anterior surface of the heart.

Right and *Left Anterior Pulmonary Plexuses*,—are formed by filaments from the superficial and deep cardiac plexuses and the anterior pulmonary branches of the vagus nerve. Branches from them accompany the ramifications of the bronchial tubes throughout the lungs. The

Right and *Left Posterior Pulmonary Plexuses* are formed by the posterior pulmonary branches of the vagus and branches from the 3rd and 4th thoracic ganglia of the sympathetic. They are not connected with the cardiac plexuses. They are situated on the posterior aspect of the roots of the lungs, and their branches accompany the ramifications of the bronchial tubes.

The Deep Cardiac Plexus is formed by the cardiac nerves derived from the cervical ganglia of the sympathetic and the cardiac branches of the recurrent laryngeal and pneumogastric nerves. The only cardiac nerves which do not enter into its formation are those forming the superficial cardiac plexus, namely—the left superior cardiac and the inferior cervical cardiac branches of the vagus. This plexus lies in front of the bifurcation of the trachea and behind the arch of the aorta. Its branches on the right side pass in front and behind the right pulmonary artery to the anterior pulmonary plexuses, the anterior (right) and posterior (left) coronary plexuses, and the right auricle; those on the left side give filaments to the superficial cardiac and anterior pulmonary plexuses and the left auricle, and then form the greater part of the—

Left or Posterior Coronary Plexus,—is formed by filaments from both sides of the deep cardiac plexus. It surrounds the branches of the left coronary artery at the back of the heart, and its filaments are distributed with those vessels to the muscular substance of the ventricles.

Ganglia,—are found on the cardiac nerves, both on the surface of the heart and in its muscular substance.

The Epigastric (Cœliac) or Solar Plexus, sometimes called the *abdominal brain,* consists of a great network of nerves and ganglia, situated behind the stomach and in front of the aorta and the crura of the diaphragm, surrounding the cœliac axis and the root of the superior mesenteric artery. Its principal ganglia are the two *Semilunar (cœliac) Ganglia,* irregular gangliform masses, formed by the aggregation of smaller ganglia with interspaces between them, situated one on each side of the plexus, and in front of the crura of the diaphragm, close to the supra-renal capsules. This plexus and its connected ganglia receive the great and small splanchnic nerves of both sides, and some filaments from the right pneumogastric. It distributes filaments over all the branches from the front of the abdominal aorta, forming the following plexuses:—

Phrenic or *Diaphragmatic Plexus,*—arises from the upper part of the semilunar ganglion, and receives one or two branches from the phrenic nerve. It accompanies the phrenic artery and supplies the diaphragm, some filaments going to the supra-renal capsule. At its junction with the phrenic nerve on the right side is the—

Ganglion Diaphragmaticum,—a small ganglion at the juncture with the right phrenic nerve, it is situated on the under surface of the diaphragm, near the right supra-renal capsule.

Supra-renal Plexus,—is formed by branches from the solar plexus, the semilunar ganglion, the phrenic and great splanchnic nerves. Its branches are large, and supply the supra-renal capsule.

Renal Plexus,—is formed by filaments from the solar plexus, the semilunar ganglion, the aortic plexus, and the lesser and smallest splanchnic nerves, some 15 or 20 in all, which have numerous ganglia on them. They accompany the branches of the renal artery into the kidney, some filaments going to the inferior vena cava and to the spermatic plexus.

Spermatic Plexus,—is derived from the renal plexus and receives fila-ments from the aortic plexus. It accompanies the spermatic vessels to the testes. In the female it is called the *Ovarian Plexus*, and is distributed to the ovaries and the fundus of the uterus.

Superior Gastric or *Coronary Plexus,*—joins with branches from the left pneumogastric nerve, and accompanies the gastric left artery along the lesser curvature of the stomach, being distributed to that viscus.

Hepatic Plexus,—receives filaments from the left pneumogastric and the right phrenic nerves, accompanies the hepatic artery, and ramifies in the substance of the liver upon the branches of that artery and those of the portal vein. It gives off branches to all the divisions of the hepatic artery, forming pyloric, gastro-duodenal, gastro-epiploic (inferior gastric), and cystic plexuses, on the arteries similarly named.

Splenic or *Lienal Plexus,*—is formed by branches from the cœliac plexus, the left semilunar ganglion, and the right pneumogastric nerve. It accompanies the splenic artery and its branches to the substance of the spleen, and gives off filaments to the pancreas and the left gastro-epiploic plexus.

Superior Mesenteric Plexus,—is a continuation of the solar plexus, and receives a branch from the right pneumogastric nerve. It surrounds the superior mesenteric artery, and divides into pancreatic, intes-tinal, ileo-colic, right colic, and middle colic branches, which are distributed to all the parts supplied by that artery. Its nerves have numerous ganglia upon them near their origin.

Aortic Plexus,—on the sides and front of the aorta, between the origins of the superior and inferior mesenteric arteries; is formed by branches from the solar (cœliac) plexus and semilunar (cœliac) ganglia, and receives filaments from the lumbar ganglia. It sends branches to the spermatic, inferior mesenteric, and hypogastric plexuses, also some filaments to the inferior vena cava. A part of it is the—

Inferior Mesenteric Plexus,—divides into left colic, sigmoid, and superior hæmorrhoidal plexuses, and supplies the descending colon and the rectum.

The Hypogastric Plexus is formed by filaments from the aortic plexus and the lumbar ganglia, and is situated in front of the promontory of the sacrum between the two common iliac arteries. It contains no evident ganglia, and bifurcates into two lateral divisions, the *Pelvic* or *Inferior Hypogastric Plexuses*, one on each side of the rectum, which receive branches from the 2nd, 3rd, and 4th sacral nerves, and the first two sacral ganglia. They give off numerous branches along the branches of the internal iliac arteries to the pelvic viscera, forming the following secondary plexuses, viz.—

Inferior Hæmorrhoidal Plexus,—to the rectum.

Vesical Plexus,—to the bladder, vesiculæ seminales, and vas deferens.

Prostatic Plexus,—to that gland and the vesiculæ seminales, also to the erectile tissue of the penis as the *large* and *small cavernous nerves.*

Vaginal Plexus,—to the vagina, gives off anteriorly the *cavernous plexus* of the clitoris from which arise the greater and lesser cavernous nerves of the clitoris.

Uterine Plexus,—to the uterus and Fallopian tube.

TABLES AND PLATES

OF THE

NERVOUS SYSTEM

NOTE.—The following Tables are of original arrangement, and are designed to show the origin, formation and distribution of each nerve. They are self-explanatory with the aid of the accompanying Plates.

THE CRANIAL NERVES

1st NERVE,—Olfactory. *Function,*—smell. *Exit,—* { Ethmoidal foramina, 20 in cribriform plate of Ethmoid bone.
(See page 216)

Ext. Root, Posterior division of the Rhin-encephalon or "Limbic lobe."
Mid. Root, Optic thalamus.
Int. Root, Posterior division of the Rhin-encephalon or "Limbic lobe."
} 1st N. and Bulb. { *Ext. Filaments,* to Schneiderian membrane over sup. turbinal and ethmoid bones.
Int. Filaments, to Septum (upper third).

2nd NERVE,—Optic.   *Function,*—sight.   *Exit,*—Optic foramen.
(See page 217)

This table is too long for the width of the page, and breaks at the Optic Commissure, which is repeated again where the table continues below.

Optic thalamus
Ext. geniculate
Corp. quad. ant.
} Fibres { *Longitudinal*
Decussating
Commissural
} Left Optic Tract } OPTIC COMMISSURE or CHIASM.

Corp. quad. ant.
Ext. geniculate
Optic thalamus
} Fibres { *Commissural*
Decussating
Longitudinal
} Right Optic Tract }

OPTIC COMMISSURE or CHIASM. { **Optic N.** 2d { *Longitudinal,* to temporal ½ of retina
Decussating, fr. opp. tract to nasal ½ of ret.
Inter-retinal, fr. opp. retina to retina.
} L. Eye.

Optic N. { *Inter-retinal,* fr. opp. retina to retina.
Decussating, fr. opp. tract to nasal ½ of ret.
Longitudinal, to temporal ½ of retina.
} R. Eye.

3d NERVE,—Motor Oculi.   *Function,*—motion.   *Exit,*—Sphenoidal fissure.
(See page 217)

Nucleus in
floor of the
Aqued. of Syl.
Crus cerebri.
} 3d N. { *Sup. Branch,* to Lev. palp. sup., Rectus superior.
Inf. Branch { to Rectus int., Rect. Inf., Inf. oblique.
motor root to Ciliary Ganglion.

Supplies all the muscles of the orbit (except the superior oblique and ext. rectus), also the sphincter of the iris and the ciliary muscle through the ciliary ganglion.

4th NERVE,—Trochlear.   *Function,*—motion.   *Exit,*—Sphenoidal fissure.
(See page 217)

Aq. of Sylvius.
Crus cerebri.
} 4th N. { to Sup. Oblique on upper (orbital) surface.
Branch to Cavernous Plexus of Sympathetic.
Recurrent Branch, to lateral sinus.

Is the smallest cranial nerve, with the longest nerve-course in the cranial cavity.

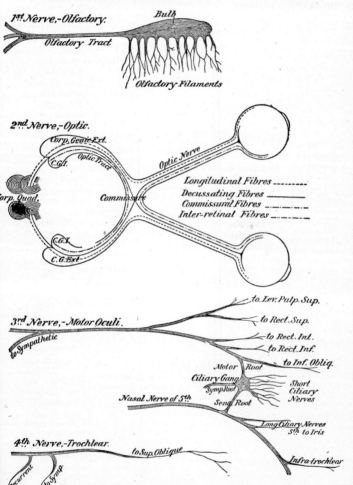

1st Nerve,-Olfactory.
Bulb
Olfactory Tract
Olfactory Filaments

2nd Nerve,-Optic.
Corp. Genic. Ext.
C.G.I.
Optic Tract
Optic Nerve
Corp. Quad.
Commissure
Longitudinal Fibres
Decussating Fibres
Commissural Fibres
Inter-retinal Fibres
C.G.I.
C.G. Ext.

3rd Nerve,-Motor Oculi.
to Lev. Palp. Sup.
to Rect. Sup.
to Sympathetic
to Rect. Int.
to Rect. Inf.
to Inf. Obliq.
Motor Root
Ciliary Gang.
Symp. Root
Short Ciliary Nerves
Nasal Nerve of 5th
Sens. Root
Long Ciliary Nerves 5th to Iris

4th Nerve,-Trochlear.
to Sup. Oblique
Recurrent
to Symp.
Infra-trochlear

Potter. del.

245

5th NERVE,—Trigeminus.   *Functions,* Sensation, Motion.
(See page 218.)

Origin.
Nucleus and
Locus Cæ-
rul. in the
medulla
oblongata
for the
Sensory Root.

Nuclei in floor
of 4th Ven-
tricle, and
Aq. of Syl-
vius, for the
Motor Root or
*Masticator
Nerve.*

**5th N.
Trigeminus
or Trifacial.**

(1) OPHTHALMIC
by Sphenoidal
fissure.

Frontal { Supraorbital. / Supratrochlear.
Lacrimal, to gland, etc.
Nasal. { Ganglionic. / Long Ciliary. / Infratrochlear. / Int. Nasal. / Ext. Nasal.

(2) MAXILLARY
by For. rotund.

Meningeal.
Orbital, { Temporal. / Malar.
Spheno-palatine.
Post. Sup. Dental.
Mid Sup. Dental. } in canal.
Ant. Sup. Dental.
Palpebral,
Nasal, } on the face.
Labial,

(3) MANDIBU-
LAR. (including
masticator) by
For. Ovale.

Recurrent.
*Int. Pterygoid,** { Ant. Br.* / Post. Br.*
*Masseteric.**
*Deep Temporal** { Ant. Br.* / Post. Br.*
Buccal.

*Ext. Pterygoid.**

*Auriculo-
Temporal.* { Br. to facial n. / Br. to otic g. / Ant. Auricular. / to Meat. Aud. / to articulation. / Parotid. / Sup. Temporal.

Lingual { Br. of Comm'n. / Br. of Distrib'n.

*Inferior
Dental.* { Mylo-hyoid.* / Dental Brs. / Incisive. } terminal / Mental.

* *Motor Branches (Masticator Nerve), going to the muscles of mastication.*

THE CRANIAL NERVES.
5th Nerve.—Trigeminus.

Plate 7

Potter, del

7th NERVE,—Facial, or Portio Dura.   *Function,*—Motion, Special Sense (taste)
       (See page 220.)

Origin.
Nucleus in floor of the 4th Ventricle, and groove between Olivary and Restiform bodies of medulla oblongata. Solitary Tract.

7th N. Facial

Branches of Communication.

In auditory canal.
- *Br.* to Auditory nerve.

In Aqueduct of Fallopius.
- *Large Superf. Petrosal,* to Meckel's ganglion.
- *Small Superf. Petrosal,* to otic ganglion.
- *Ext. Superf. Petrosal,* to meningeal plex.
- *Br.* to Auricular of pneumogastric.

At exit from the Stylo-mastoid Foramen.
- *Br.* to Great Auricular (cerv. plex.).
- *Br.* to Auriculo-Temporal (5th).
- *Br.* to Pneumogastric.
- *Br.* to Glosso-pharyngeal.

Behind the ear.
- *Br.* to small Occipital.

On the face.
- *Brs.* to 3 divisions of the 5th nerve.

In the neck.
- *Br.* to Superficial Cervical.

Branches of Distribution.

In Aqueduct of Fallopius.
- *Tympanic Nerve,* to Stapedius muscle.
- *Chorda Tympani Nerve* (glosso-palatine), to the tongue and palate.

Near Stylo-mastoid Foramen.
- *Post. Auricular*
  - Auricular.
  - Occipital.
- *Br.* to Digastric muscle.
- *Br.* to Stylo-hyoid muscle.

On the face.*
- *Temporo-facial*
  - Temporal.
  - Malar.
  - Infra-orbital.
- *Cervico-facial*
  - Buccal.
  - Mandibular.
  - Cervical.

* Forming the *Pes Anserinus,* or Goose's-foot, as these branches are named.

THE CRANIAL NERVES.

Plate 8

7th Nerve - Facial, or Portia Dura.

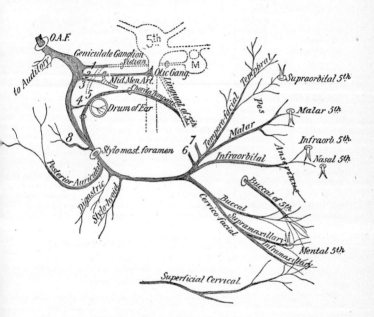

O.A.F.
Geniculate Ganglion
Vidian
Olic Gang.
M
5th
to Auditory
Mid. Men. Art.
Chorda Tympani of 5th
Drum of Ear
Stylo mast. foramen
Posterior Auricular
Digastric
Stylo-Hyoid
Temporofacial
Pes
Temporal
Supraorbital 5th
Malar
Malar 5th
Infraorbital
Infraorb. 5th
Nasal 5th
Ansa nasi
Buccal of 5th
Buccal
Cervico-facial
Supramaxillary
Inframaxillary
Mental 5th
Superficial Cervical.

References.
1. Large Superf. Petrosal, to form Vidian with Nº5.
2 Small Superf. Petrosal, to Optic Ganglion.
3 External Superf. Petrosal, to Plexus on Mid. Meningeal Artery.
4 Tympanic Br. to Stapedius, etc.
5. Br from Carotid Plexus, Making Vidian, with Nº I.
6. 7. Brs. to Auricule -Temporal of 5th
8. Br to Auricular of Vagus.
M. The Ganglion of Meckel.   Potter. del.
O.A.F Orifice of Aquæductus Fallopii.

249

9th NERVE,—Glossopharyngeal.   *Functions,*—Sensation, Special Sense.
(See page 221.)

			Communicating Brs. to	{ Large Petrosal. Small Petrosal. Carotid Plexus.
Origin. Tractus solitarius and floor of 4th vent. and the medulla oblong. behind the olivary body.	9th Nerve Glossopharyngeal, by Jugular Foramen.	*Tympanic* or *Jacobson's N.*	Distributing Brs. to	{ Fenestra vestibuli. Fenestra cochleæ. Eustachian tube.

Carotid Branches,—along Int. Carotid artery.
Pharyngeal Br.—to Pharyngeal Plexus.
Muscular Br.—to Stylo-pharyngeus.
Tonsillar Brs.—to Tonsillar Plexus.
Lingual Brs.—to base and posterior ½ of tongue; nerve of taste.

10th NERVE,—Pneumogastric, or Vagus.   *Function,*—Motion, Sensation.
(See page 221.)

Origin.	10th Nerve Vagus, by Jugular Foramen.	
Funic. solitarius, nucleus ambiguus, floor of 4th ventricle and the medulla oblongata between olivary and restiform bodies.		*Meningeal,* to dura mater. *Auricular* (Arnold's Nerve), to external ear. *Pharyngeal,* to that plexus.

Sup. Laryngeal { Ext. Laryng. (crico-thyroid). Int. Laryng. { supplies all the laryngeal muscles except crico-thyroid and arytenoideus.

Recurrent Laryngeal, ...
Cervical Cardiac. } to cardiac plexus.
Thoracic Cardiac.
Ant. Pulmonary. } to pulmonary plexus.
Post. Pulmonary.
Œsophageal, to that plexus.
Gastric Brs., to the stomach. } terminal brs.
Hepatic, to the hepatic plexus.

Gives sensation to external ear and larynx, motion to other parts, also vasomotor, inhibitory, trophic and secretory influences. A nerve of deglutition, phonation, respiration, circulation, and digestion. The Auriculo-Laryngo-Pharyngo-Œsophago-Tracheo-Pulmono-Cardio-Gastro-Hepatic Nerve.

11th NERVE,—Spinal Accessory (N. ACCESSORIUS).   *Function,*—Motion.
(See page 222.)

Origin. Floor of 4th ventricle, and gray horn of cord, down to 6th Cervical N.	11th Nerve, by Jugular Foramen.	*Branches,* to Pharyngeal and Sup. Laryngeal of Vagus. *Internal,* anastomosing with Vagus, is probably the Recurrent Laryngeal Br. of the latter nerve. *External,* or *Muscular,* to { Sterno-mastoid. Trapezius.

A motor nerve to the muscles named, and probably to the larynx also.

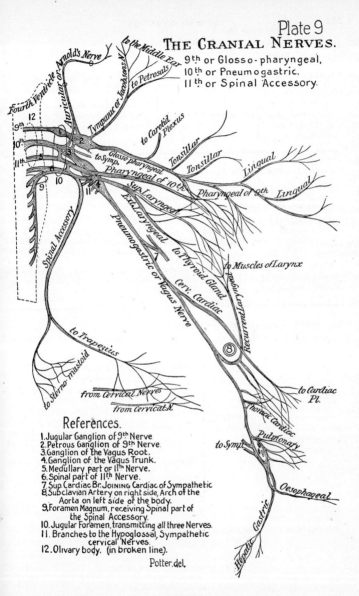

Plate 9

THE CRANIAL NERVES.

9th or Glosso-pharyngeal,
10th or Pneumogastric,
11th or Spinal Accessory.

Fourth Ventricle or Arnold's Nerve

to the Middle Ear

Auricular or Jacobson's N.

to Petrosals

9th 12
10th
11th

Tympanic or Jacobson's N.

to Carotid Plexus

Glosso-pharyngeal
to Symp.

Tonsillar

Tonsillar

Lingual

Pharyngeal of 10th

Pharyngeal of 9th

Lingual

Sup. Laryngeal

Ext. Laryngeal

to Thyroid Gland

to Muscles of Larynx

Spinal Accessory

Pneumogastric or Vagus Nerve

Cerv. Cardiac

Recurrent Laryngeal

to Trapezius

to Sterno-mastoid

from Cervical Nerves

from Cervical N.

to Cardiac Pl.

Thoracic Cardiac

Pulmonary

to Symp.

Oesophageal

Hepatic

Gastric

References.

1. Jugular Ganglion of 9th Nerve.
2. Petrous Ganglion of 9th Nerve.
3. Ganglion of the Vagus Root.
4. Ganglion of the Vagus Trunk.
5. Medullary part of 11th Nerve.
6. Spinal part of 11th Nerve.
7. Sup. Cardiac Br. JOINING Cardiac of Sympathetic.
8. Subclavian Artery on right side, Arch of the
    Aorta on left side of the body.
9. Foramen Magnum, receiving Spinal part of
    the Spinal Accessory.
10. Jugular Foramen, transmitting all three Nerves.
11. Branches to the Hypoglossal, Sympathetic
    cervical Nerves.
12. Olivary body. (in broken line).

Potter. del.

6th NERVE,—Abducens (see page 219).   *Function,*—Motion.

Origin.—A nucleus in floor of 4th ventricle, and the pyramid of the medulla oblongata. }6th Nerve, Abducens.{ *Exit* by sphenoidal fissure to the Ext. Rectus muscle of the eyeball. *Branch,* to the sympathetic.

8th NERVE,—Auditory, or Acustic.   *Function,*—Special Sense.

Origin.—Striæ in floor of the 4th ventricle, and groove between the pons and medulla. } **8th Nerve, Auditory.** {

Vestibular, to { 2 Semi-circ. canals. Utricle. Saccule.

Cochlear, to { Post. Semi-circ. canal. Saccule and Utricle. Cochlea, and Organ of Corti.

A nerve of special sense (hearing), described on page 220, *ante.* It goes by the Internal Auditory Meatus, through the Internal Auditory Canal, to the internal ear. It is the only cranial nerve which does not leave the cranial wall.

12th NERVE,—Hypoglossal (Nonus or 9th of Willis).
    (See page 222.)   *Function,*—Motor of tongue, etc.

Origin.—Floor of 4th ventricle, and groove between the pyramid and olivary body of medulla. } **12th Nerve, Hypoglossal.** {

Communicating Brs. to { Lingual of 5th. Symphatic. 1, 2 Cervical. Vagus.

Descendens Hypoglossi. { Br. to Sterno-hyoid. Br. to Sterno-thyroid. Br. to Omo-hyoid. Joins Communicans Hypoglossi.

Thyro-hyoid, to that muscle.

Muscular, to .. { Stylo-glossus. Hyo-glossus. Genio-hyoid. Genio-hyo-glossus.

Exit, by Ant. Condylar foramen (Canalis hypoglossi).

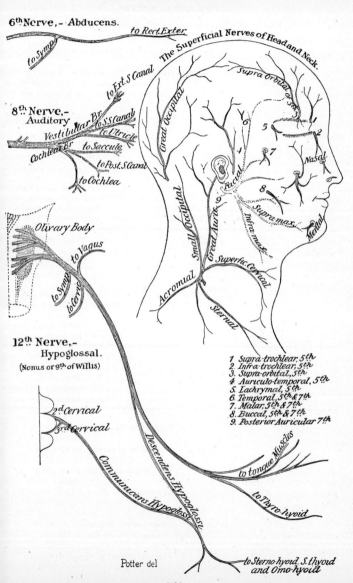

THE CRANIAL NERVES.

Plate 10

6th Nerve, - Abducens.

to Rect. Exter.

to Symp.

The Superficial Nerves of Head and Neck.

to Ext. S. Canal

Supra Orbital or 3 & 3

8th Nerve, - Auditory

Vestibular Br.

to S. S. Canal

to Utricle

Cochlear Br.

to Saccule

to Post. S. Canal

to Cochlea

Great Occipital

6

5

7

Nasal

1

2

Facial

8

Olivary Body

to Symp.

to Vagus

to Vagus

Small Occipital

Great Auric.

9

Supra-max.

Infra-max.

Mental

12th Nerve, - Hypoglossal.
(Nonus or 9th of Willis)

Acromial

Superfic. Cervical

Sternal

1 Supra-trochlear, 5th
2 Infra-trochlear, 5th
3 Supra-orbital, 5th
4 Auriculo-temporal, 5th
5 Lachrymal, 5th
6 Temporal, 5th & 7th
7 Malar, 5th & 7th
8 Buccal, 5th & 7th
9 Posterior Auricular 7th

2d Cervical

3rd Cervical

Descendens Hypogloss.

to tongue Muscles

Communicans Hypogloss.

to Thyro-hyoid

Potter del

to Sterno-hyoid, S. thyoid
and Omo-hyoid

THE SPINAL NERVES

8 CERVICAL, 12 THORACIC, 5 LUMBAR, 5 SACRAL, 1 COCCYGEAL

N. B.—Read from the **Black Type** *outwards to left and right*

Post Div. of 2d N.
Post M. of head, etc. } POST. } **1st Cervical** { ANT. { Brs. 3, to Recti cap. Muscle
Complexus Muscle. } DIV. } **Nerve.** { DIV. { Commun'g { 2 Cerv. N.
Skin of occiput. } *Sub-occipital* { Brs. to { Vagus N.
{ Hypogl. N.
{ Sup. Cerv.
{ Gang.
{ Br. to Occip-atloid artic'n.

Splenius
Cerv. ascendens
Transv.-colli } *Ext. Branch*
Trach-mastoid } supplying
Complexus } POST. } **2d** { ANT. { Br. to Spinal accessor
DIV. } **Cervical** { DIV. { Fil. to Sterno-mastoid M
to 1st Cerv. N. } *Int. Br.* or } **Nerve.** { Asc. Br. to 1st Cerv. N
Skin of occiput. } *Great Occip.* } { Desc. Br. to 3d Cerv. N
Auricular. } { Fil. to Commun. Hyp
{ *Occipitalis Minor N.*

Splenius
Cerv. ascend. } *Ext. Br.* { Ascen. { Auric. Magnus N.
Trans. colli } supplies { Br. { Superf. Cervical N
Trach-mast. } POST. } **3d** { ANT. { Br. to 2d Cerv. N.
DIV. } **Cervical** { DIV. { Br. to Spinal-ac.
} **Nerve.**
Integument } *Int. Br.* { Descen. { Fil. to 4th Nerve.
of occiput. } to { Br. { Fil. to Lev. ang. sca
} supply { Supra-clavicular.
{ Fil. to Com. Hypog
{ Fil. to Phrenic N.

Muscles of the Back. { POST. } **4th Cervical** { ANT. { Fil. to 3d Cerv. N.
DIV. } **Nerve.** { DIV. { Fil. to 5th Cerv. N.
{ Fil. to Phrenic N.
{ Fil. to Scalenus medius.
{ Fil. to Supra-clavic. N.

Anterior
Divisions of
1st Cerv. N. } **Cervical** } *Superficial* { *Occipitalis Minor*, to head.
2d Cerv. N. } **Plexus.** { *Auricularis Magnus* { Facial.
3d Cerv. N. { Auricular.
4th Cerv. N. { Mastoid.
{ *Superficialis Colli*, has 2 branches.
{ *Communicating* to { Vagus.
{ Hypoglossus.
{ Sympathetic.
} *Deep Brs.* { *Muscular*, to ant. rectus and rect. later.
{ *Communicans Hypoglossi N.* 2.
(See page 227.) { *Phrenic Nerve*, to the diaphragm.
{ *Muscular* 4, to Sterno-mastoid, etc.
{ *Communicating*, to Spinal accessory.

THE SPINAL NERVES.

Plate II.

Cervical Plexus.

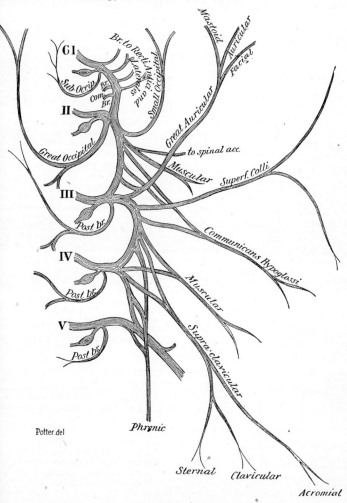

CI

Br. to Recti Antici
Laterales

Sub-Occip. Br.
Com. Br.

Mastoid

Auricular

facial

II

Small Occipital

Great Auricular

Great Occipital

to spinal acc.

Muscular   Superf. Colli

III

Post br.

Communicans Hypoglossi

IV

Post br.

Muscular

V

Post br.

Supra-clavicular

Potter.del

Phrenic

Sternal   Clavicular

Acromial

The Cervical Plexus { lies upon the { Scalenus Medius and Levator anguli Scapulae } Muscles.
is covered by the Sterno-Cleido-Mastoid Muscle.

THE BRACHIAL PLEXUS

(See page 228.)

Ant. Div. 5th Cervical Nerve.
Ant. Div. 6th Cervical Nerve. — UPPER PRIMARY CORD.
Ant. Div. 7th Cervical Nerve. — Brachial Plexus
Ant. Div. 8th Cervical Nerve. — LOWER PRIMARY CORD.
Ant. Div. 1st Thoracic Nerve.

OUTER or LATERAL CORD.

Above the Clavicle.

Communicating Br. to phrenic nerve.

Post. or *Long Thoracic,* the *Ext. Respiratory N.* of Bell. — to Serrat. mag.

Supra-scapular, to — Supra-spinatus. Infra-spinatus. Shoulder-joint.

Muscu-lar, to —
- Rhomboidei (5, 6, Cerv.)
- Subclavius (5, 6, Cerv.)
- Scaleni (6, 7, Cerv.)
- Long. colli (6, 7, Cerv.)
- Lev. ang. scap. (5, Cerv.)

Below Clavicle.

Br. to Post. Cord of Brachial Plexus.
External Ant. Thoracic, to Pect. major.

Musculo-cutaneous. (No. 2.) — Muscular. Anterior. Posterior. Articular.

Median Nerve (outer head) (No. 3).

POSTERIOR CORD.

1st *Subscapular,* to Subscap. M.
2d *Subscapular,* to Lat. dorsi.
3d *Scapular,* to Teres major.
Circumflex, to Deltoid and skin. (n. Axillaris.)

Musculo-spiral (No. 6). (n. Radialis.) — Muscular. Cutaneous. Radial. Post. Interosseous.

INNER or MEDIAL CORD.

Muscular, to —
- Scaleni (8, Cerv.)
- Long. colli (8 Cerv.)
- Above Clavicle.

Br. to Post. Cord of Brachial Plexus.
Int. Ant. Thoracic, to Pectoral muscles.
Internal Cutaneous (No. 8) (medial Anti-brachial cutaneous).
Lesser Int. Cutan. (*N. of Wrisberg*) (medial brachial cutaneous).
Median Nerve (inner head) (No. 3).
Ulnar Nerve (No. 10).

Note.—Nos. 1, 2, 3, etc., refer to the next two tables.

Plate 12

THE SPINAL NERVES

Brachial Plexus

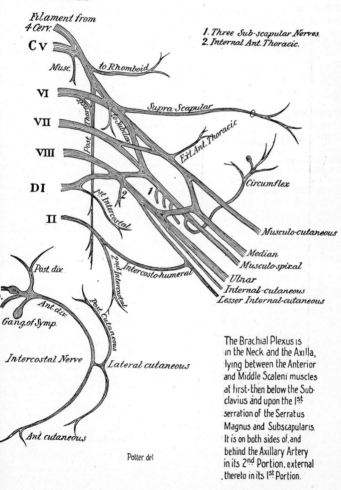

Filament from
4 Cerv.

C v

Musc.   to Rhomboid

VI

Supra-Scapular

VII

Post. Thoracic

VIII

to Subclav.

DI

1st Intercostal

II

2

1

Ext. Ant. Thoracic

Circumflex

Musculo-cutaneous

Median

Musculo-spiral

Ulnar

Internal-cutaneous

Lesser Internal-cutaneous

1. Three Sub-scapular Nerves.
2. Internal Ant. Thoracic.

2nd Intercosto-humeral

Post. dix.

Ant. dix.

Gang. of Symp.

O.

2nd Intercostal

Post. Cutaneous

Intercostal Nerve

Lateral cutaneous

Ant. cutaneous

Potter del

The Brachial Plexus is
in the Neck and the Axilla,
lying between the Anterior
and Middle Scaleni muscles
at first - then below the Subclavius and upon the 1st
serration of the Serratus
Magnus and Subscapularis.
It is on both sides of, and
behind the Axillary Artery
in its 2nd Portion, external
thereto in its 1st Portion.

17

257

NERVES OF THE UPPER EXTREMITY

Terminal Branches of the Brachial Plexus

Lateral or Outer Cord of the Brachial Plexus.

(1) External Anterior Thoracic, to Pectoralis major muscle.

(2) Musculo-Cutaneous.

- *Muscular*, to..
  - Coraco-brachialis.
  - Biceps.
  - Brachialis anticus.

- *Anterior Br.*
  - Skin of forearm (front).
  - Skin of ball of thumb.
  - Joins Radial Nerve.

- *Posterior Br.*
  - Skin of forearm (back).
  - Joins Radial Nerve.
  - Joins Ext. Cutan. Br. of Musculo spiral N.

- *Articular Br.*, to Elbow-joint.

(3) Median, from both outer and inner cords.

In Forearm.

- *Muscular*, to..
  - Pronator radii teres.
  - Flex. carpi radialis.
  - Palm. longus.
  - Flex. subl. digitorum.

- *Anterior Interosseous.*
  - to Flex. long. pollicis.
  - to Flex. prof. digit. (Ext. ½).
  - to Pronat. quadratus.

- *Palmar Cutaneous.*
  - Skin of palm.
  - Skin of ball of thumb.

In the Hand.

- *External Br...*
  - to Abduct. pollicis.
  - to Opponens pollicis.
  - to Flex. brev. pollicis.
  - *Digital*, to thumb.
  - *Digital*, to 1st finger.

- *Internal Br...*
  - *Digital*, to contiguous sides of in dex, middle and ring fingers.
  - *Filaments*, to two outer Lum bricales.

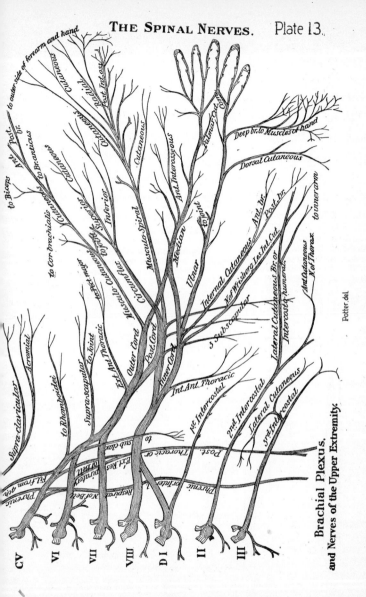

to outer side of forearm and hand

Cutaneous

Post Int oss

Radial

Cutaneous

Cutaneous

Ant Post. br.

Cutaneous

to Biceps

to Cor brachialis

to Brachialis

Musculo-Cutaneous

Superior

Inferior

Cutaneous

Ant. Interosseous

Flexor Prof. Dig. Cord

Deep br. to Muscles of hand

Dorsal Cutaneous

Musculo-Spiral

Median

to Joint

Ulnar

Internal Cutaneous

Ant. Br.

Post. br.

N of Wrisberg Les Int Cut.

to upper arm

Lateral Cutaneous Br. or Intercosto-humeral

Ant.Cutaneous N of Thorax

Potter. del.

Supra clavicular

Acromial

to Rhomboidei

Supra-scapular

to Joint

Ext Ant Thoracic

Infra Cutaneous to Joint

Act. maj.

Outer Cord

Post.Cord

Circumflex

Inner Cord

3 Subscapular

Int.Ant.Thoracic

1st Intercostal

2nd Intercostal

Lateral Cutaneous

3rd Intercostal

Fil. from 4th

Phrenic

Respiratory N of Bell

Post. Duration or

Ext Res.

to sub-clav.

Thoracic or

Phrenic

Long Posterior or

Respiratory N of Bell

Fil. from 4th

CV

VI

VII

VIII

DI

II

III

**Brachial Plexus,
and Nerves of the Upper Extremity.**

NERVES OF THE UPPER EXTREMITY.—Continued.

Posterior Cord of the Brachial Plexus.

(4) SUBSCAPULAR 3
- 1st, *Upper*, to Subscapular muscle.
- 2d, *Long*, to Latiss. dorsi.
- 3d, *Lower*, to Teres major.

(5) CIRCUMFLEX (n. Axillaris).
- *Superior Br.*..to
  - Deltoid.
  - Skin of shoulder.
- *Inferior Br.*..to
  - Teres minor.
  - Deltoid (posteriorly).
  - Skin of shoulder.

(6) MUSCULO-SPIRAL (n. Radialis).
- *Muscular*...to
  - Triceps, Anconeus.
  - Brach. anticus.
  - Supin. longus.
  - Extensor carpi long.
- *Cutaneous*, to skin of arm.
- *Radial*,
  - *External Br.* to skin of thumb.
  - *Internal Br.* to ulnar side of thumb and adjacent sides of 2½ fingers.
- *Posterior Interosseous.*
  - to all muscles on back of forearm, except Anconeus, Sup. long. and Extensor carpi longior.
  - Filaments to wrist-joints.

Medial or Inner Cord of the Brachial Plexus.

(7) INTERNAL ANTERIOR THORACIC, to both Pectoral muscles.

(8) INTERNAL CUTANEOUS (med. Ant. Brach. Cuta.)
- *Anterior Br.* to skin of forearm, inner side.
- *Posterior Br.* to skin of forearm, inner side.

(9) LESSER INTERNAL CUTANEOUS. (N. of Wrisberg.) (medial Brach. Cutan.)
- Is often wanting, Intercosto-humeral taking its place, to post. surface of lower ⅓ of skin of arm.

(10) ULNAR

In Forearm.
- *Articular*, ...to Elbow-joint.
- *Muscular*,.... to
  - Flex. carp. ulnaris.
  - Flex. prof. dig. (inner ½).
- *Cutaneous*, to skin of front wrist, and palm of hand.
- *Dorsal Cutaneous*, to skin of back wrist, and 1½ fingers.
- *Articular*,.... to Wrist-joint.

In Hand.
- *Superficial Palmar*, ... to
  - Palmaris brevis.
  - Skin of 1½ fingers.
- *Deep Palmar*,..to
  - Muscles of little finger. Interossei.
  - 2 inner Lumbricales.
  - Adduc. pollicis.
  - Flex. brev. poll. (inner head).

THE THORACIC NERVES

N. B.—Read from the Black Types outwards to left and right

ansv. colli.
ngis. dorsi.
achelo-mast.   } *Ext. Brs.*
vat. costar.   ← to
cro-lumbal.
cessorius.

mi-sp. dorsi.
ultif. Spinæ. } *Int. Brs.*
in of back.   ← to

Post. Div. { **Each of Upper 6 Thoracic Nerves.** } Ant. Div. *Thoracic Intercostals.*

Muscular. { Intercos. Tri. Ster.

Lateral Cutaneous. { Skin of Chest, Breast, Side, Back.

Anterior Cutaneous. { Skin of Chest, Breast.

---

me as above.
in of back.   } *Ext. Brs.*

me as above.
. br. of skin. } *Int. Brs.*

Post. Div. { **Each of Lower 6 Thoracic Nerves.** } Ant. Div. or *Thoracico-abdominal Intercostals.*

Muscular. { Intercos. Abdom. M.

Lateral Cutaneous. { Skin of Abdomen, etc.

Anterior Cutaneous. { Recti M. Skin of Abdomen.

12th Thoracic } Ant. Div. { Also sends a branch to the Lumbo-sacral Cord.

THE LUMBAR AND SACRAL NERVES

(See page 232)

(DISTRIBUTION SHOWN ON THE NEXT TWO TABLES)

An **External Branch**, sending filaments to the Erector spinæ and Intertransversales muscles, and the skin of the gluteal region, posteriorly.	The Posterior Division of each of these nerves has	1st Lumbar.	Ant. Div.	Nos. 1, 2, 3, *Comm. Br.* to 2d Lum.
		2d Lumbar.	Ant. Div.	Nos. 3, 4, 7, *Comm. Br.* to 3d Lum.
An **Internal Branch**, sending filaments to the Multifid. spinæ, and Interspinales, and the skin over spinal vertebræ.		3d Lumbar.	Ant. Div.	Part of 5, 6, 7, *Comm. Br.* to 4th Lum.
		4th Lumbar.	Ant. Div.	Part of 5, 6, 7, *Lumbo-Sacral Cord*
		5th Lumbar.	Ant. Div.	Joins the *Lumbo-Sacral Cord*
An **External Branch**, forming loop on sacrum and great Sac.-Sciat. lig. to supply skin over glutei.	The Posterior Division of each of these nerves has	1st Sacral.	Ant. Div.	Joins the *Lumbo-Sacral Cord* and 2d Sacral.
		2d Sacral.	Ant. Div.	Joins with 1st Sacral.
An **Internal Branch**, to Multifidus Spinæ and skin of the gluteal region; the lower nerve to Extensor Coccygis and skin over the coccyx.		3d Sacral.	Ant. Div.	Joins with 2d Sacral and part of the 4th.
		4th Sacral.	Ant. Div.	*Br.* to Plexus, Visc. Brs. Mus. Brs. Fil. to 5th.
Join together in loops over back of sacrum, sending filaments to skin over coccyx and **Extensor Coccygis.**		Post. Div.	5th Sacral. Ant. Div.	Br. to skin of coccyx. Br. to Coccygeus M. Br. to Cocc. Nerve.
		Post. Div.	Coccygeal. Ant. Div.	A delicate filament, going to sk over coccyx.

Lumbar Plexus.
Branches:
(1) *Ilio-hypogastric.*
(2) *Ilio-inguinal.*
(3) *Genito-crural.*
(4) *Ext. Cutaneous.*
(5) *Obturator.*
(6) *Accessory Obturato*
(7) *Anterior Crural.*

Sacral Plexus.
Branches:
(1) *Sup. Gluteal.*
(2) *Inf. Gluteal.*
(3) *Muscular.*
(4) *Articular.*
(5) *Small Sciatic.*
(6) *Pudic.*
(7) *Great Sciatic.*

Plate 14

THE SPINAL NERVES.
Lumbar & Sacral Plexuses.

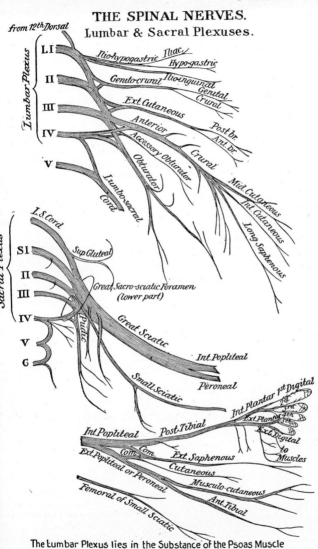

The Lumbar Plexus lies in the Substance of the Psoas Muscle

The Sacral Plexus { Lies upon the Pyriformis Muscle in the Pelvis and is covered by the Pelvic Fascia, and the Sciatic and Pudic Arteries.

Potter, del.

DISTRIBUTION OF THE BRANCHES

FROM THE 7 GREAT TRUNKS OF THE LUMBAR PLEXUS

(A CONTINUATION OF THE TABLE ON PAGE 261)

ILIO-HYPOGASTRIC,
from 1st Lumbar.
- *Iliac*, to skin of gluteal region.
- *Hypogastric*, to skin of that region.
- *Communicating Br.*, with 12th thoracic nerve.

ILIO-INGUINAL,
from 1st Lumbar.
- *Branch*, to ilio-hypogastric nerve.
- to Internal Oblique muscle.
- to skin of upper and inner thigh, scrotum.

GENITO-CRURAL,
or GENITO-FEMORAL
from 1st, 2nd Lumbar.
- *Genital*, to Cremaster, scrotum, round ligament.
- *Crural*, to skin of upper and front thigh.
- *Branch*, to femoral artery.

EXTERNAL CUTANEOUS,
from 2nd, 3d Lumbar.
- *Ant. Br.* to skin of ant. and outer thigh.
- *Post. Br.* to skin of post. and outer thigh.

OBTURATOR,
from 2d, 3d,
4th Lumbar.

Ant. Br.
- *Articular Brs.* to hip-joint.
- *Muscular Brs.* to Adductors, Gracilis and Pectineus.
- *Anastomotic Brs.* with Int. Cutan. and Int. Saphenous.

Post. Br.
- *Articular Brs.* to knee-joint.
- *Muscular Brs.* to Adduc. mag. and Obturator externus

ACCESSORY OBTURATOR,
from 3d, 4th Lumbar.
- *Muscular Br.* to Pectineus.
- *Articular Br.* to hip-joint.
- *Cutaneous Br.* to skin of thigh and leg.
} often absent.

ANTERIOR
FEMORAL or
CRURAL,
from 2d, 3d,
4th Lumbar.

- *Muscular Brs.* to Iliacus muscle.
- *Arterial*, to the femoral artery.
} within abdomen.

Ant. Div.
- *Mid. Cutaneous.* — to Sartorius, and skin of ant. thi as low as the knee.
- *Int. Cutaneous.* — *Ext. Br.* to skin, lateral of knee. *Post. Br.* to skin of inner thigh a leg.
- *Long Saphenous.* — to skin of knee and of front a inner leg and foot.

Post. Div.
- *Muscular Brs.* to the 4 parts of the Quadriceps Extens muscle.
- *Articular Brs.* 2, to capsules of knee- and hip-joints.

The Lumbar Plexus lies in the substance of the Psoas muscle, in front of the tra[n]sverse processes of the lumbar vertebræ.

Lumbar & Sacral Plexuses.

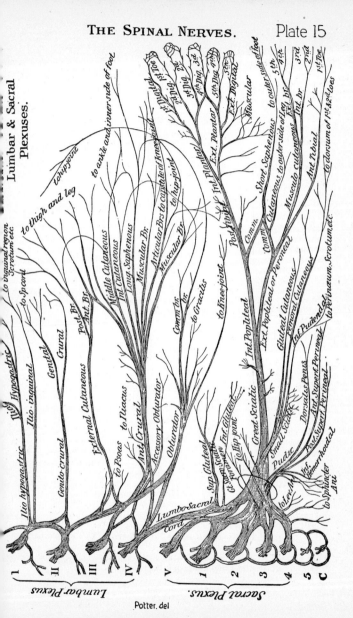

Potter. del

DISTRIBUTION OF THE BRANCHES OF THE SACRAL PLEXUS

[CONTINUATION OF TABLE ON PAGE 261]

SUPERIOR GLUTEAL,
from Lumbo-sacral cord.
- *Sup. Br.* to the Gluteus medius muscle.
- *Inf. Br.*
  - to the Gluteus medius and minimus.
  - to the Tensor vaginæ femoris.

INFERIOR GLUTEAL,..to the Gluteus maximus muscle.

MUSCULAR BRANCHES, to
- Pyriformis, Obturator internus, the two Gemelli, an the Quadratus femoris muscles.

ARTICULAR BRANCHES, to the hip-joint.

SMALL SCIATIC, or POSTERIOR FEMORAL CUTANEOUS, from 2d, 3d Sacral.
- *Gluteal Cutaneous*, to skin over Gluteus maximus.
- *Perineal Cutaneous,*
  - to skin of upper and inner thigh.
  - *Inf. Pudendal*, skin of scrotum.
- *Femoral Cutaneous,*
  - to back of thigh, popliteal space, an upper part of the leg.

PERFORATING CUTANEOUS, from 2d, 3d Sacral.
- to skin covering lower part of Gluteus maximus muscle: pass through the sacro-sciatic ligament.

PUDIC or PUDENDAL, from 3d, 4th Sacral.
- *Inferior Hemorrhoidal,*
  - to Sphincter ani muscle.
  - to skin of anal region.
- *Perineal,*
  - *Superficial Perineal,*
    - to Skin of anus, scrotu penis and labia, and th Sphincter ani muscle.
  - *Muscular*, to perineal muscles, and corpus spongi sum of penis.
- *Dorsal of Penis,*
  - Skin of dorsum of penis.
  - *Br.* to Corpora cavernosa.

GREAT SCIATIC (n. ischiadicus), from lumbo-sacral cord, 4 upper sacral.
- *Articular*,..to the hip-joint.
- *Muscular*, to
  - Adductus magnus, Biceps.
  - Semi-membranosus, Semi-tendinosus.
- *External Popliteal* or *Peroneal.* } terminal branches.
- *Internal Popliteal* or *Tibial Nerve.* } (*See next page.*)

The Sacral Plexus lies in the pelvis upon the Pyriformis muscle, and is cover by the Pelvic fascia, and the Sciatic and Pudic arteries.

NERVES OF THE LEG AND FOOT

[TERMINAL BRANCHES OF THE GREAT SCIATIC NERVE]

INTERNAL POPLITEAL or TIBIAL NERVE.

Articular 3, to knee-joint.

Muscular, to Gastrocnemius, Plantaris, Soleus, and Popliteus.

Communicans Tibialis, to form the Ext. Saphenous nerve.

External or *Short Saphenous*, { formed by a filament from each of the Popliteal nerves, to skin of outer side of the foot and little toe.

Continues as the— POSTERIOR TIBIAL.

Muscular, to { Flexor longus pollicis. Flexor longus digitorum. Tibialis posticus. Soleus.

Calcaneo-Plantar, to skin of heel and sole of the foot.

Articular, to the ankle-joint.

Internal Plantar. { *Digital*, to skin, 3½ inner toes. *Muscular*, to flexors, etc. *Articular*, to tarsal joints. *Cutaneous*, to sole of foot.

External Plantar. { *Muscular*, to Flexor accessorius. *Superficial*, { to 1½ outer toes. Flexor brevis min. digiti. 4th Interosseous. *Deep Br.* to the { 3d and 4th Lumbricales. rest of Interossei.

EXTERNAL POPLITEAL or COMMON PERONEAL NERVE.

Articular 3, distributed to the knee-joint.

Cutaneous 2, to skin of leg, exteriorly and posteriorly.

Communicans Peronei, to form the Ext. Saphenous nerve.

Anterior Tibial or Deep Peroneal { *Muscular*, to { front muscles of leg. Peroneus tertius. *External Br.* { Extensor brevis digitorum. Tarsal articulations. *Internal Br.* to skin of sides of great and 2nd toes.

Musculo-cutaneous or Superficial Peroneal. { *External Br.* { Peroneus longus and brevis muscles. Skin, outer side of foot and ankle. Skin, contig. sides, 3d, 4th, 5th toes. *Internal Br.* { Skin, inner side of foot and ankle. Skin, contig. sides, 2d and 3d toes and inner side of great toe.

THE SYMPATHETIC SYSTEM

Begins in the—	**Ganglion of Ribes.**	on the Anterior Communicating artery, at the base of the brain.

External Branches to join the 1st, 2d, 3d, 4th Cervical Nerves.	**Superior Cervical Ganglion.**	*Sup. Brs.*	*Some* to Pneumogastric, Glossopharyngeal, and Hypoglossal Nerves. *Ascend. Br.* { *Ext. Br.* forms Carotid Plexus. / *Int. Br.* forms Cavernous Plex. along Int. Carotid Artery. *Anterior Branches*, to Plexus on Ext. Carotid Artery.
		Int. Brs.	*Pharyngeal*, to Pharyngeal Plexus. *Superior Cardiac Nerve*, to Cardiac Plexus; goes to Deep Pl. on right side, to Superficial Pl. left side of body.

Ext. Brs. to 5th and 6th Cerv. N.	**Middle Cervical Ganglion.**	*Int. Brs.*	*Filaments* along Inf. Thyroid Art. to Thyroid body and Larynx. *Mid. Cardiac Nerve*, to Deep Cardiac Plexus.

Ext. Brs. to 7th and 8th Cerv. N.	**Inferior Cervical Ganglion.**	*Int. Brs.*	*Filaments* along Vertebral Art. to cranium. *Inf. Cardiac Nerve*, to Deep Cardiac Plexus.

Ext. Brs. to *Thoracic* N.	**12 Thoracic Ganglia.**	*Int. Brs.*	Upper 5 or 6 to Aorta and Vertebral column. 3d and 4th to Post. Pulmonary Plexus. Lower 6 form the 3 Splanchnic Nerves, thus— 6-10, *Great Splanchnic*, to Semi-lunar Gang. 10, 11, *Lesser Splanchnic*, to Cœliac Plexus. 12, *Smaller Splanchnic*, to Renal and Solar Plexuses.

Ext. Brs. to Lumbar N.	**4 Lumbar Ganglia.**	*Int. Brs.*	Some to Aortic Plexus. Some to Hypogastric Plexus.

Ext. Brs. to Sacral N.	**4 or 5 Sacral Ganglia.**	*Int. Brs.*	to Pelvic Plexus. to Plexus on Middle Sacral Artery.

Ends in the—	**Coccygeal G., or Ganglion Impar.**	In which ends the double chain of gangliated cords enumerated above, and called THE SYMPATHETIC NERVE

[FOR THE VARIOUS CONNECTED GANGLIA, ETC., SEE PAGES 223 TO 227.]

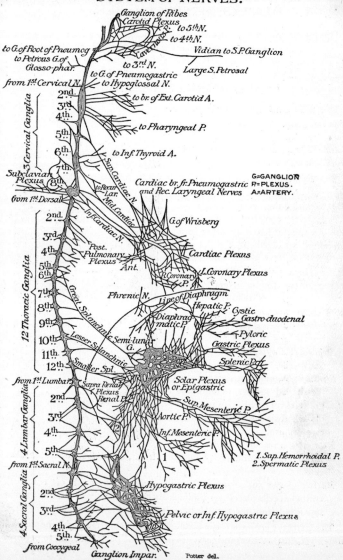

Ganglion of Ribes
Carotid Plexus
to 5th N.
to 4th N.
Vidian to S.P. Ganglion
to G. of Root of Pneumog.
to Petrous G. of
Glosso-phar.
to 3rd N.
Large S. Petrosal
to G. of Pneumogastric
from 1st Cervical N.
to Hypoglossal N.
2nd.
to br. of Ext. Carotid A.
3rd Cervical Ganglia
3rd.
4th.
to Pharyngeal P.
5th.
6th.
to Inf. Thyroid A.
7th.
Subclavian
Plexus
8th.
Sup. Cardiac N.
from 1st Dorsal
to Recur.
Lar.
Cardiac br. fr. Pneumogastric
and Rec. Laryngeal Nerves
G=GANGLION
P=PLEXUS.
A=ARTERY.
2nd.
Mid. Cardiac
Inf. Cardiac N.
G. of Wrisberg
3rd.
4th.
Post.
Pulmonary
Plexus
Ant.
Cardiac Plexus
5th.
6th.
R. Coronary
P.
L. Coronary Plexus
12 Thoracic Ganglia
7th.
Great Splanchnic
Phrenic N.
Line of Diaphragm
8th.
Hepatic P.
Cystic.
9th.
Diaphrag-
matic P.
Gastro-duodenal
Semi-lunar
G.
Pyloric
10th.
Lesser Splanchnic
Gastric Plexus
11th.
Smaller Spl.
Splenic P.
12th.
from 1st Lumbar
Supra Renal
Plexus
Renal P.
Solar Plexus
or Epigastric
4 Lumbar Ganglia
2nd.
Sup. Mesenteric P.
3rd.
Aortic P.
4th.
Inf. Mesenteric P.
5th.
1
1. Sup. Hemorrhoidal P.
2. Spermatic Plexus
from 1st Sacral N.
4 Sacral Ganglia
2nd.
Hypogastric Plexus
3rd.
Pelvic or Inf. Hypogastric Plexus
4th.
5th.
from Coccygeal
Ganglion Impar.
Potter del.

ORGANS OF SPECIAL SENSE

The Special Senses are those of touch, taste, smell, sight and hearing. The Skin is the principal seat of the sense of touch, the Tongue is the organ of taste, the Nose is the peripheral organ of smell, the Eye of sight and the Ear of hearing.

THE SKIN AND ITS APPENDAGES

The Skin consists of—the *Epidermis* or *Cuticle*, the scarf-skin, composed of 3 superficial and 2 deep layers; and the *Derma*, *Corium*, or *Cutis Vera*, the true skin, composed of a papillary layer above and a reticular layer below.

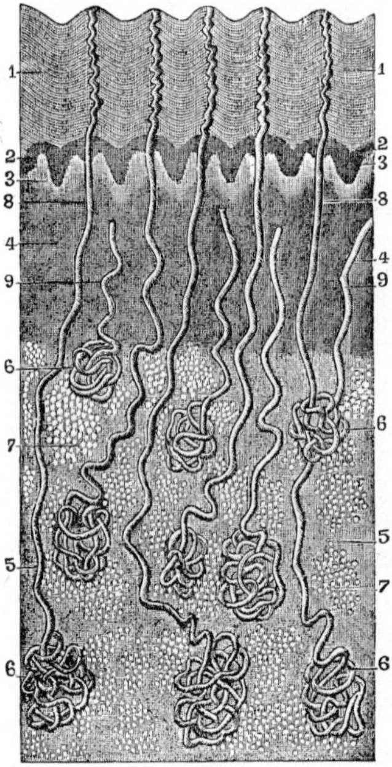

The Epidermis, *Cuticle* or *Scarf-skin*, is an unorganized epithelial structure, having neither vessels nor nerves. Its constituent epithelial cells are agglutinated together in a laminated arrangement, are flat and dry on the surface, round and softer in the central portion, columnar and softest in the deepest layers. They are arranged in the following layers, from above downward, viz.—

FIG. 81.

> *Stratum Corneum* (1),—horny epithelial cells, without nuclei.
>
> *Stratum Lucidum,*—closely packed, scaly cells.
>
> *Stratum Granulosum,*—flat, spindle-shaped cells, containing granules of *eleidin,* an intermediate substance in the formation of horn.
>
> *Rete Mucosum* or *Stratum Malpighii* (2),—contains pigment cells.
>
> *Basilar Layer* or *Stratum Germinativum,*—composed of columnar epithelial cells placed perpendicularly on the surface of the derma, and separated from the papillæ by a homogeneous basement membrane.

The Derma, *Corium* or *Cutis Vera* (4), the true skin, is a highly organized, tough yet elastic tissue, and serves to protect the parts beneath, to perform the functions of excretion and absorption, and as the chief seat of the sense of touch. It consists of felted connective tissue, elastic fibres, blood-vessels, lymphatics, and nerves; also unstriped muscular fibres in various situations. It is formed in two layers, as follows:—

Papillary Layer (3),—situated next to the epidermis, is covered with minute conical elevations (papillæ), $\frac{1}{100}$ inch high, $\frac{1}{250}$ inch in diameter at their base, very numerous and arranged in parallel curved lines wherever sensibility is greatest. Each papilla contains a capillary loop or plexus, the termination of one or more sensory nerves,—and in highly sensitive parts, an oval-shaped body, the *Tactile Corpuscle*, a special sensory nerve ending.

Reticular Layer,—the deep layer, is composed chiefly of interlacing bundles of white fibrous tissue, in which are mingled some yellow elastic fibres; also plain muscular fibres wherever hairs are found, and lymphatic vessels, blood-vessels, and nerves in plexiform arrangement. Below this the elements of the skin become blended with the subcutaneous tela or areolar tissue (5), which contains fat, except in a few situations.

Mucous Membrane is a soft, velvety structure, analogous to the skin, and found as the lining of the gastro-intestinal, pulmonary and genito-urinary tracts. It is composed of—*Epithelium* of various forms, including the squamous, columnar, and ciliated, often arranged in several layers; and *Corium*, analogous to the derma of the skin, consists of connective tissue, blood-vessels, lymphatics, nerves, and unstriped muscle cells; and is separated from the epithelium by a transparent basement membrane. The mucous membrane has numerous *glands* embedded in it, which secrete *mucus* to cover the surface for its protection from foreign substances. Projecting from it in certain parts are *villi* and *papillæ*, processes which are analogous to the papillæ of the skin.

Structures lying in the Skin, and directly beneath it, include the following, viz.—

Sensitive Papillæ, containing *Tactile Corpuscles* in very sensitive parts,—in the papillary layer of the derma.

Hair Follicles,—in the reticular layer of the derma, perforating the derma and the epidermis: sometimes extending into the subcutaneous tissue.

Sebaceous Glands (6),—in the reticular layer of the derma; their ducts (8, 9) opening usually into the hair-follicles, but occasionally on the surface of the epidermis.

Sudoriferous or *Sweat Glands*,—usually in the subcutaneous areolar tissue; their ducts perforating the derma and epidermis, to open on the surface of the latter.

Fat Cells,—in the subcutaneous areolar tissue.

Organs of Touch are the various sensory nerve-endings in the skin or its vicinity and in mucous membranes. They include minute, primitive *fibrillæ* or networks thereof, and certain special terminal organs, as follows:—

FIG. 82.

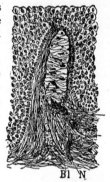

End-bulbs of Krause,—minute bodies, $\frac{1}{600}$ inch in diameter, consisting of a capsule surrounding a soft core, in which the axis-cylinder of the nerve terminates, in a bulbous expansion or in a coiled plexiform mass. They are found chiefly in mucous membranes, the genital organs, and the synovial membranes of the finger-joints.

Tactile Corpuscles,—are oval bodies, $\frac{1}{300}$ inch long, formed of connective tissue, and consisting of a capsule and imperfect septa, which penetrate the interior. The axis-cylinders of the nerve fibres (N) terminate within the corpuscle in a globular enlargement. They are found in papillæ of

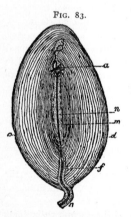

FIG. 83.

the derma of the hand, foot, forearm, lips, nipple, etc. Other tactile corpuscles, in the papillæ of parts devoid of hair, consist of a capsule, containing two or more granular cells, between which the nerve-fibre is supposed to terminate.

Pacinian Corpuscles,—are composed of lamellæ (*d*), consisting of connective tissue fibres, arranged concentrically around a central clear space (*m*), in which the nerve-fibre (*n*) terminates at the distal extremity in a rounded end (*a*), which is often bifid or even trifid. They are found chiefly on the nerves of the palm of the hand and the sole of the foot, the ends of the fingers, and the genital organs, lying in the subcutaneous tissue.

APPENDAGES OF THE SKIN

The Nails (Ungues) are curved, horny structures, a modification of the epidermis, molded upon the derma at the dorsal surface of the terminal

halanges of the fingers and toes. Each nail is convex on its outward
surface, and is embedded by its *Root* (radix unguis) into a fold of the skin.
ss—

Matrix,—is that portion of the derma directly beneath the nail. It is
covered with highly vascular papillæ. The—

Lunula,—is a white crescentic portion of the nail nearest to its root,
produced by the diminution in number and size of the papillæ beneath.

The Hairs (Pili) are also a modified form of the epidermis, found over
nearly the whole surface of the body, much varied in size and color. Each
hair consists of a Root and a Shaft. The—

Root (radix pili),—is lodged in an involution of the epidermis called the
Hair-follicle, which sometimes extends into the subcutaneous cellular
tissue. The root rests on a vascular papilla, at the bottom or *Bulb*
of the follicle, which supplies it with material for its growth.

Shaft (scapus pili),—is the projecting portion of the hair. It consists
of a medulla in the centre, next a fibrous portion, externally a cortex
of thin, flat scales. The finest hairs have no medulla.

Point (apex pili),—consists of the fibrous portion and the cortex, the
medulla being wanting.

Sebaceous Glands (Glandulæ Sebaceæ) are small, glandular bodies
situated in the corium over most of the body, but not in that of the palmar
surface of the hands nor on the plantar surface of the feet. Each gland
consists of a single sacculated duct, usually opening into a hair-follicle,
but sometimes ending on the surface of the epidermis. They are most
abundant in the scalp, the face, around the anus, and the apertures of the
nose, mouth and external ear. The largest are the—

Meibomian Glands,—situated in the eyelids.

Sudoriferous or **Sweat Glands** (Glandulæ Sudoriferæ) consist each of a
single convoluted tube, situated usually in the subcutaneous cellular
tissue, and opening on the surface of the integument by a spiral duct
which pierces the derma and the epidermis. The duct has two coats, an
external fibro-cellular, which is continuous with the corium, and an
epithelial lining, continuous with the epidermis. These glands are
estimated as varying, in different parts of the integument, from 417 to
3oo to the square inch, giving for the whole body a total number of nearly
two millions and a half, representing an evaporating surface of about 8
square inches. They are most numerous on the palm of the hand.

THE TONGUE (LINGUA)

The Tongue is the organ of taste. It is composed of striated muscle,
covered with mucous membrane, and is supplied with blood-vessels,

18

lymphatics and nerves. Its *base* (radix linguæ) is connected with the hyoid bone by the hyo-glossi and genio-hyo-glossi (mm. genioglossi) muscles and the hyo-glossal membrane; with the epiglottis, by the glosso-epiglottic folds of mucous membrane; with the soft palate, by the anterior pillars (arci glosso-palatini) of the fauces; and with the pharynx by the superior constrictor muscles and the mucous membrane. Its *tip* (apex linguæ), thin and narrow, is free in the mouth, and rests when quiet against the lower incisor teeth. Its *under surface* (facies inferior linguæ) is connected with the lower jaw by the genio-hyo-glossi (mm. genioglossi) muscles. Its mucous covering is reflected laterally on the inner surface of the gums, forming in front the *frænum linguæ* (frenulum linguæ), a vertical fold below the tip. The tongue presents the—

FIG. 84.

Raphê (sulcus medianus linguæ),—a vertical, fibrous septum, in the median line, dividing the tongue into two symmetrical halves, and terminating behind in a depression, the *foramen cæcum*, about an inch from the base of the organ.

Papillæ Vallatæ (1) (circumvallate),—8 to 12 in number, in two rows on the *dorsum* of the tongue, the rows forming a V and meeting in front of the *foramen cæcum*.

Papillæ Fungiformes (2) (lenticular),— scattered irregularly over the dorsum, chiefly at its sides and apex.

Papillæ Filiformes (conical),—cover the anterior two-thirds of the dorsum and have numerous filiform processes or secondary papillæ projecting from their apices.

Taste-buds,—flask-shaped bodies, found in the epidermis of the circumvallate papillæ, and in some of the fungiform (described below).

Glands of Blandin or *Nuhn*,—mucous glands, one on either side of the frænum, having 4 to 6 ducts which open on the under surface of the apex.

Racemose Serous Glands of Ebner,—at the back of the tongue, their ducts opening into the fossæ of the vallate papillæ.

Hyo-glossal Membrane,—a strong, fibrous lamina, connecting the under surface of the base of the tongue to the body of the hyoid bone.

Extrinsic Muscles of the Tongue,—are the stylo-, hyo-, chondro-, genio-hyo-, palato-glossi muscles, and part of the superior constrictors of the pharynx (pharyngeo-glossi). These have been described on page 82.

Intrinsic Muscles of the Tongue,—are the various fibres of the lingualis muscle,—superior, inferior, transverse and vertical. (See page 83.)

Taste-buds are flask-shaped bodies, situated in the epidermis (*e*) of the vallate and some of the fungiform papillæ; also found at the sides of the base of the tongue, on the epiglottis and the soft palate. Each bud has a broad base, which rests on the corium, and a neck opening on the mucous surface by an orifice, the *gustatory pore* (*o*). The buds are formed by *supporting cells*, mostly arranged like the staves of a cask; and spindle-shaped, nucleated *gustatory cells* in the central portion, each terminating at the gustatory pore in a fine filament, the *gustatory hair*. Terminal nerve-fibrils ramify between the gustatory cells, and others are found between the cortical cells.

FIG. 85.

Vessels of the Tongue. The *Arteries* are derived from the lingual, facial, and ascending pharyngeal, branches of the external carotid. The *Veins* open into the internal jugular. The *Lymphatics* of the posterior half of the tongue pass to one or two small glands on the hyo-glossus muscle, and thence to the deep glands of the neck; those of the anterior half are connected with the sub-mandibular lymphatics.

Nerves of the Tongue are as follows: the—

Lingual Branch of the Mandibular Division of the 5th,—to the papillæ of the fore part and sides of the tongue, endowing the anterior two-thirds of the organ with ordinary sensibility.

Chorda Tympani is the continuation of the glosso-palatine nerve (n. intermedius) or "pars intermedia," the sensory root of the facial,—it runs in the sheath of the lingual nerve and is distributed to the same region, being the nerve of taste for the anterior two-thirds of the tongue.

Lingual Branches of the 9th or Glosso-pharyngeal,—to the mucous membrane of the base and sides and the circumvallate papillæ, being the nerves of taste and ordinary sensation for the posterior third of the tongue.

Hypo-glossal or 12th Nerve,—the motor nerve of the tongue, distributed to the intrinsic and extrinsic muscles.

Superior Laryngeal Branch of the 10th or Vagus,—sends a few filaments, by way of its internal laryngeal branch, to the root of the tongue.

Sympathetic Filaments,—from the nervi molles on the lingual and other arteries supplying the organ (Spitzka).

Special Nerves of Taste in the Tongue, are the-

Chorda Tympani, the continuation of the sensory root (glosso-palatine nerve or n. intermedius) *of the Facial,*—for its anterior two-thirds; perceiving saline, acid and styptic qualities (Flint).

Lingual Branches of the Glosso-pharyngeal,—for its posterior third; appreciating alkaline, metallic, sweet and bitter tastes (Flint).

Sapolini's view of the Chorda Tympani Nerve. From repeated dissections, Dr. Sapolini, of Milan, believes the chorda tympani to be a separate cranial nerve, a continuation of the *pars intermedia* of Wrisberg (glosso-palatine nerve or n. intermedius) which has its deep origin in the upper end of the nucleus of the glosso-pharyngeal nerve in the floor of the 4th ventricle and the solitary or "trineural" tract in the medulla, joins the facial in the internal auditory meatus, and terminates in a dense plexus with the lingual branch of the 5th in the muscular substance of the tongue. He further concludes that the chorda tympani is the nerve governing the movements of the tongue in speech, and that the nerves of taste are the Lingual Branches of the 5th and 9th nerves.

THE NOSE (NASUS)

The Nose is the peripheral organ of smell, and consists of the outer nose (nasus externus) and the nasal fossæ (cavum nasi). The *Outer Nose* projects from the centre of the face, and is composed of a framework of bones and cartilages, covered by skin, lined by mucous membrane, and supplied with vessels and nerves. At its base it presents two elliptical orifices, the nostrils or *anterior nares,* separated by a septum, the *columna* (septum mobile nasi), and guarded at their margins by numerous stiff hairs, the *vibrissæ.* The—

Bony Framework,—is formed by the nasal bones and the nasal processes of the maxillæ (see page 27).

Cartilages (cartilagines nasi) are 5,—two upper lateral (cartilago nasi lateralis), two lower lateral (cartilago alaris nasi major), and the cartilage of the septum (cartilago septi nasi), connected together and to the bones by a tough, fibrous membrane, which permits of free movement between them.

Septum Nasi, the nasal septum,—is formed anteriorly by the cartilage of the septum, posteriorly by the perpendicular plate of the ethmoid bone above and the vomer below.

The Nasal Fossæ (cavum nasi) are two irregular cavities in the middle of the face, separated by the septum nasi, opening in front by the anterior nares, behind by the posterior nares (choanæ) into the naso-pharynx. Their osteological description has been given on page 37. Each fossa is divided into an *olfactory* portion (regio olfactoria), containing the upper part of the septum and the superior turbinal process and a *respiratory* portion (regio respiratoria), comprising the rest of the fossa. It is further divided, from above downward, into the superior, middle and

FIG. 86.

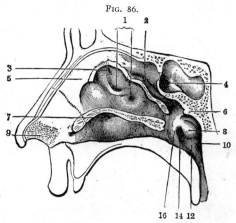

inferior *meatuses* of the nose, which are separated from each other by the middle (concha nasalis media) (2) and inferior turbinal (concha nasalis inferior) bones. Each fossa presents the—

Vestibule (9),—a slight dilatation inside the aperture of the nostril, extending as a small pouch, the *ventricle*, toward the point of the nose.

Spheno-ethmoidal Recess,—on the outer wall, above the superior turbinal process into which the sphenoidal sinus (4) opens.

Bulla Ethmoidalis,—an elevation on the outer wall of the middle meatus, on or above which are the orifices of the middle ethmoidal cells.

Hiatus Semilunaris,—a narrow groove in the outer wall, in front of the bulla ethmoidalis, into which open the anterior ethmoidal cells and the antrum (sinus maxillaris) of Highmore (1).

Infundibulum (3),—the superior prolongation of the middle meatus, leading into anterior ethmoidal cells and the frontal sinus (see page 38).

Atrium (atrium meatus medii nasi) (5),—a depressed area above the vestibule, forming the anterior extremity of the middle meatus.

Orifice of the Nasal Duct (ductus naso-lacrimalis) (7),—on the outer wall, in the anterior part of the inferior meatus.

Naso-palatine Recess,—a depression at the lower edge of the cartilage of the septum; near it a minute orifice leads into a blind pouch, the rudimentary *organ of Jacobson* (organon vomero-nasale).

The Schneiderian or **Pituitary Membrane** is the mucous membrane lining the nasal fossæ, thick and vascular over the septum and the turbinal processes, but very thin elsewhere. On it, in the upper portion of the fossæ, are distributed the terminal filaments of the *olfactory nerve*, the

FIG. 87.

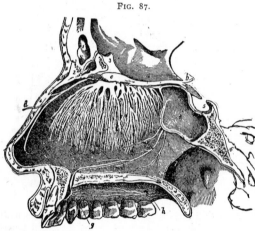

special nerve of the sense of smell. It is continuous with the mucous lining of the pharynx, Eustachian tube (tuba auditiva), tympanum and mastoid cells; also with that of the frontal, ethmoidal and sphenoidal sinuses, the maxillary antrum, nasal duct, and the conjunctiva. It is covered with columnar epithelium, which is ciliated throughout most of its extent, contains much adenoid tissue, is provided with mucous and serous glands, and in the olfactory region it contains the—

Olfactory Cells of Schultze,—spindle-shaped, epithelial cells, grouped around and between the columnar cells of the epithelium, having at one end hair-like processes, the *olfactory hairs*, and joined together by other processes, forming an intricate plexus on which the terminal fibres of the olfactory nerves are supposed to end.

Glands of Bowman,—are tubular, often branched, serous glands, in a layer beneath the epithelium, extending through the thickness of the mucous membrane, in the olfactory region.

Nerves supplying the *Outer Nose* are branches from the facial nerve to the muscles; branches from the infraorbital and infratrochlear, and the nasal branch of the ophthalmic, supplying the integument. Those supplying the *Nasal Fossæ* are the—

Olfactory or 1st Nerve (a),—over the upper third of the septum (i), the superior turbinal process and the surface of the ethmoid in front of it.

Nasal Branch of the Ophthalmic (d),—to the septum and outer walls.

Anterior Dental or Alveolar Branch of the Maxillary,—to the inferior meatus of the nose and the inferior turbinal bone.

Vidian Nerve (n. canalis pterygoidei),—to the septum and the inferior turbinal bone.

Naso-palatine (e),—from the spheno-palatine ganglion, to the middle of the septum; thence through the anterior palatine foramen (f).

Anterior Palatine (h),—from the spheno-palatine ganglion, to the middle and lower turbinal bones, by its inferior nasal branches.

Superior Nasal Branches,—from the spheno-palatine ganglion, to the septum and the superior and middle turbinal bones.

Arteries of the Nose. The arteries supplying the *Outer Nose* are— the lateralis nasi branch of the facial (a. maxillaris externa); the inferior artery of the septum, from the superior coronary branch of the facial (a. maxillaris externa); and the nasal branch of the ophthalmic and the infraorbital, which go to the dorsum and sides of the nose. The *Arteries of the Nasal Fossæ* form a close, plexiform network beneath and in the mucous membrane, and are the—

Ant. and Post. Ethmoidal, from the ophthalmic,—to the roof.

Spheno-palatine, branch of the internal maxillary,—to the mucous membrane over the turbinal bones, the meatuses, and the septum.

Infraorbital and *Alveolar,* branches of the internal maxillary,—to the mucous lining of the antrum.

Inferior Artery of the Septum, from the superior coronary branch of the facial (a. maxillaris externa),—to the mucous membrane of the septum.

Veins of the Nose. Those of the *outer nose* terminate in the facial and ophthalmic veins. Those of the *nasal fossæ* form a close, cavernous-like network beneath the mucous membrane, and terminate in the facial and ophthalmic veins, a few going to the veins in the interior of the skull.

THE EYE

[For an osteological description of the Orbit, see page 35.]

The Eyeball (bulbus oculi) is situated in the anterior part of the orbital cavity, on a cushion of connective tissue and fat, where it is retained by its muscles, the optic nerve, the conjunctiva, etc., and protected in front by the eyelids and eyebrows. It is composed of segments of two spheres of different sizes; the anterior segment being the smaller, forming about ⅙ of the eyeball, and named the *cornea;* the posterior and larger segment, is formed by the *sclerotic coat* (tunica fibrosa oculi), and constitutes the remaining ⅚ of the globe. It is surrounded by a thin, membranous sac, the *capsule* (fascia bulbi oculi) *of Tenon,* and has the following—

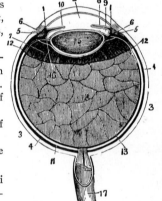

Fig. 88.

> *Diameters,*—in the adult, antero-posterior and transverse, nearly an inch, vertical about $\frac{9}{10}$ of an inch.
>
> *Anterior Pole,*—the central point of the anterior curvature.
>
> *Posterior Pole,*—the central point of the posterior curvature.
>
> *Sagittal Axis* (axis optica),—a line joining the two poles.

The Capsule of Tenon (fascia bulbi oculi) (3) is a thin membrane which envelops the eyeball from the optic nerve to the ciliary region, where it blends with the ocular conjunctiva. Its smooth, inner surface is in contact with the outer surface of the sclerotic coat (tunica fibrosa oculi), with which it is connected by delicate bands of connective tissue. Posteriorly it is continuous with the sheath (17) of the optic nerve, and from it tubular sheaths are prolonged over the muscles which move the eyeball, giving off slips to the bones of the orbit. The—

> *Check Ligaments,*—internal and external, are expansions from the sheaths of the internal and external recti muscles, and are attached to the lacrimal and malar bones respectively.

Suspensory Ligament of the Eye (Lockwood's),—is a thickening of the
  lower part of the capsule, slung like a hammock below the eyeball,
  and attached to the lacrimal and malar bones.
Peri-sclerotic Lymph-space,—intervenes between the capsule and the
  sclerotic, and is continuous with the subdural and subarachnoid
  spaces.

Tunics of the Eyeball are 3 in number, named from without inward as
follows: the—

Sclerotic (fibrosa) (3) and *Coronea* (1),—the external, fibrous, and
  protective tunic.
Choroid (choroidea) (4), *Ciliary Body* (corpus ciliare) (5), and *Iris* (8),
  —the vascular tunic, sometimes called the Uveal Tract.
Retina (tunica interna) (13),—the innermost, nervous tunic.

Refracting Media are 3 in number, and are named as follows: the—

Aqueous Humor (humor aqueus) (2), ⁓fills the anterior (2) and posterior
  (9) chambers (cameræ).
Vitreous Body (corpus vitreum) (18),—fills the concavity of the retina.
Crystalline Lens (lens crystallina) (15),—in front of the vitreous body.

THE SCLEROTIC AND CORNEA

The Sclerotic, or hard coat (tunica fibrosa oculi), is the posterior five-
sixths of the external tunic of the eyeball, the anterior one-sixth being the
Cornea. Externally it is of a white color, covered anteriorly by the
conjunctival mucous membrane, posteriorly being continuous with the
fibrous sheath of the optic nerve. Internally its color is brown, and its
surface marked by grooves for the ciliary nerves. The optic nerve pierces
it posteriorly, also the long and short ciliary arteries, posterior ciliary
veins and short ciliary nerves. In the equatorial region it is pierced
obliquely by the venæ vorticosæ, and around the corneal border by the
anterior ciliary arteries and veins. It is composed of white fibrous tissue,
intermixed with elastic fibres, and of flattened connective-tissue corpuscles,
some of which are pigmented. The Sclerotic presents for consideration
the following points:—

Thickness,—⅟₂₅ inch posteriorly, ⅟₆₀ inch anteriorly.
Lamina Fusca,—a layer of very fine pigmented connective tissue, connecting the sclerotic with the outer surface of the choroid.
Lamina Cribrosa (lamina cribrosa scleræ),—the posterior perforated
  portion of the sclerotic, which at this point is a thin, cribriform
  lamina. Its largest opening transmits the arteria centralis retinæ.

Arteries,—from the ciliary, are few and in a coarse network, the capillaries uniting at long and wide intervals.

Nerves,—from the ciliary, their mode of ending unknown.

The Cornea, or horny body, is the anterior transparent projecting portion of the external tunic of the eyeball, forming about one-sixth thereof. It is set into the sclerotic as a watch-crystal into its case, is of nearly circular base, and its curvature varies in degree in different persons, and in the same person at different ages, becoming flattened in advanced life. It consists of 4 layers,—centrally the true fibrous corneal tissue, having in front the conjunctival epithelium; behind, a homogeneous elastic lamina and the epithelial lining of the anterior chamber. The—

Conjunctival Epithelium,—consists of several layers of epithelial cells, the deepest being columnar, the central polyhedral with processes and the superficial scaly with flattened nuclei.

Proper Corneal Substance,—a transparent, firm, fibrous structure, continuous with the sclerotic, and composed of about 60 *lamellæ* of modified connective tissue, superimposed one on the other, and connected by a cement, in which are *spaces* of stellate shape, each containing a cell, the *corneal corpuscle.* The anterior layer of the corneal substance was called by Bowman the *anterior elastic lamina.*

Posterior Elastic Lamina, Membrane of Descemet, or Demours,—is a structureless basement membrane, of extreme thinness and transparency, the latter being unaffected by water, alcohol or acids; very brittle, exceedingly elastic, and curls up inwardly upon itself, when detached from the true cornea. At the corneal margin it breaks up into fibres, some of which are continuous with the ligamentum pectinatum of the iris.

Fontana's Spaces (spatia anguli iridis),—are small, cavernous spaces between the fibres which go to form the ligamentum pectinatum. In some animals, as the ox, they form regular canals. They communicate with the anterior chamber and with the—

Canal of Schlemm, or *Sinus Venosus Scleræ,*—a minute canal at the internal corneo-sclerotic junction, extending around the circumference of the attached border of the iris. It communicates with the anterior chamber through the spaces of Fontana, also with the scleral veins.

Posterior Endothelial Layer (endothelium cameræ anterioris),—a single layer of flattened, polygonal, transparent, nucleated cells, covers the posterior surface of the elastic lamina, lines the anterior chamber and the spaces of Fontana, and is reflected on to the front of the iris.

Vessels,—none, the capillary vessels terminating in loops at its circumference, so that it is practically a non-vascular structure.

Nerves,—are numerous; 24 to 36 twigs from the Ciliary nerves form an intricate plexus throughout its laminated substance.

THE CHOROID, CILIARY BODY AND IRIS

The Middle Tunic (Tunica Vasculosa Oculi) of the Eye is formed from behind forward by the Choroid, the Ciliary Body and the Iris; the former being the vascular and pigmented tunic; the latter a circular, muscular curtain or septum, with the *pupil,* an opening in its centre; while the ciliary body connects the choroid with the iris.

The Choroid is a thin, vascular membrane, of dark-brown or chocolate color, which invests the posterior ⅚ of the globe, extending from the optic nerve entrance behind to the ora serrata of the retina. It is loosely connected externally by the lamina fusca to the sclerotic, the space between being the *peri-choroidal lymph-space,* and is covered by a thin membrane, the *lamina superchoroidea,* containing spaces between its constituent lamellæ. Internally it is connected with the pigmentary layer of the retina by the *lamina basalis* or membrane of Bruch, a very thin, structureless membrane. The Choroid terminates anteriorly in the *ciliary processes* (see below), and is composed of 2 layers, as follows:—

Lamina Vasculosa, the external layer,—consists chiefly of the venæ vorticosæ, the larger branches of the short ciliary arteries, and dark pigment cells.

Lamina Chorio-capillaris or *Tunica Ruyschiana,* the internal layer,— consists of a very fine capillary plexus, formed by the short ciliary vessels.

Tapetum,—is the name applied to the iridescent appearance seen in the outer and posterior part of the choroid of many animals.

Arteries,—are the short ciliary and recurrent branches from the long and anterior ciliary arteries.

Veins (2),—unite into 4 or 5 trunks (4), which pass out through the sclerotic near its equator.

Nerves (3),—are derived from the 3d, 5th and sympathetic, through the long ciliary and the ciliary branches of the ophthalmic ganglion.

The Ciliary Body (corpus ciliare) (5), comprises the orbiculus ciliaris, (annulus ciliaris), the ciliary processes, and the ciliary muscle. It connects the choroid with the circumference of the iris. The—

Orbiculus Ciliaris (annulus ciliaris),—is a zone about ⅙ inch wide, directly continuous with the anterior part of the choroid.

Ciliary Processes,—are 60 to 80 folds, formed by the plaiting of the choroid and its lamina basalis at their anterior margin, and are received into corresponding folds of the suspensory ligament of the lens. They form a sort of plaited frill behind the iris, around the margin of the lens, and are similar in structure to the choroid.

Ciliary Muscle or *Muscle of Bowman* (m. ciliaris),—is a ring of un-striped muscular fibres on the outer surface of the anterior part of the choroid, and consists of radiating (fibræ meridianales) and cir-cular fibres (fibræ circulares). The former arise from the corneo-sclerotic junction and pass backward to the choroid in front of the

FIG. 89.

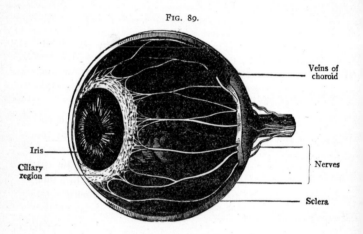

retina. The circular fibres are internal to the radiating ones, have a circular course around the attachment of the iris, and by drawing on the ciliary processes they relax the suspensory ligament of the lens, permitting the lens to become more convex by its own elasticity. It is supplied by the 3d nerve.

The Iris (6) is a perforated contractile curtain, suspended in the aqueous humor behind the cornea and in front of the lens, and is the anterior portion of the middle tunic of the eyeball, being continuous with the ciliary body and the choroid. It is about ⅙ inch wide, ¹⁄₁₀₀ inch thick, and is composed of radiating and circular muscular fibres, a fibrous stroma and pigment cells, covered by a layer of endothelial cells continuous with those of the posterior elastic lamina of the cornea. The—

Pupil (pupilla),—is the central opening in the iris, situated a little to the nasal side of the centre, diameter $\frac{1}{12}$ to $\frac{1}{4}$ inch.

Ligamentum Pectinatum Iridis, or Dollinger's band,—is the suspensory ligament of the iris, connecting its ciliary margin with the posterior elastic lamina of the cornea.

Pars Iridica Retinæ or *Uvea*,—pigmented epithelium of deep purple color, on the posterior surface of the iris.

Sphincter Pupillæ,—a layer of circular muscular fibres around the pupillary margin, supplied by the 3d nerve.

Dilator Pupillæ,—radiating muscular fibres from the pupillary margin toward the ciliary border, supplied by fibres of the sympathetic from the ciliary ganglion.

Membrana Pupillaris,—a vascular membrane which covers the pupil in the fœtus, disappearing about the eighth month, occasionally permanent.

Arteries,—are derived from the long and anterior ciliary, forming the *circulus major* at the ciliary border, and the *circulus minor* near the pupillary margin.

Veins,—empty into those of the ciliary processes and the anterior ciliary veins.

Nerves of the Iris,—are derived from the 3d, 5th and the sympathetic, through the long and short ciliary nerves. The 3d supplies the circular fibres, the sympathetic the radiating ones, the 5th being nerves of common sensation.

THE RETINA (TUNICA INTERNA)

The Retina, the innermost or nervous tunic of the eye, is a delicate, grayish, transparent membrane, about $\frac{1}{75}$ of an inch thick at the fundus, $\frac{1}{200}$ inch at the anterior margin. It is formed by a membranous expansion of the optic nerve elements, and extends from the termination of that nerve nearly as far forward as the ciliary processes, terminating in a ragged margin, the *ora serrata*, though its fibrous stroma is continued as the *pars ciliaris retinæ* over the ciliary body. The Retina presents for examination the following points:—

Macula Lutea, or Yellow Spot,—situated on the retina, exactly in the visual axis; in an elevated oval spot where vision is very acute, the retina being very thin and full of nerve elements closely packed together at the expense of its connective tissue. No rods, no nerve-fibre layer here, but the cones and ganglion-cells are very numerous.

Fovea Centralis,—a depression at the centre of the macula lutea, $\frac{1}{125}$ to $\frac{1}{60}$ inch in diameter, in which the sense of vision is most acute.

Porus Opticus or *Optic Disk*,—the point where the optic nerve enters, lies about ⅛ inch internal to the yellow spot. It is often called the *blind spot*, being the only part of the fundus from which the power of vision is absent.

Colliculus Nervi Optici or *Optic Papilla*,—is a slight eminence of the nervous substance at the porus opticus; the central artery of the retina pierces its centre which is depressed slightly, forming the Optic Cup (excavatio papillæ nervi optici).

Pars Ciliaris Retinæ,—is that portion of the retinal stroma which is prolonged over the ciliary body, and continued over the back of the iris as the *pars iridica retinæ*. It is destitute of nerve-elements.

Arteries of the Retina,—arise from the arteria centralis retinæ (branch of the ophthalmic artery), just behind the porus opticus; run chiefly upward and downward, accompanied by veins, to terminate in a minute capillary plexus. They do not anastomose with each other, being terminal arteries. No vessels exist in the fovea centralis, and only the finest capillaries in the macula lutea.

Structure of the Retina. The retina is composed of nervous elements, blood-vessels, pigmented epithelium, and modified connective tissue resembling the neuroglia of the brain; the latter being called the *radiating fibres* or *fibres of Müller*, which form the two limiting membranes and stretch between them, passing through all the nervous layers except Jacob's membrane. The structures are arranged in 10 layers, as follows:—

Membrana Limitans Interna,—derived from the supporting frame-work and shown in the cut by the lowest line.

Layer of Nerve-fibres (stratum opticum) (1),—formed by the expansion of the optic nerve, the fibres of which, as simple axis-cylinders, pass through all the succeeding layers of the retina.

Ganglionic Layer (2),—a single layer of large ganglion-cells, which give off their axons into the preceding layer and their dendrites into the inner molecular layer.

Inner Plexiform Layer (3),—is made up of a dense reticulum of minute fibrils, formed by the interlacement of the dendrites of the ganglion-cells with those of the cells of the next layer.

Inner Nuclear or *Granular Layer* (4),—consists of closely packed cells of 3 kinds, bipolar, amacrine, and cells connected with the fibres of Müller.

Outer Plexiform Layer (5),—a dense network of minute fibrils derived from the processes of the cells in the adjoining layers.

Outer Nuclear or *Granular Layer* (6),—contains several strata of oval nuclear bodies, named rod-granules and cone-granules, which are

respectively continuous with the rods and cones of Jacob's membrane.
Membrana Limitans Externa,—derived from the supporting framework of the retina, is shown in the cut by a horizontal line between
layers 6 and 7.

Jacob's Membrane, or *Layer of Rods and Cones* (7),—the perceptive

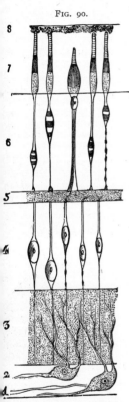

FIG. 90.

portion of the retina, is composed of a
palisade-like arrangement of rods and
cones, the terminal organs probably
of the optic nerve fibres.

Pigmentary Layer, or *Tapetum Nigrum*
(8),—formerly described as a part of
the choroid, consists of a single layer
of hexagonal epithelial cells, loaded
with pigment-granules. It extends
with the retinal stroma as the *pars
ciliaris retinæ,* (see page 285), beyond
the ora serrata, where the nervous
layers terminate.

REFRACTING MEDIA

The Aqueous Humor (humor aqueus) is
a clear, alkaline, serous fluid, composed of
water 96.7, albumen 0.1, chloride of sodium
and extractive matters 3.2, weighing 4 to 5
grains, and filling the anterior (camera oculi
anterior) and posterior aqueous chambers
(camera oculi posterior) which communicate
with each other when the pupil is dilated
sufficiently to remove the pupillary margin
of the iris from the surface of the lens.
The—

Anterior Chamber (camera oculi anterior)
of the Eyeball,—has the cornea in front
and the iris behind. The peripheral
angle of this chamber is called the Fil-
tration Angle (angulus iridis).

Posterior Chamber (camera oculi posterior) *of the Eyeball,*—is a narrow
chink between the peripheral part of the iris, the suspensory ligament
of the lens, and the ciliary processes.

The Vitreous Body (corpus vitreum) is a transparent jelly-like substance, composed of an albuminous fluid enclosed in a delicate membrane,

also transparent and named the *hyaloid membrane* (membrana hyaloidea).
It is apparently structureless, has neither vessels nor nerves, and is situated
in the concavity of the retina, which it fills, forming about ⅘ of the entire
globe.　Running antero-posteriorly in its centre is a canal, filled with fluid
and lined by a prolongation of the hyaloid membrane, called the—

　　Canal of Stilling (canalis hyaloideus),—which in the fœtus conveyed the
　　　　hyaloid artery to the membrana pupillaris.　It extends from the
　　　　entrance of the optic nerve, forwards directly through the centre
　　　　of the vitreous humor to the back of the crystalline lens.

　　Fossa Patellaris,—is a deep concavity on the front of the vitreous, for
　　　　the posterior convex surface of the lens.

　　Hyaloid Membrane,—is the delicate capsule which encloses the vitreous
　　　　humor, and has been supposed to give off delicate septa into its sub-
　　　　stance.　In front of the ora serrata it is thickened and is termed the—

　　Zonula Ciliaris or *Zonule of Zinn,*—presents a series of furrows, radially
　　　　arranged, for the reception of the ciliary processes.　It splits into
　　　　layers, one of which lines the fossa patellaris, the other is the—

　　Suspensory Ligament of the Lens,—passes over the ciliary body to be
　　　　attached to the capsule of the lens.

　　Canal of Petit (spatia zonularia),—a sacculated canal, behind the
　　　　suspensory ligament, encircles the equator of the lens, and lies
　　　　between the two layers into which the zonule of Zinn is split.

The Crystalline Lens (lens crystallina) is a bi-convex, elastic, transparent body, enclosed in a capsule, held in place by a suspensory ligament,
and situated immediately behind the pupil
and in front of the vitreous body, in the fossa
patellaris of which its posterior and most convex surface rests.　The ciliary processes encircle it and slightly overlap its margin.　It
consists of concentric layers formed of minute
parallel fibres, which are hexagonal prisms with
dentated edges fitting accurately into each
other.　Faint lines, six or more in number,
radiate from the anterior and posterior poles
to the circumference and correspond to the free edges of septa in the
lens.　The external layers are soft, the deeper are firmer, and the central
ones form a hard nucleus, the *nucleus lentis*.　The lens is unorganized,
having neither vessels nor nerves, but is nourished by imbibition from
neighboring structures, possibly from the aqueous humor.　Its—

FIG. 91.

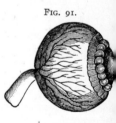

　　Capsule (capsula lentis),—is transparent, elastic, ½₀₀₀ inch thick
　　　　anteriorly, ⅙₀₀₀ inch posteriorly; has a layer of flat cells between its

anterior portion and the lens, which, after death, break down into a fluid, the *liquor morgagni.*

Suspensory Ligament,—connects the capsule with the ciliary body, and is the anterior of the two layers formed by the splitting of the zonule of Zinn (zonula ciliaris) (see p. 287). It is shown exaggerated in the cut.

Canal of Petit, (spatia zonularia),—is a triangular space around the circumference of the lens, formed by the separation of the two portions of the zonule of Zinn (zonula ciliaris) (shown inflated in the cut).

MUSCLES AND NERVES OF THE EYEBALL

Muscles of the Eyeball, are 6 in number, 4 Recti and 2 Oblique, which are inserted into the sclerotic coat (tunica fibrosa), just behind the margin of the cornea. The insertions of the superior, inferior, internal and external recti correspond to the ends of the four arms of an equal-armed cross, imagined to exist behind the corneo-sclerotic junction. The insertion of the superior oblique (14) lies between the insertions of the superior and external rect, that of the inferior oblique (13) somewhat behind the insertion of the superior oblique. These muscles are described on page 76. The tendon of the superior oblique passes through a pulley or *trochlea* on the internal angular process of the frontal bone, before being inserted into the eyeball: (see Fig. 92).

FIG. 92.

Nerves supplying the muscles of the eyeball are the 3d, 4th and 6th cranial nerves; the 3d supplies the superior, inferior and internal recti and the inferior oblique, the 4th supplies the superior oblique, and the 6th supplies the external rectus.

VESSELS OF THE EYE

Arteries supplying the eye and its appendages are,—the Ophthalmic and Anterior Cerebral branches of the internal carotid artery; and the Infra-orbital branch of the internal maxillary, from the external carotid. The *Ophthalmic Artery* arises from the cavernous portion of the internal carotid, enters the optic foramen to the orbit, and gives off the following branches to the eye and its appendages:—

Arteria Centralis Retinæ (2),—pierces the optic nerve (1) obliquely, and is distributed to the retina.

Muscular Branches, 2,—superior and inferior, supply the muscles of the eyeball, and give off the anterior ciliary (see below).

19

Lacrimal,—to the lacrimal gland, the eyelids, and the conjunctiva anastomosing with the palpebral.

Supra-orbital,—supplies the superior rectus and levator palpebræ muscles.

Internal Palpebral (aa. palpebrales mediales),—superior and inferior —to the eyelids.

Nasal, (a. dorsalis nasi),—to the lacrimal sac, and the nose.

Short Ciliary (aa. ciliares posteriores breves), 6 to 12,—pierce the sclerotic at the lamina cribrosa, supplying the choroid and the ciliary processes.

Long Ciliary (aa. ciliares posteriores longæ), 2,—pierce the sclerotic, and pass forward between it and the choroid, to supply the iris, forming two arterial circles thereon, the circulus major at the ciliary border and the circulus minor near the pupillary margin.

Anterior Ciliary (aa. ciliares anteriores) (3),—arise from the muscular branches, form a zone beneath the conjunctiva, then pierce the sclerotic, and join the circulus major on the iris.

Anterior Cerebral, branch of the Internal Carotid,—sends nutrient capillaries to the optic nerve.

Infra-orbital, branch of the Internal Maxillary artery,—sends branches to the inferior rectus and inferior oblique muscles, and to the lacrimal gland.

Veins of the Eye are collected into two main trunks, the *Superior* and *Inferior Ophthalmic Veins,* which empty into the cavernous sinus, after collecting the blood from the smaller venous channels through the *Venæ Vorticosæ* of the choroid. The veins of the eye anastomose freely with the facial veins, thus permitting the escape of venous blood in either direction.

Lymph-spaces of the Eye. The principal lymph-spaces found in the eyeball and its connected structures are the—

Canal of Schlemm (sinus venosus scleræ),—around the circumference of the iris.

Peri-choroidal Space,—between the choroid and the sclerotic (tunica fibrosa).

Peri-sclerotic Space,—between the sclerotic (tunica fibrosa) and the capsule of Tenon (fascia bulbi), is continuous with the subdural and subarachnoid spaces.

Vaginal Spaces,—have been described as existing between the sheaths of the optic nerve.

NERVES OF THE EYE

Nerves of the Eye. Besides the 3d, 4th and 6th nerves, already mentioned as supplying the muscles of the eyeball, the eye is supplied with common *sensation* by branches from the ophthalmic division of the 5th and the ophthalmic ganglion, also *motor* filaments from the 5th, and its special *sense* of sight, from the 2d or optic nerve.   The—

Sympathetic Branches,—arise from the medulla, and the cavernous and carotid plexuses, and join the 3d, 4th, 5th, and 6th nerves, sending filaments to the dilator fibres of the iris, to the muscles of the orbit and lids, to the ophthalmic ganglion, and to the walls of the arteries.

Short Ciliary,—some 6 to 10 in number, arise from the ophthalmic ganglion (see page 224), pierce the sclerotic and go to the ciliary muscle, iris, cornea, and to the sheath of the optic nerve.

Ascending,—from Meckel's (spheno-palatine) ganglion (see page 224), enter the orbit by the spheno-maxillary fissure, going to the optic nerve, the 6th nerve, and the ciliary ganglion.

FIG. 93.

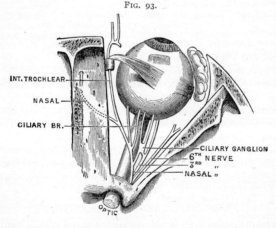

The Optic Nerve, 2d Cranial (Plate 6, page 244), begins at the anterior part of the optic commissure, passes into the orbit by the optic foramen in company with the ophthalmic artery, is pierced by the central artery of the retina, and enters the eyeball posteriorly ⅛ inch inwardly from its axis, piercing the sclerotic (tunic fibrosa) and choroid coats, and finally expanding in the retina.   It is surrounded by a tubular process of dura mater, which as the nerve enters the orbit, subdivides to form both the sheath of the nerve and the periosteum of the orbit.   The two nerves are connected together at the commissure, from the back of which most of their fibres may be traced through the *optic tracts* to the lower visual centres of the brain, viz.—the external (lateral) geniculate body, the upper quadrigeminal body, (colliculus superior), and the pulvinar of the optic thalamus.

The Optic Commissure or **Chiasma** (Plate 6, page 244), is seen at the base of the brain in front of the tuber cinereum and behind the lamina cinerea. It contains four sets of fibres, one of which decussates in the commissure with its fellow set of the opposite side. The four sets of fibres are arranged in the following manner:—

    Crossed or *Decussating Fibres* (1),—are the most numerous; lying in the centre of the commissure, they pass from the optic tract of one side to the optic nerve of the other side, connecting the retina of each eye with the opposite hemisphere of the brain.

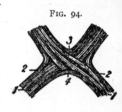

FIG. 94.

    Uncrossed or *Longitudinal Fibres* (2),—occupy the outer sides of the commissure and tracts, passing from the tracts to the nerves of the same sides, and connecting the temporal side of each retina with the cerebral hemisphere of its own side.

    Inter-retinal Fibres (3),—in the anterior portion of the commissure, pass from one optic nerve to the other, connecting the nasal sides of the retinas of both eyes with each other.

    Commissural Fibres (4) or *Commissure of Gudden,*—in the posterior portion of the commissure, have nothing to do with vision, but pass from one internal (medial) geniculate body to the other, or to the opposite posterior quadrigeminal body (colliculus inferior) (Whitaker).

The Optic Tract arises from the brain by two bands, an external and an internal. The *external* (lateral) *band* arises from the external (lateral) geniculate body, the upper quadrigeminal body (colliculus superior) and the pulvinar of the optic thalamus, the lower visual centres. The *internal* (medial) *band* arises from the internal (medial) geniculate body and the inferior quadrigeminal body (colliculus inferior), most of its fibres being commissural between the two internal (medial) geniculates. The two bands wind around the crus (cerebral peduncle) and join together opposite its centre in a flattened band, which becomes cylindrical and continues on to connect with the tract of the opposite side in the optic commissure. In its course the tract is attached to the surface of the crus by its anterior margin, and receives some fibres from the tuber cinereum and the lamina cinerea (lamina terminalis).

Meynert's Commissure (fasciculus retroflexus),—consists of the fibres from the epithalamic habenular nucleus, which cross in the optic commissure and enter the crus (cerebral peduncle) on the opposite side, passing obliquely through the red nucleus into the hypothalamic nucleus. It is concerned with olfactory impulses.

Visual Centres in the Brain. The *lower visual centres* are the external (lateral) geniculate body, the upper quadrigeminal body (colliculus superior), and the pulvinar of the optic thalamus, to which the optic nerve fibres are traced. From these nuclei other fibres go to the *cortical visual centre*, which is located in the cuneus of the occipital lobe, and probably also in the adjacent lingual lobule of the temporal lobe.

APPENDAGES OF THE EYE

The Tutamina Oculi (organa oculi accessoria) or appendages of the eye, include the eyebrows, the eyelids, the conjunctiva, the lacrimal gland, the lacrimal sac, and the nasal duct (ductus naso-lacrimalis).

The Eyebrows, or **Supercilia,** are two arched eminences of thickened integument over the supra-orbital arches, and connected beneath with the orbicularis palpebrarum, corrugator supercilii and occipito-frontalis muscles. They are covered with short, thick hairs, and are drawn downward and inward by the corrugator supercilli: (see page 75).

The Eyelids, or **Palpebræ,** are two thin, movable folds, placed in front of the eye, for its protection. The upper lid is the more movable one, having its own levator muscle, the levator palpebræ superioris. They are composed externally of skin, internally of mucous membrane (the palpebral conjunctiva), and between these lie areolar tissue, the orbicularis muscle, tarsal cartilage, fibrous membrane, Meibomian glands (glandulæ tarsales), vessels and nerves. The upper lid has, in addition, the aponeurosis of the levator palpebræ.

Eyelashes, or *Cilia,*—are a double or triple row of short hairs, situated on the free margins of the lids; their follicles lying in the connective tissue beneath the tarsal cartilages.

Glands of Moll (glandulæ ciliares),—are enlarged and modified sweat-glands, the openings of which are in several rows, near the attachment of the eyelashes.

Palpebral Fissure (rima palpebrarum),—is the space between the free margin of the lids, its outer and inner angles being termed respectively the *external* (commissura palpebrarum lateralis) and *internal* (commissura palpebrarum medialis) *canthus.*

Lacus Lacrimalis,—is a small triangular space at the internal canthus, between the lids and the globe.

Lacrimal Papilla,—on the edge of each lid, about ¼ inch from the internal canthus.

Punctum Lacrimale,—a minute orifice on each papilla, and the beginning of the lacrimal canal.

Tarsal Plates (tarsi),—are two thin, elongated plates of dense connective tissue, about an inch in length, placed one in each lid, giving it form and support. The upper one is crescentic in shape, the lower one is elliptical and smaller.

Tarsal Ligaments, external (ligamentum palpebralis laterale),—connects the outer angle of the tarsal plate to the malar bone. The internal (ligamentum palpebralis mediale) connects the inner angle of the plate to the nasal process of the maxilla. The internal one is often called the *tendo oculi.*

Meibomian Glands (glandulæ tarsales) (1),—are sebaceous glands embedded in grooves in the inner surface of the tarsal plates, about 30 in the upper eyelid, less in the lower one. Their ducts open on the inner edge of the free margin of the lids by minute foramina, through which their secretion is furnished to prevent the lids adhering to each other.

Fig. 95.

Muscles,—the palpebral portion of the orbicularis muscle is very thin and pale; the tensor tarsi compresses the punctum lacrimale and the lacrimal sac: (see page 75).

Arteries,—are the palpebral branches of the ophthalmic artery, forming the *superior and inferior tarsal arches,* and anastomosing with the orbital branch of the temporal, the lacrimal, transverse facial, and angular arteries.

Nerves,—the 3d, facial, and sympathetic to the muscles; the 5th to the skin and conjunctiva.

The Conjunctiva (Tunica Conjunctiva) is the mucous membrane lining the inner surface of the eyelids, and reflected over the front of the sclerotic and cornea. It is continuous with the mucous lining of the Meibomian glands (glandulæ tarsales), lacrimal ducts, lacrimal sac, naso-lacrimal duct, duct and lacrimal gland. The—

Palpebral Conjunctiva (tunica conjunctiva palpebrarum),—consists of connective tissue covered by epithelium, is traversed by furrows, and has papillæ, follicular glands, and lymphoid tissue.

Ocular Conjunctiva (tunica conjunctiva bulbi),—is very thin and transparent, loosely attached on the sclerotic, firmly adherent over the cornea, where it has no vessels in its structure. It has very few papillæ, and no glands.

Palpebral Folds, superior and inferior,—are where the conjunctiva is reflected over the globe, the *fornix conjunctivæ* lying between them, and containing mucous glands and trachoma glands, the latter being analogous to lymphoid follicles.

Plica Semilunaris, or Semi-lunar Fold,—a crescentic fold of conjunctiva at the inner canthus, considered to be the rudiment of the *membrana nictitans* or 3d eyelid of birds.

Caruncula lacrimalis,—is a small, red, conical body, situated in the lacus lacrimalis, at the inner canthus of the eye; consisting of a small island of skin, containing sebaceous and sweat glands, and a few slender hairs. It is the source of the whitish secretion which collects at the inner angle of the eye. It is connected by tendinous fibres to the capsule (fascia bulbi) of Tenon and to the rectus internus muscle.

The Lacrimal Gland (1) is an oval gland situated in a depression on the orbital portion of the frontal bone, at the outer angle of the orbit, its

FIG. 96.

inferior surface resting on the eyeball, its lower margin or lobe being covered by conjunctiva. Its front portion is separated from the rest of the gland by a fibrous septum, and is called the *accessory gland of Rosenmüller* (glandula lacrimalis inferior). Its *ducts*, from 6 to 12 in number, open by a row of orifices on the upper and outer portion of the palpebral conjunctiva. Its *secretion*, the tears, lubricates the surface of the eyeball; the excess evaporating or being collected in the lacus, from which it passes through the puncta (2) into the canaliculi (3) and the lacrimal sac (4), and thence by the naso-lacrimal duct (5) to the inferior meatus of the nose.

The Canaliculi (3) or *lacrimal canals* are two minute canals, $\frac{1}{25}$ inch in diameter and $\frac{1}{3}$ inch long, which extend from the punctum (2) in each lid to the lacrimal sac (4). They are lined with mucous membrane, and enveloped by fibres of the tensor tarsi muscle.

The Lacrimal Sac (4) is the superior dilated extremity of the nasal duct (5), and is situated in the groove formed by the lacrimal bone and the nasal process of the maxilla. Its form is oval, flattened anteroposteriorly; its dimensions about ⅖ inch long and ⅙ inch wide. Its fundus is crossed by the tarsal ligament, and by the tensor tarsi muscle. Its junction with the nasal duct may be interrupted by folds of the lining mucous membrane.

The Nasal Duct (ductus naso-lacrimalis) (5) is a membranous canal extending from the lacrimal sac to the inferior meatus of the nose. It is about ¾ inch long, ⅛ inch in diameter, is contained in the osseous lacrimal canal, curving downward, backward and outward, and its calibre is narrowest about its middle. Its mucous lining is thick, and continuous with the Schneiderian membrane of the nasal cavity. The—

Valve of Hasner (plica lacrimalis),—is an imperfect valve at the terminal orifice (6) of the naso-lacrimal duct, and is formed by a fold of mucous membrane.

THE EAR (AURIS OR ORGANON AUDITUS)

The Organ of Hearing is divisible into 3 parts—the external ear (auris externa), the middle ear (auris media) or tympanum, and the internal ear or labyrinth (auris interna); which are situated in or upon the mastoid and petrous portions of the temporal bone (described on page 20): The—

External Ear (auris externa),—consists of the *auricle* or *pinna*, and the auditory canal (meatus acusticus externus), which extends to the membrana tympani.

Middle Ear or *Tympanum* (auris media),—consists of the *atrium* or tympanic cavity proper (cavum tympani), and the *attic* or *epitympanic recess;* it contains the membrana tympani, the ossicles of the tympanum (ossicula auditus) and the tympanic orifice of the Eustachian tube (tuba auditiva).

Internal Ear or *Labyrinth* (auris interna),—consists of the *osseous* labyrinth (labyrinthus osseus) and the membranous labyrinth (labyrinthus membranaceus), the latter being contained within the former, which comprises the *vestibule* (vestibulum), the *semicircular canals* (canales semicirculares ossei), and the *cochlea*. The membranous labyrinth (labyrinthus membranaceus) consists of the *utricle* (utriculus), the *saccule* (sacculus), and the *membranous semicircular canals* (ductus semicirculares), and contains the terminal filaments of the auditory nerve (n. acusticus).

The External Ear (Auris Externa)

The Auricle or **Pinna** (auricula) is the external irregularly shaped appendage, fastened to the malar and temporal bones by ligaments. It consists of a thin plate of yellow fibro-cartilage, deficient in places where its parts are joined together by fibrous tissue, and is covered by peri-chondrium and integument, the latter containing sebaceous and sweat glands, and provided with short, downy hairs. The Auricle presents several elevations and depressions, which are due to the folding of its cartilage, and are named as follows:—

Helix,—the outer curved edge of the pinna, beneath which is a deep groove, the *fossa navicularis* (scapha) or fossa of the helix.

Anti-helix,—a curved ridge, parallel with and in front of the helix, bifur-cating above forming the crura antihelicis which enclose a triangular depression, the *fossa triangularis* auriculæ.

Concha Auriculæ,—the central cavity leading into the auditory canal (meatus acusticus externus).

Tragus,—a conical eminence in front of the concha, usually covered with hair along its inferior border.

Anti-tragus,—a smaller projection facing the tragus, from which it is separated by a deep fissure, the *incisura intertragica*.

Tubercle (tuberculum auriculæ) of Darwin,—a small tubercle frequently seen, where the helix turns downward.

Lobe or Lobule Auriculæ,—the soft, pendulous portion, composed of integumentary, adipose and connective tissues.

Muscles of the Auricle. The extrinsic muscles are the Attollens, Attrahens and Retrahens Auriculam, described on page 75. The intrinsic muscles are very slightly developed (see page 79) and are the—

Musculus Helicis Major,—vertically on the anterior border of the helix.

Musculus Helicis Minor,—on the lateral surface of the root of the helix.

Musculus Tragicus,—lies vertically on the outer surface of the tragus.

Musculus Anti-tragicus,—on the posterior wall of the auditory canal.

Musculus Transversus Auriculæ,—on the posterior surface of the auricle, radiating outward from the convexity of the concha.

Musculus Obliquus Auriculæ,—also on the posterior surface, radiating upward from the convexity of the concha.

The Auditory Canal (meatus acusticus externus) is an osseo-cartilaginous tube, about 1¼ inches long, extending from the concha to the membrana tympani, and curved irregularly in its course. The cartilaginous, or external portion, is about ½ inch long, and deficient posteriorly and above, where it is filled by strong fibrous tissue. The canal is lined with integument, having numerous hair follicles, sebaceous and ceruminous glands. Its relations are—*in front*, the condyle of the lower jaw; *below and in front*, the parotid gland; *behind*, the mastoid cells and the lateral sinus, separated from it by a very thin bony plate; *above*, the mastoid cells and the dura mater of the brain, separated from it by a thin osseous plate. The—

> *Sulcus Tympanicus*,—is a circumferential groove at the bottom of the canal for the insertion of the membrana tympani. It is interrupted above by a notch, the *incisura Rivinii*.

Vessels and Nerves. The *Arteries* of the auricle are derived from the external carotid artery, viz.—the anterior and posterior auricular, and the auricular branch of the occipital. Those of the auditory canal are branches from the posterior auricular, internal maxillary, and temporal arteries. The *Nerves* of the canal are derived from the temporo-auricular branch of the maxillary division of the 5th, and the auricular branch of the Vagus. Those of the auricle are the—

> *Auricularis Magnus*,—from the cervical plexus.
>
> *Auricular*,—branch of the vagus (also called Arnold's nerve).
>
> *Auriculo-temporal*, branch of the mandibular div. of the 5th.
>
> *Occipitalis Maior*,—from the post. division of the 2nd cervical nerve.
>
> *Occipitalis Minor*,—from the cervical plexus.
>
> *Posterior Auricular*,—branch of the facial, to the muscles.

The Membrana Tympani

The Membrana Tympani, or Drumhead, is an oval, inelastic, semi-transparent membrane, about $\frac{1}{250}$ inch in thickness, situated obliquely at the bottom of the auditory canal, inclined inward and forward, so as to form almost a continuation of the posterior wall of the canal. As seen through the canal, it is of a delicate blue-gray color, arched inward, and presents for consideration the following points:—

> *Malleolar Eminence*,—white in color at the upper border, made by the short process of the malleus behind.
>
> *Malleolar Stripe*,—also white, running downward from the eminence and formed by the handle of the malleus behind.
>
> *Light-spot*,—a triangular reflection, its apex at the tip of the malleus handle, its base extending to the periphery of the membrane. It is due to the concavity of the exterior surface of the membrane.
>
> *Umbo*, or *Navel*,—is the dark, central, depressed part of the membrane
>
> *Shrapnell's Membrane* (pars flaccida),—is the upper posterior part of the drumhead, where it is somewhat flaccid.

Structure. The Membrana Tympani is composed of 3 layers, an external or cuticular layer (stratum cutaneum), a middle or fibrous (membrana propria), and an internal or mucous layer (stratum mucosum). Its circumference is thickened to form an incomplete ring (annulus fibrocartilagineus), which is received into the sulcus tympanicus at the inner end of the auditory canal. The anterior and posterior ends of this ring are shown by (*v*) and (*h*) in the figure. The—

Fig. 97.

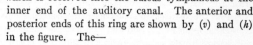
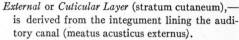

> *External* or *Cuticular Layer* (stratum cutaneum),—
>   is derived from the integument lining the auditory canal (meatus acusticus externus).
>
> *Middle* or *Fibrous Layer* (membrana propria),—
>   consists of an outer layer of fibres which radiate from the handle of the malleus; and an inner

layer of circular fibres, most numerous around the circumference. Between these two sets of fibres are situated the short process and handle of the malleus.

> *Internal* or *Mucous Layer* (stratum mucosum),—is continuous with the mucous lining of the tympanum.

The Internal Surface of the *Membrana Tympani* is convex, and presents the curved handle of the *malleus* pointing downward between its layers, also the *chorda tympani* nerve passing along the upper margin to the iter chordæ anterius in the Glaserian (tympano-squamous) fissure.

Nerves and Vessels. The Membrana Tympani receives its *nervous supply* from the auriculo-temporal branch of the mandibular, the auricular branch of the vagus and the tympanic branch of the glosso-pharyngeal. The *Veins* open into the external jugular, except those on the inner surface, which drain partly into the lateral sinus and veins of the dura mater, and partly into a plexus on the Eustachian tube (tuba auditiva). The *Arteries* are the—

> *Deep Auricular*, branch of the internal maxillary,—supplies the external layer, and forms with the tympanic branches a capillary plexus in the middle layer.
>
> *Tympanic Branches*, of the internal maxillary and internal carotid arteries,—supply the internal layer, the former with the stylo-mastoid artery forming a vascular circle around the membrane, and both anastomosing on the membrane with the—
>
> *Vidian* (a. canalis pterygoidea),—branch of the internal maxillary, and the—
>
> *Stylo-mastoid*,—from the posterior auricular branch of the external carotid.

The Middle Ear or Tympanum (Auris Media)

The Tympanum, or *Drum* (auris media), is an irregular cavity within the petrous portion of the temporal bone, lying between the membrana tympani and the tympanic surface of the petrous bone and communicating with the naso-pharynx by the Eustachian tube (tuba auditiva). It contains the ossicles (ossicula auditus) of the tympanum, part of the chorda tympani nerve, and air. Its average diameters are about ½ inch antero-posteriorly, ⅕ to ⅗ inch vertically, and 1/12 to ⅛ inch transversely. It consists of two parts, the *atrium* or tympanic cavity proper (cavum tympani), opposite the tympanic membrane; and the *attic* or *epitympanic recess* above, containing the upper half of the malleus and the greater part of the incus. Its roof and floor are formed by thin osseous laminæ, the floor separating it from the jugular fossa and vein, and presenting, near the inner wall, a small aperture for *Jacobson's nerve* (tympanic branch of the glosso-pharyngeal). The other walls of the tympanum present for examination the following points:—

OUTER WALL (paries membranacea),—is formed by the membrana tympani and presents the—

  Iter Chordæ Posterius,—opens close to the posterior edge of the drumhead, for the passage of the chorda tympani nerve.

  Iter Chordæ Anterius (canal of Huguier),—opens just in front of the drumhead, for the passage of the chorda tympani nerve.

  Glaserian (tympano-squamous) *Fissure,*—opens above and in front of the drumhead, receiving the long process (processus gracilis or anterior) of the malleus, the anterior ligament of the malleus, (*laxator tympani tendon*) and the tympanic branch of the internal maxillary artery.

INNER WALL (paries labyrinthica),—is the outer wall of the labyrinth, presents the—

  Fenestra Vestibuli or *Ovalis,*—an oval opening, leading into the vestibule, and closed by a membrane, to which is attached the base of the stapes.

  Fenestra Cochleæ or *Rotunda,*—a smaller opening, below the fenestra vestibuli, leading into the scala tympani of the cochlea, and closed by the *membrana tympani secundaria,* a membrane of 3 layers.

  Promontory,—an elevation corresponding to the first turn of the cochlea, situated between the fenestræ and in front of them. It is grooved by the tympanic plexus.

  Ridge of the Aquæductus Fallopii (prominentia canalis facialis),—above the fenestra vestibuli, behind which it curves downward along the posterior wall.

POSTERIOR WALL (paries mastoidea), separates it from the mastoid cells, and presents the—

Opening of the Tympanic or Mastoid Antrum,—which in turn communicates with the mastoid cells.

Pyramid (eminentia pyramidalis),—a hollow conical eminence, behind the fenestra vestibuli, contains the stapedius muscle, and a minute canal communicating with the aquæductus Fallopii (canalis facialis) and transmitting a nerve to the stapedius.

ANTERIOR WALL (paries carotica), separates it from the carotid canal, and presents the—

Opening of Canal (semicanalis m. tensoris tympani) *for the Tensor Tympani Muscle,*—above, situated on a small projection, sometimes called the anterior pyramid.

Opening of the Eustachian Tube (semicanalis tubæ auditivæ),—next below, the two canals being separated from each other by a thin, horizontal, bony plate, the *processus cochleariformis* (septum canalis musculotubarii).

The Ossicles (ossicula auditus) **of the Tympanum** are three small bones, which form a chain across the tympanic cavity, connecting the membrana tympani with the fenestra vestibuli, and named the—

Malleus, or Hammer *(A),*—consists of a head, neck, short process (processus lateralis), long process or *processus gracilis* (processus anterior), and handle or *manubrium.* The short process and handle are fastened to the middle layer of the drumhead. The long process (never found in adults) is received into the Glaserian (tympano-squamous) fissure, and the head articulates with the head of the incus.

FIG. 98.

Incus, or Anvil *(B),*—resembles a two-pronged tooth; it has a head, also a long and a short process. The head articulates with the head of the malleus, the short process with the *fossa incudis* in the epitympanic recess, the long process with the head of the stapes, by the *os orbiculare,* its convex extremity.

Stapes, or Stirrup *(C),*—presents a head, neck, base and two crura. Its head articulates with the incus, its base rests on the membrane closing the fenestra vestibuli, its neck receives the tendon of the stapedius muscle.

Ligaments of the Ossicles are 5 in number, besides the capsular ligaments of their articulations, 3 for the malleus, 1 for the incus, and 1 for the stapes, as follows:—

Anterior Ligament of the Malleus,—is the degenerated laxator tympani muscle, from the neck of the malleus through the tympano-squamous fissure or its petro-tympanic subdivision to the base of the *alar spine* of the sphenoid. It is an active muscle in most infants and about 75 per cent. of adults.

Superior of the Malleus,—from the head of the malleus to the roof of the epitympanic recess.

External of the Malleus,—from the short process of the malleus to the posterior part of the notch in the tympanic ring.

Posterior of the Incus,—from the end of the short process of the incus to the posterior part of the epitympanic recess. [The so-called superior ligament of the incus is merely a fold of mucous membrane.]

Annular Ligament of the Stapes (ligamentum annulare baseos stapedis), —around the circumference of the base of the stapes, connecting it to the margin of the fenestra vestibuli.

Muscles of the Tympanum are 2, the Tensor Tympani Stapedius and the laxator tympani.

Tensor Tympani,—arises from the under surface of the petrous portion of the temporal bone, the cartilaginous Eustachian tube (pars cartilaginea tubæ auditivæ), and its own osseous canal (semicanalis m. tensoris tympani); and is inserted into the handle of the malleus. It draws the membrana tympani inward and tense. Its *nerve* is a branch from the trigeminal, through the otic ganglion.

Stapedius,—arises from a conical cavity in the interior of the pyramid; its tendon emerges from the orifice at the apex of the pyramid, and is inserted into the neck of the stapes. It draws the head of the stapes backward, and probably compresses the contents of the vestibule. Its *nerve* is the tympanic branch of the facial.

Laxator Tympani,—see anterior ligament of malleus (see page 80).

Vessels of the Tympanum. The *Veins* terminate in the pterygoid plexus and in the superior petrosal sinus. The *Arteries* are 6 in number, as follows:—

Tympanic,—branch of the internal maxillary, entering by the petrotympanic fissure, anastomosing on the membrana tympani, in a vascular circle with the Stylo-mastoid and Vidian arteries, and the Tympanic br. of the internal carotid.

Stylo-mastoid,—br. of the posterior auricular br. of the external carotid entering at the stylo-mastoid foramen.

Petrosal,—br. of middle meningeal artery, entering by the hiatus Fallopii.

Tympanic,—br. from the internal carotid artery.

Branch from the Ascending Pharyngeal,—from the external carotid; also accompanying the Eustachian tube.

Nerves of the Tympanum. Besides the nerves supplying the two muscles (see above), the *Chorda Tympani Nerve* enters the tympanum by the iter chordæ posterius, crosses the cavity between the handle of the malleus and the long process of the incus, and makes its exit by the iter chordæ anterius, after passing close along the upper part of the membrana tympani. The mucous membrane lining the tympanum is supplied by the branches of distribution of the *Tympanic Plexus*, which lies on the inner wall around the promontory, and is formed by the—

Tympanic Branch of the Glosso-pharyngeal,—also known as Jacobson's nerve, enters by an aperture in the floor near the inner wall.

Small Deep Petrosal,—from the carotid plexus of the sympathetic, enters from the carotid canal.

Small Superficial Petrosal,—from the otic ganglion, enters near the canal for the tensor tympani muscle.

Branch from the Great Superficial Petrosal,—enters through the inner wall, just in front of the fenestra vestibuli.

The Eustachian or Auditory Tube (tuba auditiva) is an osseo-cartilaginous canal, about 1½ inches long, ⅟₁₂ to ⅓ inch in diameter, which forms a channel of communication between the tympanum and the pharynx. It passes obliquely downward, forward and inward, from the anterior wall of the tympanum to the naso-pharynx, where it ends in an oval orifice on the side wall of the pharynx just behind the inferior meatus of the nose. The osseous part (pars ossea tubæ auditivæ), ½ inch long, terminates at the retiring angle of junction of the petrous and squamous portions of the temporal bone, in a jagged margin, to which the cartilaginous part (pars cartilaginea tubæ auditivæ) is attached. The latter, 1 inch long, is formed by a triangular plate of elastic fibro-cartilage, folded on itself above so as to leave a deficiency below, which is filled by fibrous tissue. This portion of the tube expands as it descends into a trumpet-shaped lower extremity. The tube is lined by ciliated mucous membrane, continuous with that of the tympanum and pharynx, and containing mucous glands, also adenoid tissue near its lower end. The—

Tube-tonsil of Gerlach,—is formed by the adenoid tissue in the mucous lining near the pharyngeal orifice.

Isthmus,—is the narrowest part of the tube, at the junction of the osseous and cartilaginous portions.

Muscles,—are the dilator tubæ fibres of the tensor palati (m. tensor veli palatini), which open the tube during deglutition, aided by the salpingo-pharyngeus when present. The levator palati closes the pharyngeal orifice. For these muscles see page 80.

Arteries,—are the ascending pharyngeal, from the external carotid, and the Vidian (a. canalis pterygoidea) from the internal maxillary.

Nerves,—are pharyngeal branches from the glosso-pharyngeal, pneumogastric and sympathetic, through the pharyngeal plexus, also the upper posterior nasal branches of Meckel's (spheno-palatine) ganglion. The otic ganglion lies on the outer side of the cartilaginous portion of the tube (pars cartilaginea tubæ auditivæ), and supplies the tensor palati muscle (m. tensor veli palatini).

The Internal Ear or Labyrinth (Auris Interna)

The Internal Ear or **Labyrinth** is the essential part of the organ of hearing. It lies internal to the tympanum, within the petrous portion of the temporal bone, and consists of a series of osseous chambers, the *Osseous Labyrinth,* containing a fluid, the *perilymph,* in which lies a membranous reproduction of the chambers, the *Membranous Labyrinth,* which also contains a fluid, the *endolymph.* Within the membranous labyrinth are distributed the terminal filaments of the auditory nerve, which being suspended between two fluids, are not only protected from injury, but enabled to receive the most delicate vibrations communicated to the fluids surrounding them. The Internal Ear comprises the following-named structures:—

Osseous Labyrinth.....
- *Vestibule* (4), the central cavity.
- *Semicircular Canals,* behind the vestibule.
- *Cochlea* (8), in front of the vestibule.

Membranous Labyrinth.
- *Utricle,* a membranous sac, in the recessus ellipticus of the vestibule.
- *Membranous Semicircular Canals* (ductus semicirculares), in the osseous canals.
- *Saccule,* a membranous sac, in the recessus sphæricus of the vestibule.
- *Membranous Cochlea* (ductus cochlearis), a spiral tube, enclosed in the osseous cochlea.

Auditory Nerve (n. acusticus),—the 8th cranial nerve, Portio Mollis of the 7th pair.

Organ of Corti (organon spirale),—the terminal auditory apparatus, in the membranous cochlea (ductus cochlearis).

Internal Auditory Meatus (meatus acusticus internus),—by which the auditory nerve enters from the brain.

The Vestibule (4) is the central common cavity of communication between the osseous parts of the internal ear, and measures in vertical diameter about ⅕ inch, laterally about 1/10 inch. It is situated internal to the tympanum, behind the cochlea (8), and in front of the semicircular canals (2), communicating in front with the scala vestibuli of the cochlea, and behind by five openings with the semicircular canals. It contains a fluid, the *perilymph*, also the *utricle* and *saccule* of the membranous labyrinth, and presents the following points:—

FIG. 99.

> *Fenestra Vestibuli* (fenestra ovalis),—on its outer wall, closed by the base of the stapes and its annular ligament.
>
> *Recessus Sphæricus* (fovea hemisphærica) (7),—a small circular depression on the inner wall, for the saccule, medially, it presents a small area, macula cribrosa media, which is perforated by 12 to 15 minute orifices for filaments of the acoustic nerve.

Crista Vestibuli,—a vertical ridge on the inner wall behind the recessus sphæricus. It bifurcates below to enclose the—

Recessus Cochlearis,—a small depression, perforated for the passage of about 8 filaments of the acoustic nerve.

Aquæductus Vestibuli,—opens behind the crista, ending on the posterior surface of the petrous portion of the temporal bone. It transmits a small vein, and contains the *ductus endo-lymphaticus*, a tubular prolongation of the lining membrane of the vestibule, which ends in a cul-de-sac between the layers of the dura mater in the cranial cavity.

Recessus Ellipticus or *Fovea Semi-elliptica* (6),—a transverse oval depression on the roof for the utricle; behind it are the 5 orifices of the semicircular canals, and in front is the opening into the scala vestibuli of the cochlea.

The Semicircular Canals (canales semicirculares ossei) are three C-shaped bony tubes, each about 1/20 inch in diameter, situated above and behind the vestibule, into which they open by 5 apertures. Each canal lies at a right angle with the other two. The external (lateral) canals of both ears are virtually in the same plane, while the superior canal of one ear is in a plane parallel to that of the posterior canal of the other ear

(Crum Brown). The superior and posterior canals are each nearly an inch long, and are placed vertically; they join together behind in the *crus commune*, which opens into the vestibule. The external canal is about $\frac{1}{5}$ inch long, placed horizontally, its arch being directed outward and backward. The canals contain the *perilymph*, and the membranous semicircular canals. The—

 Ampulla,—is a flask-shaped dilatation of each canal at one extremity, having a diameter of about $\frac{1}{10}$ inch.

The Cochlea is a spiral canal situated in the eburnated (ivory-like) portion of the petrous bone, diametrically opposite to the internal auditory canal (meatus acusticus internus). The depth at which it lies from the cerebral surface of the bone varies, in different individuals, from $\frac{1}{64}$ to $\frac{10}{64}$ of an inch. The promontory in the tympanum is the only part of the cochlea that is exposed, elsewhere it is completely imbedded in solid bone. It is about $1\frac{1}{2}$ inches long, tapering from $\frac{1}{10}$ to $\frac{1}{20}$ inch in diameter, coiled around a central conical axis for $2\frac{3}{4}$ turns. By removal of surrounding bone, in conformity with its interior,

Fig. 100.

the cochlea can be made to resemble a snail-shell in appearance with its apex pointing forward and outward. Its *first turn* is separated from the carotid canal in front by a thin wall. Its central axis, the *modiolus*, is of conical shape, and is channeled by small canals for the passage of arteries and nerves, and by a central one, the *canalis centralis modioli*. Its apex is the last coil of the cochlea, and is expanded into a funnel-shaped lamella, the *infundibulum*. The—

 Canalis Spiralis Modioli, or Spiral Canal,—is the space between the modiolus and the outer wall of the cochlea. It makes $2\frac{3}{4}$ turns, from left to right in the right ear, from right to left in the left ear, or in other words, that of the right ear corresponds to a "right hand" screw; and terminates in the *cupola*, a cul-de-sac at the apex of the cochlea. It presents 3 openings,—the *fenestra cochleæ* (fenestra rotunda), communicating with the tympanum; the opening into the vestibule, and the orifice of the aquæductus cochleæ (see below).

 Lamina Spiralis (*b*),—is a thin, osseous plate, projecting from the modiolus half way across the spiral canal, and winding around the modiolus terminates near the apex in a hook-like process, the *hamulus*. Its deficiency in the last half turn of the cochlea forms the *Helicotrema*, a space in which the two scalæ unite. It consists of two laminæ, between which pass the filaments of the cochlear nerve. From its free edge the structures composing the membranous cochlea pass to their attachment on the opposite wall of the cavity. It partially divides the spiral canal into 2 passages, the *scala vestibuli* above and the *scala tympani* below.

Aquæductus Cochleæ,—is a minute funnel-shaped canal which begins by a small orifice in the lower wall of the scala tympani near the promontory, and runs in the inner wall of the jugular fossa, ending in the small deep triangular depression on the posterior border of the basilar surface of the petrous portion of the temporal bone. It transmits a vein from the cochlea to the jugular vein, or to the inferior petrosal sinus, and forms a communication between the perilymph in the scala tympani and the subarachnoidean space of the brain.

The Membranous Labyrinth (labyrinthus membranaceus) is situated within the osseous labyrinth, and consists of two membranous sacs, the *Utricle* (utriculus) (1) and *Saccule* (sacculus) (2), together with the *Mem-

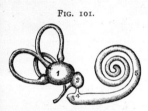

FIG. 101.

A cast of left labyrinth as seen from behind.

branous Semicircular Canals* (ductus semicirculares) (6), and the *Membranous Cochlea* (ductus cochlearis) (5). The utricle and saccule communicate with each other indirectly by a small canal contained in the aquæductus vestibuli. The saccule communicates with the membranous cochlea by the *canalis reuniens* of Hensen (4), and the membranous semicircular canals open into the utricle; so that the membranous labyrinth affords an uninterrupted channel for the *endolymph* which it contains. The walls consist of 3 layers,—an outer fibrous coat, a middle one resembling the hyaloid membrane, and an inner layer, formed of polygonal, nucleated epithelial cells. In the walls of the utricle and saccule are contained 2 small gelatinoid bodies, the *Maculæ Acusticæ* which contain flask-shaped *Hair Cells* and

Otoliths (otoconia),—minute crystals of calcium carbonate, held together in a mesh of delicate fibrous tissue in which ramify many minute fibres of the acoustic nerve.

The Utricle (utriculus) (1) is a flattened, oblong membranous sac, fastened to the inner wall of the vestibule in the fovea semi-elliptica (recessus ellipticus). It is filled with endolymph, nearly surrounded by perilymph, and communicates with the saccule through the small tube in the aquæductus vestibuli. The membranous semicircular canals open into its cavity behind by 5 orifices. The—

    Macula Acustica Utricularis,—is a thickened spot in the wall where it is lodged in the fovea (recessus), receiving the utricular filaments of the acoustic nerve.

    Ductus Utriculosaccularis,—is given off from the medial wall; it is joined by a similar duct coming from the saccule; together they form the Ductus Endolymphaticus which passes through the aquæductus vestibuli.

The Saccule (sacculus) (2) is the smaller of the two membranous sacs, about $\frac{1}{15}$ inch in diameter, attached at one point to the utricle, and also to the fovea hemispherica (recessus sphæricus) of the vestibule, being elsewhere surrounded by perilymph, and containing endolymph. It communicates with the utricle through the *ductus endolymphaticus* in the aquæductus vestibuli, and also with the membranous cochlea by the—

    Canalis Reuniens of Hensen (4),—about $\frac{1}{35}$ inch long and $\frac{1}{120}$ inch in diameter, connects the cavity of the saccule and the vestibular end of the membranous cochlea (ductus cochlearis) (3).

    Macula Acustica Saccularis,—is a circular area, $\frac{1}{12}$ inch in diameter, on the wall of the saccule, where the saccular filaments of the acoustic nerve originate.

Fig. 102.

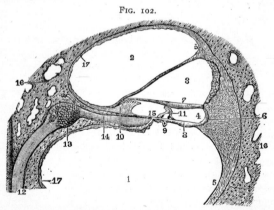

The **Membranous Semicircular Canals** (ductus semicirculares) have the same shape as the osseous ones in which they are contained but are $\frac{1}{3}$ their diameter. They are fastened thereto by the convex curves, and are elsewhere surrounded by perilymph, except at the ampullary enlargements, where they fill the osseous canals and present a thickened fiddle-shaped elevation projecting into the cavity and called the *septum transversum*, in which the nerves end. They are held in position by numerous fibrous bands, connecting them to the walls of the osseous canals. They constitute the *Organ* of *Orientation* and *Equilibration*.

The Membranous Cochlea, also called the *Ductus Cochlearis* or *Scala Media*, is a spiral tube enclosed in the spiral canal of the osseous cochlea (16), lying along its outer wall, to which it is attached, being also attached to the lamina spiralis (10) on the opposite side of the cavity. It is formed by the *membrana* or *lamina basilaris* (8) below, the *vestibular membrane of Reissner* (18) above, and the periosteum of the cochlear wall on the outer side, its cross-section being of triangular form. It is filled with endolymph, and contains the *organ of Corti* (organon spirale) (11) overhung by the *membrana tectoria* (7). The—

Limbus Laminæ Spiralis (10),—is the soft structure of periosteum on the edge of the lamina spiralis, and lies in the membranous cochlea. It has two lips,—an upper, the *labium vestibulare*, and a lower, the *labium tympanicum*, with a C-shaped concavity, the *sulcus spiralis internus*, between them.

Vestibular Membrane of Reissner (18),—extends from the edge of the lamina spiralis to the outer cochlear wall, separating the membranous cochlea from the scala vestibuli (2).

Membrana or Lamina Basilaris (8),—is the tympanic wall of the membranous cochlea, extending from the labium tympanicum of the lamina spiralis to the outer cochlear wall, where its insertion is called the *ligamentum spirale* (5), or *muscle of Todd and Bowman*. On it rests the *Spiral Organ of Corti* (11),—covered by the membrana tectoria.

Membrana Tectoria (7),—extends parallel to the membrana or lamina basilaris from the labium vestibulare, over the spiral organ of Corti, to be attached externally to the outer row of Deiters' cells (see below).

Vas Spirale (9),—a vessel in the vascular connective tissue of the membrana or lamina basilaris, below the spiral organ of Corti.

Zona Arctuata,—is the inner area, and the *zona pectinata* is the outer area, of the membrana or lamina basilaris.

The Organ of Corti (organon spirale) (11), or *Papilla Spiralis*, is situated on the inner surface of the membrana or lamina basilaris (8), is overlapped by the free edge of the membrana tectoria (7), and appears as a papilla winding spirally throughout the length of the membranous cochlea. It is an arrangement of cells, some of which are rod-like in form, and others

are epithelial hair-cells, the whole being supposed to be the essential orga
of hearing.   The—

> *Rods of Corti*,—are arranged in two rows, resting, by their pedestals
> on the lamina basilaris, and uniting with each other by their heads
> so as to form an arched tunnel, the *tunnel of Corti*, between them an
> the membrana basilaris all along the length of the cochlea.   Numbe
> of rods in inner row about 6,000, in outer row 4,000.   Average di
> ameter of the rods, from $\frac{1}{25000}$ to $\frac{1}{35000}$ inch.
>
> *Head-plates*,—are attached to the heads of the inner rods, for the recep
> tion of the rods of the opposite row.

FIG. 103.   FIG. 104.

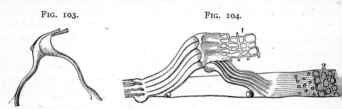

> *Lamina Reticularis* (1),—a delicate perforated membrane which extend
> from the articulations of the rods outward to the external row o
> the outer hair-cells.
>
> *Auditory Cells* (2),—are epithelial structures covering the inner surface
> of the walls and the floor of the membranous cochlea.   Those whic
> cover the inner rods by a single row number about 3,500, are nucleated
> covered with tufts of cilia, and called the *inner hair-cells*.   On th
> outer rods are 3 or 4 rows of similar cells, numbering about 12,000
> and named the *outer hair-cells*.   Between the latter are rows of sup-
> porting cells, called the *cells of Deiters*, and outside them are 5 or
> rows of columnar cells, the *cells of Hensen*, beyond which are the *cell
> of Claudius*, covering the outer part of the zona pectinata of the
> membrana or lamina basilaris.

The Auditory Nerve (n. acusticus), the 8th or *Portio Mollis* of the 7th
pair, arises by two roots from the same groove in the medulla as does the
facial nerve which is in front and separated from it by the *pars intermedia*
or glosso-palatine nerve (n. intermedius), the medial or *vestibular root* from
the *area acustica* or trigonum acusticum in the floor of the 4th ventricle,
the lateral or *cochlear root* from the accessory nucleus and the tuberculum
acusticum, in the medulla, close to the restiform body.   It emerges from
the medulla at the lower border of the pons Varolii, in company with the
facial nerve, from which it receives one or two filaments, both nerves

passing into the internal auditory meatus, at the bottom of which the auditory divides into two branches, vestibular and cochlear. The—

Vestibular Nerve,—has a ganglion, the *vestibular ganglion of Scarpa,* on it in the internal auditory meatus; it then divides into 3 branches, which pass through minute orifices in the bottom of the meatus, and entering the vestibule, are distributed to the utricle and the ampullæ of the external and superior semicircular canals respectively. This nerve has nothing to do with hearing, it is purely a nerve of *orientation* and *equilibration.*

Cochlear Nerve,—is the true nerve of hearing, it gives off branches to the saccule and the ampulla of the posterior semicircular canal, and then divides at the base of the modiolus of the cochlea into numerous filaments (14), which pass through the little foramena in the tractus spiralis foramenosus at the bottom of the internal acoustic meatus, then between the lamellæ of the lamina spiralis, and through the central canal of the modiolus, to the hair-cells of the spiral organ of Corti (Fig. 101). On it in the spiral canal of the modiolus is the—

Ganglion Spirale (13),—consisting of bipolar nerve-cells, which are the true cells of origin of this nerve, one pole being prolonged centrally to the brain, and the other peripherally to the hair-cells of Corti's spiral organ (see lateral lemniscus, page 199).

The Internal Auditory Meatus (meatus acusticus internus) is a large orifice on the cerebellar surface of the petrous portion of the temporal bone, leading into a short canal, which runs outward for $\frac{1}{3}$ inch, and is closed by a vertical plate, the *fundus* or *lamina cribrosa,* divided by a crest, the *crista falciformis* (crista transversa), into 4 depressions, which are perforated by foramina for the passage of the branches of the auditory nerve into the labyrinth. The—

Tractus Spiralis Foraminosus,—is the anterior lower depression; has a number of foramina spirally arranged and opening into the central canal of the cochlea, transmitting the nerves to the cochlea.

Area Cribrosa Media (area vestibularis inferior),—just below the posterior part of the crest, transmits the nerves to the saccule.

Foramen Singulare,—behind the preceding area, for the nerve to the posterior semicircular canal.

Area Cribrosa Superior (area vestibularis superior),—above the crest posteriorly, for the filaments to the utricle and the superior and external semicircular canals.

Opening of the Aquæductus Fallopii (area n. facialis) above and in front, for the passage of the facial nerve.

Vessels of the Internal Ear.　The *Veins* accompany the arteries, and uniting at the base of the modiolus empty into the superior petrosal sinus or into the lateral sinus.　The *Arteries* are the—

Internal Auditory, br. of the basilar (from the vertebral),—accompanies the acoustic nerve into the internal auditory meatus, where it divides into vestibular and cochlear branches.

Stylo-mastoid, br. of the posterior auricular (from the external carotid), —sends some small branches to the cochlea.

ORGANS OF DIGESTION (APPARATUS DIGESTORIUS)

The Alimentary Canal is a musculo-membranous tube, about 30 feet in length, extending from the mouth to the anus, lined throughout with mucous membrane, furnished with several accessory organs, and performing the functions of ingestion, mastication, insalivation, deglutition, digestion, assimilation, and egestion.　Its subdivisions are named the— Mouth, Pharynx, Œsophagus, Stomach, Small Intestine (duodénum, jejúnum and ileum) and Large Intestine (cæcum, colon and rectum). The first three lie above the diaphragm, the rest below it.　The portion from the pharynx down is the "*tubus digestorius.*"

Accessory Organs of Digestion are the—Teeth, Salivary glands (parotid, sub-mandibular, sub-lingual), Liver, and Pancreas.

THE MOUTH (CAVUM ORIS)

The Mouth is an oval-shaped cavity, placed at the commencement of the alimentary canal, and consists of the vestibule, and the cavity proper. The *vestibule* (vestibulum oris) is a slit-like aperture between the lips and cheeks externally and the gums and teeth internally.　It is partially interrupted in front in the mid-line by the *frenula* which attach the lips to the gums, the frenulum of the upper lip being the more developed of the two.　The *cavity proper* (cavum oris proprium) extends from the alveolar arches and their teeth in front and laterally to the isthmus of the fauces behind, by which constricted aperture it communicates with the pharynx. Its roof is formed by the palate, its floor by the tongue and its mucous membrane reflected to the lower gum.　The *lips* (labia oris) are the two fleshy folds, which surround the orifice (rima oris) of the mouth, the *cheeks* (buccæ) forming its sides and being continuous with the lips in front; both are formed of skin externally, and mucous membrane internally; between which are muscle, fat, areolar tissue, vessels, nerves and glands.　The mouth presents for examination the tongue (see page 272), the gums and teeth (described separately), the palate, fauces, tonsils, and openings of ducts from the salivary glands. Special anatomical features presented by the mouth are the—

Hamular Process of the Medial Pterygoid Lamina of the Sphenoid Bone,—may be felt behind the last upper molar tooth; also the *internal pterygoid plate* (medial pterygoid lamina), and part of the *pterygoid fossa.*

Coronoid Process,—of the lower jaw, at its anterior border.

Posterior Palatine Artery,—at the inner side of the last upper molar tooth, and in front of the hamular process.

Pterygo-mandibular Ligament,—is felt as a fold posteriorly to the last lower molar tooth.

Lingual Branch of the 5th,—the gustatory nerve,—passes over the inner side of the ramus of the lower jaw, close to the last lower molar tooth.

Openings of Stenson's Ducts, from the parotid glands,—in the vestibule, one on each cheek, opposite the 2nd upper molar tooth.

Openings of Wharton's Ducts, from the submandibular or submaxillary glands,—in the cavity proper, one on each side of the frænum (frenulum linguæ) of the tongue.

Openings of the Ducts of Rivinus, from the sublingual glands,—8 to 20 on each side, open into the cavity proper, on either side of the frænum (frenulum linguæ) of the tongue.

The Palate (Palatum) and Tonsils (Tonsillæ Palatinæ)

The Palate forms the roof of the mouth, and consists of the hard palate (palatum durum) in front, and the soft palate (palatum molle) behind. The *Hard Palate* (palatum durum) is formed by the palate process of the maxilla and the horizontal plate of the palate bone, is covered with mucous membrane, which is closely adherent to the periosteum, and presents along the median line, a linear ridge or *raphé*, which terminates anteriorly in a papilla corresponding to the inferior opening of the anterior palatine fossa. The *Soft Palate* (palatum molle) is a movable fold suspended from the posterior border of the hard palate, and forming an incomplete septum between the mouth and the pharynx. It consists of a fold of mucous membrane, enclosing muscular fibres, an aponeurosis, adenoid tissue, vessels, nerves and mucous glands; and is formed by fibres of the following—

Muscles, 5 on each side, the—levator palati, tensor veli palati, palato-glossus (m. glosso-palatinus), palato-pharyngeus (m. pharyngo-palatinus), and the azygos uvulæ (m. uvulæ);—the latter forming with its fellow the—

Uvula,—a conical-shaped, pendulous process, which hangs down from
the middle of the free border of the soft palate.

Glosso-palatine Arch or *Anterior Pillar of the Fauces,*—arches downward
and forward to the base of the tongue, and contains the glosso-palatine
muscle.

Pharyngo-palatine Arch or *Posterior Pillar of the Fauces,*—arches downward and backward to the sides of the pharynx, and contains the
palato-pharyngei (m. pharyngo-palatinus) muscle.

Isthmus Faucium,—the space bounded by the glosso-palatine arches of
both sides, the free border of the palate, and the base of the tongue.
It communicates with the mouth anteriorly and with the pharynx
posteriorly.

The Tonsils (tonsillæ palatinæ) or *Amygdalæ,* are two prominent bodies,
situated one on each side, in the *sinus tonsillaris* between the anterior and
posterior pillars (glosso-palatine and pharyngo-palatine arches) of the
fauces, and nearly an inch in front of the internal carotid artery. Their
inner surfaces show 12 to 15 orifices, leading into recesses, from which
follicles branch out into the substance of the gland. The follicles are
numerous, and are surrounded by a layer of closed capsules of adenoid
tissue, and a plexus of lymphatic vessels communicating with the deep
cervical glands. The—

Fossa Supra-tonsillaris,—is a recess above the tonsil, and is covered by
the *plica semilunaris,* a fold of mucous membrane.

Arteries, as usually given, are—the dorsalis linguæ, from the lingual; the
ascending palatine and tonsillar, from the facial (a. maxillaris
externa); the ascending pharyngeal, from the external carotid;
the descending palatine, from the internal maxillary; and a twig
from the small meningeal. As a matter of fact, in 95 per cent. of
all cases none of these arteries that surround the tonsillar fossa
(sinus tonsillaris) and form a plexus around it, actually penetrate
directly through the wall and capsule into the tonsil. The *ascending
palatine* branch of the facial (external maxillary) and the *descending
palatine* branch of the internal maxillary arteries form a plexiform
anastomosis which is quite outside of the fossa (sinus tonsillaris)
and well above and behind it.

    The True Tonsillar Artery is formed by this anastomosis, it passes
downwards between the capsule and muscular aponeurosis for a
distance of about ½ inch before penetrating the capsule to reach
the tonsil (J. Leslie Davis).

Veins,—accompanying the *true tonsillar artery* is a vein which runs upwards to the *palatine plexus*, a smaller vein emerges from the tonsil in company with the other vein, then turns downwards and runs between the capsule and the wall of the fossa (sinus tonsillaris) to reach the *pharyngeal plexus* (J. Leslie Davis).

Nerves,—are derived from the spheno-palatine ganglion, and from the glosso-pharyngeal.

THE SALIVARY GLANDS (GLANDULÆ SALIVALES)

The Salivary Glands, communicating with the mouth, are the *Parotid*, the *Submandibular*, and the *Sublingual* glands. They are compound, race-mose glands, consisting of numerous lobes, made up of smaller lobules connected together by dense areolar tissue, vessels and ducts. Each lobule consists of the ramifications of a duct, the branches terminating in dilated ends or *alveoli*, on which the capillaries are distributed, and which are enclosed by a reticulated basement membrane. The alveoli are lined by cells, which secrete a *mucous* secretion in the sublingual gland, or a *serous* fluid in the parotid gland; the submandibular producing both kinds. *Mucous Glands* are also found in the mouth, in the tongue, the tonsil, and the soft palate.

The Parotid Gland (glandula parotis) (1) is the largest of the three salivary glands, and weighs from ½ oz. to 1 oz. Superficially, it lies upon

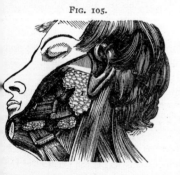

FIG. 105.

the side of the face, below and in front of the external ear, and passes over the masseter muscle anteriorly. Deeply, it lies on the tympanic plate of the temporal bone behind the articulation of the lower jaw. The parotid is surrounded by a capsule which blends deeply with the back of the stylo-mandibular ligament. The superficial portion of this capsule is the parotid fascia (fascia parotideo-masseterica). The capsule is derived from the deep cervical fascia, it is strongly attached to the lower border of the zygoma, the acoustic meatus, anterior border of the sterno-mastoid muscle, stylo-mandibular ligament, and the bucco-pharyngeal fascia. It is tenaciously adherent to the gland itself. Passing through it are the following—

Structures,—the external carotid artery and its terminal branches, the posterior auricular, temporal, and internal maxillary; the vein formed by the union of the temporal and internal maxillary veins, the facial nerve and its branches, branches of the great auricular nerve, and the auriculo-temporal branch of the mandibular nerve. The internal carotid artery and the internal jugular vein lie close to its deep surface.

Stenson's Duct (ductus parotideus) (2),—is the duct of the parotid gland, and is about $2\frac{1}{2}$ inches long. It begins by numerous branches from the anterior part of the gland, crosses the masseter muscle, pierces the buccinator, and opens on the inner surface of the cheek by a small orifice opposite the 2nd molar tooth of the upper jaw.

Socia Parotidis,—is a small, detached portion of the gland, which occasionally exists as a separate lobe, just beneath the zygomatic arch. Its duct empties into Stenson's duct, where the latter crosses the masseter muscle.

Arteries,—are derived from the external carotid.

Veins,—empty into tributaries of the external jugular.

Lymphatics,—terminate in the superficial and deep cervical glands.

Nerves,—are derived from the carotid plexus of the sympathetic, the facial, auriculo-temporal and great auricular nerves.

The Submandibular Gland (glandula submaxillaris) (3) lies below the jaw, in the anterior part of the submandibular triangle, and upon the mylo-hyoid, hyo-glossus, and stylo-glossus muscles, the facial artery (a. maxillaris externa) lying embedded in a groove in its upper, posterior border. Its duct—

Wharton's Duct (ductus submaxillaris) (4),—is about 2 inches long, and opens on the summit of a papilla at the side of the frænum of the tongue.

Arteries,—are branches of the facial (external maxillary) and the lingual; the veins following the course of the arteries.

Nerves,—are branches of the submandibular or submaxillary ganglion, and are derived through the ganglion from the chorda tympani, the lingual, and the sympathetic.

The Sublingual Gland (glandula sublingualis) (5) is the smallest of the salivary glands, and is situated beneath the mucous lining of the floor of the mouth, at the side of the frænum (frenulum linguæ) of the tongue, and in contact with the inner surface of the lower jaw. Its ducts, the—

Ducts of Rivinus (ductus sublinguales minores),—from 8 to 2c in number; some join Wharton's duct (ductus submaxillaris), others open on the side of the frenulum linguæ.

Duct of Bartholin,—is a tube formed by one or more of the preceding ducts; it opens into Wharton's duct (ductus submaxillaris).

Arteries,—are derived from the sublingual and submental.

Nerves,—are branches from the lingual nerve.

THE TEETH (DENTES)

The Teeth are 32 organs of digestion, situated 16 in each jaw, where they are implanted within the alveoli, and are partly surrounded by the gums. In each half of each jaw there are—

Deciduous or *Temporary Teeth* (dentes dicidui) (5)—2 Incisors, 1 Canine, 2 Milk-molars.

Permanent Teeth (dentes permanentes) (8)—2 Incisors, 1 Canine, 2 Premolar, 3 Molars.

The Gums (gingivæ) are composed of dense fibrous tissue, closely connected to the periosteum of the alveolar processes, and surrounding the necks of the teeth. They are covered with mucous membrane, presenting numerous fine papillæ around the dental margin, and reflected into the alveoli, where it is continuous with the periosteal lining membrane.

Characteristics of the Teeth. Each tooth consists of a—*crown* (corona dentis) or *body*, projecting above the gum; *root* or *fang* (radix dentis),

Fig. 106.

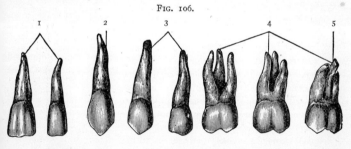

embedded within the alveolus; and the *neck* (collum dentis), the constricted portion between the crown and the fang. The roots are entirely concealed within their alveoli, and are covered by the *pericementum* (periosteum alveolare), a reflection of the periosteum lining the alveoli, which becomes continuous with the fibrous structure of the gums. The *pulp-cavity* (cavum dentis) occupies the centre of the tooth, opening (foramen apicis) at the apex of the fang for the passage of vessels and nerves to the pulp (pulpa dentis). Each class of teeth presents the following characteristics:

Incisors, or Cutters (dentes incisivi) (1),—Crown chisel-shaped, beveled posteriorly. Fang single, long, thickest antero-posteriorly.

Canines, or Tearers (dentes canini) (2),—Crown thick and conical. Fang longest and thickest of all the teeth, forming a projection on the alveolar arch. The 2 upper canines are the "eye-teeth."

Premolars, or Bicuspids (dentes præmolares) (3),—Crown has 2 cusps (tubercles). Fang single but grooved deeply, showing a marked tendency to bifurcate.

Molars, or Grinders (dentes molares) (4),—Crown large, low and cuboid in shape, has 4 cusps on upper molars, 5 on the lower ones. Fangs multiple, usually 3 on the first two upper molars, 2 on the first two lower ones. The third molar (dentes serotini) (5) is called the "wisdom-tooth," from its late eruption; its fangs are usually fused together into a grooved cone.

FIG. 107.

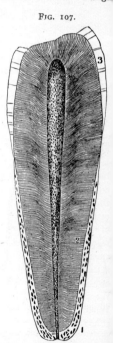

Structure of the Teeth. A tooth consists of 3 structures,—the *dentine*, or ivory (substantia eburnea) the proper dental substance, forming the larger portion; the *enamel* or *adamant* (substantia adamantina), a layer covering the crown; and the *cement* (substantia ossea), a thin layer on the surface of the fang. A central chamber, the *pulp-cavity* (cavum dentis), occupies the interior, and contains the *pulp* (pulpa dentis), a soft, vascular, and sensitive organ, surrounded by a layer of cells the *odonto-blasts* or dentine-forming cells. The—

Pulp-cavity (cavum dentis),—has a process extending down each root, and opening at the apex by a minute orifice (foramen apicis) which transmits vessels and nerves to the pulp.

Pulp (pulpa dentis),—is made up of myxomatous tissue, and contains numerous blood-vessels and nerves, but no lymphatics.

Dentine, or Ivory (substantia eburnea) (2),—consists of tubules (canaliculi dentales) surrounded by the inter-tubular tissue or matrix, and opening into the pulp cavity (cavum dentis). It resembles compact bone in appearance and in composition, consisting of 28 parts animal matter and 72 earthy matter.

Dentinal Tubuli (canaliculi dentales),—in the dentine, are delicate,
wavy canals, diameter about $\frac{1}{4500}$ of an inch, which branch outwardly
and anastomose with each other, forming concentric shadings called
Schreger's lines. They contain slender prolongations from the processes of the cells of the pulp-tissue.

Enamel (substantia adamantina) (3),—covers the crown; consists of
very dense tissue, containing but $3\frac{1}{2}$ per cent. of animal matter.
Its earthy matter, $96\frac{1}{3}$ per cent., is composed chiefly of the phosphate and carbonate of calcium. It is covered by a delicate epithelial
cuticle, *Nasmyth's Membrane* (cuticula dentis), which when intact
withstands the action of acids.

Crusta Petrosa (substantia ossea) or *Cement* (1),—the enamel of the
fang; is a thin layer of true bony tissue, containing lacunæ, canaliculi,
and occasionally Haversian canals.

Development of the Teeth. The teeth are evolved from the dermoid
system, not from the skeleton. They are developed from two of the primitive layers of the embryo,—the *epiblast* producing the enamel (adamant)
and the *mesoblast* giving rise to the dentine (ivory) pulp, cement (substantia ossea), and pericementum (periosteum alveolare). About the
7th week of fœtal life, two parallel ridges arise along the summit of each
jaw, and a corresponding epithelial *lamina* sinks into the mesoblastic tissue
beneath. This lamina sends off 10 cords, one for each tooth, from its inner
edge; the cords expand into flask-like forms, and gradually assume
the forms of the teeth, constituting their *enamel-organs*. They meet and
enclose *papillæ*, which arise from the mesoblastic tissue, forming a series
of sacs, which with their contents are the *dental follicles*, having fibrous
septa between them. In each follicle the vascular papilla has on its
surface a layer of cells, named *odontoblasts*, from which the dentine (ivory)
is developed by calcification, the remainder of the papilla forming the pulp
of the tooth. The cement (adamant) is produced later by the tissue of
the dental sac, in the same manner as bone is produced by periosteum.
When calcification has advanced sufficiently, the pressure of the teeth
causes the absorption of the gum above them, the teeth erupt, and the
fibrous septa ossify, forming the alveoli, which embrace the necks of the
teeth in a firm hold.

The 10 *permanent teeth*, which replace the temporary ones in each jaw,
are developed from special germs (enamel-organs) which arise from the
lamina behind the germs for the temporary teeth, and recede into the
tissue, to enclose mesoblastic papillæ, and go through the same process
as described for the temporary teeth. These germs appear about the 16th

week. The 6 superadded permanent teeth arise from successive backward extensions of the lamina, projected from the back of that for each preceding tooth, and thus forming a special dental germ for each added tooth.

Eruption of the Teeth. The *temporary teeth* begin to appear through the gum at the 7th month after birth, the lower central incisors appearing first. Their eruption ends with the appearance of the second molars, about the age of two years. The lower teeth slightly antedate the upper. Their formula is as follows:—

Mo. Mo. Ca. In. In. In. In. Ca. Mo. Mo.

	Upper...	1	1	1	1	1	1	1	1	1	1	= 10	
	Lower...	1	1	1	1	1	1	1	1	1	1	= 10	= 20

24 12 18 9 7 7 9 18 12 24 months.

Of the *permanent teeth*, the first molars appear about the end of the 6th year, followed by the incisors about the 7th or 8th year, the bicuspids from the 9th to the 10th year, the canines about the 11th or 12th year, the second molars from the 12th to the 13th year, and the third molars from the 17th to the 21st year. Those of the lower jaw are slightly in advance of the corresponding upper ones. Their formula is as follows:—

Wis.Mo.Mo.Pm.Pm.Ca.In.In.In.In.Ca.Pm.Pm.Mo.Mo.Wis.

	Upper.	1	1	1	1	1	1	1	1	1	1	1	1	1	1	1	1	= 16	
	Lower.	1	1	1	1	1	1	1	1	1	1	1	1	1	1	1	1	= 16	32

19 12 6 10 9 11 8 7 7 8 11 9 10 6 12 19 years.

The *greatest number of teeth* at one time in the jaws is 48,—including all the temporary and permanent teeth except the third molars, if none have been lost. This occurs between the 5th and 7th years of age.

THE PHARYNX

The Pharynx is a conical, musculo-membranous tube, about 4½ inches long, hung base up from the basilar process of the occipital bone, and extending to the lower border of the cricoid cartilage posteriorly, or the 5th cervical vertebra, where it becomes continuous with the œsophagus (5). It forms that part of the alimentary canal which lies behind the mouth, being incomplete in front where it opens into that cavity. From above downward it may be divided into—the *naso-pharynx* (pars nasalis), above the level of the soft palate; the *oral part* (pars oralis), between the levels of the soft palate and the hyoid bone; and the *laryngeal part* (pars laryngea), below the latter level. It is connected with—

Anteriorly,—the internal pterygoid plate, pterygo-mandibular ligament, lower jaw, base of the tongue, cornua of the hyoid bone, stylo-hyoid ligament, thyroid and cricoid cartilages of the larynx.

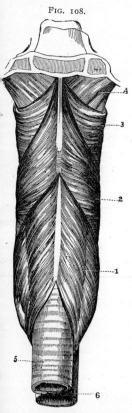

Fig. 108.

Posteriorly,—the longus colli and recti capitis anticus muscles, and by loose areolar tissue to the first 5 cervical vertebræ.

Laterally,—the styloid processes and their muscles, and is in contact with the common and internal carotid arteries, the internal jugular vein, the 9th, 10th, 12th and sympathetic nerves, and above with a small part of the internal pterygoid muscles.

Above,—it is limited by the body of the sphenoid bone, and the basilar process of the occipital bone.

Openings into the Pharynx,—are 7 in number; the 2 posterior nares, (choanæ), the 2 Eustachian tubes (tubæ auditivæ), the mouth, the larynx and the œsophagus.

The Naso-pharynx (pars nasalis pharyngis) is that portion of the pharynx lying behind the nose and above the level of the soft palate. Its cavity, unlike the rest of the pharynx, always remains open. The—

Eustachian Tube (tuba auditiva),—opens on its lateral wall, by a cleft-like orifice (ostium pharyngeum tubæ auditivæ), behind the inferior meatus of the nose, and just above the level of the floor of the nasal fossa.

Pharyngeal Tonsil,—a mass of lymphoid tissue, in the back wall of the pharynx, between the two Eustachian tubes (tubæ auditivæ).

Bursa Pharyngea,—an irregular depression of the mucous membrane in the middle line of the pharynx, above the pharyngeal tonsil.

Cushion (torus tubarius) or *Tubal Prominence*,—immediately behind

the orifice of the Eustachian tube (ostium pharyngeum tubæ auditivæ),
due to the pressure of the extremity of the cartilage of the tube.

Fossa of Rosenmüller,—a deep recess, behind the cushion (torus tubarius)

Structure of the Pharynx. The pharynx is composed of 3 coats,—a
mucous, a muscular and a fibrous, the latter lying between the other two
and called the *pharyngeal aponeurosis* (fascia pharyngo-basilaris) (4)
The mucous coat is covered with ciliated columnar epithelium above the
level of the floor of the nares—below that level with squamous epithelium
and contains racemose mucous glands, especially around the orifices of the
Eustachian tubes (ostia pharyngea tubarum auditivarum), also numerous
crypts or recesses, surrounded by lymphoid tissue.   The—

   Pharyngeal Aponeurosis (fascia pharyngo-basilaris) (4),—is thick
     above, where it is firmly attached to the basilar process of the
     occipital bone, and the petrous portion of the temporal bone.   Pos
     teriorly it presents a fibrous band or *raphé* in the median line, which
     gives attachment to the constrictor muscles.

   Muscles,—are the inferior (1), middle (2), and superior (3) constrictor
     of the pharynx, the stylo-pharyngeus and the palato-pharyngeus (m
     pharyngo-palatinus), which have been described on page 83.

Vessels and Nerves. The *Arteries* of the pharynx are the superior
thyroid and ascending pharyngeal, also the pterygo-palatine and descend
ing palatine branches of the internal maxillary; all from the external
carotid.   The nerves are branches from the—

   Pharyngeal Plexus,—formed by the pharyngeal branches of the vagus
     glosso-pharyngeal, external br. of the superior laryngeal, and superior
     cervical ganglion of the sympathetic.

THE ŒSOPHAGUS OR GULLET

The Œsophagus is a musculo-membranous tube, about 9 inches long
extending from the 5th cervical vertebra and the upper border of the
cricoid cartilage of the larynx, through the œsophageal opening (hiatu
œsophageus) in the diaphragm to the cardiac orifice (cardia ventricul
of the stomach, where it terminates opposite the 10th thoracic vertebra.
In the neck it lies between the trachea and the vertebral column, resting
in part on the longus colli muscle; then inclining to the left side it reaches
the posterior mediastinum behind the left bronchus, and descends in the
mediastinum, at first in front of the thoracic duct, lower down to its left
The Œsophagus is composed of 3 coats, as follows:—

   Muscular Coat (tunica muscularis),—has longitudinal fibres externally
     circular fibres internally, which are continuous with the fibres of the

stomach below, and with those of the inferior constrictor muscle above.

Areolar Coat (tela submucosa),—forms a loose connection between the other two coats, and contains the œsophageal vessels.

Mucous Coat (tunica mucosa),—in thick longitudinal folds, covered with a layer of stratified pavement epithelium. The œsophagus is loosely surrounded by an additional areolar coat (tunica adventitia) which loosely connects it to the surrounding structures.

Œsophageal Glands (glandulæ œsophageæ),—are compound racemose glands, situated in the submucous tissue throughout the tube, but most numerous at the lower end, close to the cardiac orifice (cardia ventriculi) of the stomach.

Arteries,—are chiefly branches from the thoracic aorta.

Veins,—empty into the vena azygos minor.

Nerves,—are branches from the *œsophageal plexus* (plexus gullæ), which is formed by branches from the vagus and the cervical sympathetic.

THE ABDOMEN

The Abdomen is a large, oval-shaped cavity, situated between the thorax above and the pelvis below, and bounded—*above*, by the diaphragm; *below*, by the brim of the pelvis; *posteriorly*, by the vertebral column, and the fasciæ covering the psoæ and quadrati lumborum muscles; *anteriorly and laterally*, by the transversalis fascia, the lower ribs and the venter of the ilium. It is invested internally by the *Peritoneum*, and it contains the—

Stomach.	*Pancreas.*	*Abdominal Aorta.*
Intestines.	*Kidneys and Ureters.*	*Inferior Vena Cava.*
Liver.	*Supra-renal Capsules.*	*Receptaculum Chyli.*
Gall-bladder.	*Bladder* (when distended).	*Thoracic Duct.*
Spleen.	*Uterus* (during pregnancy).	*Solar Plexus*, etc.

Regions of the Abdomen (Regiones Abdominis). The abdomen is divided into 9 regions by two horizontal planes,—one at the level of the cartilages of the 10th ribs (sub-costal plane), another at the level of the highest points of the crests of the ilia, and 2 vertical or lateral planes from the cartilages of the 8th ribs to the centre of Poupart's inguinal ligament. The 9 regions thus formed are named the—

Right Hypochondriac.	*Epigastric.*	*Left Hypochondriac.*
Right Lumbar.	*Umbilical.*	*Left Lumbar.*
Right Inguinal or Iliac.	*Hypogastric.*	*Left Inguinal or Iliac.*

Parts contained in each region are as follows:—

Right Hypochondriac Region,—contains the right lobe of the liver, hepatic flexure of the colon, and part of the right kidney.

Epigastric Region,—contains the right two-thirds of the stomach, left lobe and part of the right lobe of the liver, gall-bladder, duodenum, cœliac axis, solar plexus, pancreas, parts of the aorta, inferior vena cava, vena azygos, and thoracic duct, the supra-renal capsules and parts of the kidneys.

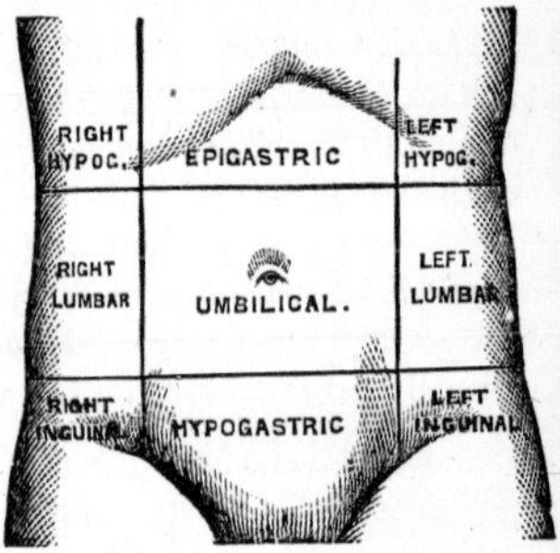

Left Hypochondriac Region,—contains the fundus of the stomach, spleen, tail of the pancreas, splenic flexure of the colon, and part of the left kidney.

Right Lumbar Region,—contains the ascending colon, lower half of the right kidney, and part of the small intestine.

FIG. 109.

Umbilical,—contains the transverse colon, transverse duodenum, part of the great omentum and mesentery, and part of the small intestine.

Left Lumbar Region,—contains the descending colon, lower half of the left kidney, and part of the small intestine.

Right Inguinal or Iliac Region,—contains the right ureter, cæcum, appendix vermiformis, and the spermatic vessels of that side.

Hypogastric Region,—contains convolutions of the small intestine, the bladder in children and in adults when distended, and the uterus during pregnancy.

Left Inguinal or Iliac Region,—contains the left ureter and spermatic vessels, and the sigmoid flexure of the colon.

Apertures in the Walls of the Abdomen are 8 in number, for the transmission of structures to or from it, as follows: the—

Opening for the Vena Cava (foramen venæ cavæ),—in the diaphragm.

Aortic Opening (hiatus aorticus),—behind the diaphragm, for the aorta, vena azygos minor, thoracic duct, and occasionally the left sympathetic nerve (see page 94).

Œsophageal Opening (hiatus œsophageus),—in the diaphragm, for the œsophagus, and the pneumogastric nerves (see page 94).

Umbilical Opening,—in the anterior wall, transmitting the umbilical vessels in the fœtus, but obliterated after birth, leaving a puckered depression, named the *umbilicus*.

Internal Abdominal Ring (annulus inguinalis abdominis),—on each side, half an inch above Poupart's ligament, for the passage of the spermatic cord in the male, and the round ligament of the uterus in the female (see page 384).

Femoral or Crural Ring (annulus femoralis),—on each side, just below Poupart's inguinal ligament; for the passage of the femoral vessels. This opening is closed by the crural or femoral septum (see page 388).

THE PERITONEUM

The Peritoneum (peritonæum) is a large serous membrane, which forms in the male a closed sac, the *parietal layer* (peritonæum parietale) of which

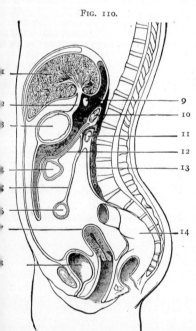

FIG. 110.

lines the abdominal walls, its *visceral layer* (peritonæum viscerale) being reflected more or less completely over all the abdominal and pelvic viscera. Its free surface is covered with endothelium, and is smooth, moist, and shining. Its attached surface is connected to the viscera and the parietes of the abdomen by the sub-peritoneal tela or areolar tissue (tela subserosa). In the female it is not a closed sac, the free extremities of the Fallopian tubes opening directly into its cavity. The peritoneum is divided by a constricted portion of its tissue, at the *foramen of Winslow* (foramen epiploicum) (9), into 2 sacs, the—

Greater Sac (cavum peritonæi),—extends over the anterior two-thirds of the liver (1), behind and above the stomach (3); below, behind, and in front of the great omentum, and below the meso-colon (12).

Lesser Sac (bursa omentalis) *or Cavity of the Great Omentum,*—extends behind and below the liver and stomach, above the meso-colon, within the great omentum, and behind the small or gastro-hepatic omentum (ligamentum hepatogastricum) (2).

The Foramen of Winslow (foramen epiploicum) (9) is an opening which connects the two peritoneal sacs with each other. It is formed by an hour-glass constriction of the peritoneum caused by the hepatic artery in its curved passage forward and upward from the cœliac axis to the transverse fissure of the liver. It is situated behind the free border of the lesser or gastro-hepatic omentum (ligamentum hepatogastricum) (2), immediately below the caudate lobe of the liver, and is bounded as follows:—

Anteriorly,—the lesser or gastro-hepatic omentum (ligamentum hepato-gastricum) (2), containing the hepatic artery, portal vein, and the ductus communis cholédochus.

Posteriorly,—the inferior vena cava, and the right crus of the diaphragm.

Superiorly,—the caudate lobe (processus caudatus) of the liver.

Inferiorly,—the duodenum, and the hepatic artery.

The Omenta are peritoneal folds which pass from the external surface of the *stomach* (3) to various other organs, and are named the *lesser* or gastro-hepatic, the *great* or gastro-colic, and the *gastro-splenic* omentum. The "B.N.A." disregards this distinction and classes them with the *true* ligaments.

Lesser or *Gastro-hepatic Omentum* (ligamentum hepatogastricum) (2), —consists of two layers of peritoneum, the anterior layer belonging to the greater sac (cavum peritonæi), the posterior to the lesser sac (bursa omentalis). It ascends from the lesser curvature of the stomach (3) to the transverse fissure of the liver (porta hepatis) (1) and the end of the œsophagus. Its right margin is free and rounded, and contains between its layers the—

Hepatic Artery and Portal Vein.   Ductus Communis Cholédochus.
Hepatic Plexus of Nerves.   Lymphatics.

Great or *Gastro-colic Omentum* (omentum majus),—consists of 4 layers of peritoneum, the most anterior and superior of which belong to the greater sac (cavum peritonæi), the two internal to the lesser sac (bursa omentalis). The two anterior layers descend from the stomach and spleen over the small intestines (6), and then ascend as the posterior layers to enclose the transverse colon (4).

Gastro-splenic Omentum (ligamentum gastrolienale),—connects the stomach with the spleen, and is continuous by its lower border with the great omentum. It contains the vasa brevia vessels (aa. gastricæ breves).

The Mesenteries (mesenteria) are folds of peritoneum connecting the various parts of the intestinal canal (except the duodenum) to the posterior abdominal wall. Each one contains the vessels of the part which it supports. They are the—

Mesentery proper (mesenterium commune) (5),—connects the convolutions of the jejunum (6) and ileum to the posterior abdominal wall, and contains between its layers the mesenteric vessels and nerves, the lacteals, and the mesenteric glands.

Transverse Meso-colon (mesocolon transversum) (12)—connects the transverse colon to the posterior abdominal wall, and is formed by the two posterior layers of the great omentum (omentum majus).

Sigmoid Meso-colon (mesocolon sigmoideum),—connects the sigmoid flexure of the colon to the left iliac fossa.

Meso-rectum,—connects the upper part of the rectum (14) to the front of the sacrum, and contains the superior hemorrhoidal vessels.

Ligaments formed by the Peritoneum are 17 folds of peritoneum which support certain organs, viz.—

Gastro-splenic (lig. gastrolienale),—from the stomach to the spleen.

Hepatic (ligamenta hepatis),—the longitudinal (lig. falciforme hepatis), coronary (lig. coronarium hepatis), and 2 lateral ligaments of the liver (lig. triangulare dextrum et lig. triangulare sinistrum).

Splenic (lig. lienorenale),—the suspensory ligament of the spleen.

Vesical,—the false ligaments of the bladder, 5 in number.

Uterine,—2 vesico-uterine, 2 recto-uterine, and 2 lateral or broad ligaments of the uterus.

Pouches formed by the Peritoneum, as it passes over the rectum (14), vagina, uterus (7) and bladder (8), are as follows: the—

Recto-vesical Pouch (excavatio rectovesicalis),—in the male, between the rectum and the bladder.

Recto-vaginal or *Douglas' Pouch* (excavatio rectouterina or cavum Douglasi),—in the female, between the rectum and the posterior vaginal wall.

Utero-vesical Pouch (excavatio vesicouterina),—in the female, between the anterior wall of the uterus and the posterior wall of the bladder.

Retro-peritoneal Fossæ are recesses of the peritoneum, forming small pouches in certain parts of the abdominal cavity; any one of which may be the site of a retro-peritoneal hernia, and hernia of the vermiform appendix (processus vermiformis) frequently occurs into one of the pericæcal group. The *lesser sac* of the peritoneum may be regarded as a recess of peritoneum through the epiploic foramen of Winslow. The others ar[e] divided into 3 groups, as follows:—

Duodenal Fossæ,—9 have been described, of which 3 are fairly constan[t] viz.; the *inferior,* and *superior,* both on the left side of the ascendin[g] portion of the duodenum (11); and the *duodeno-jejunal (recessu[s] duodenojejunalis),* bounded above by the pancreas (10), below b[y] the left renal vein, to the right by the aorta (13), and to the left by th[e] left kidney.

Pericæcal Fossæ,—are the *ileo-colic* (recessus ileocecalis anterior), i[n] front of the cæcum; the *ileo-cæcal* (recessus ileocecalis,posterior) behind the angle of junction of the ileum and cæcum; and the *sub- cæcal* (recessus ileocecalis inferior), immediately behind the cæcum.

Intersigmoid Fossa,—lies behind the sigmoid meso-colon, and in fron[t] of the parietal peritoneum, on the external iliac vessels. It is con[n]stant in the fœtus and during infancy, but disappears in a certai[n] percentage of cases as age advances.

Appendices Epiploicæ,—are small pouches of peritoneum situated alon[g] the colon and upper third of the rectum, and filled with fat. The[y] are chiefly found along the transverse colon.

Viscera invested by Peritoneum are the following-named:—

Liver (1) (almost wholly).	*Transverse Colon* (4).
Stomach (3) (almost wholly).	*Sigmoid Flexure.*
Spleen.	*Rectum* (upper ⅓).
Duodenum (11) (first part).	*Ovaries.*
Small Intestine (6).	*Uterus* (7).

Those partially invested by peritoneum are the—

Duodenun (descending and transverse portions).	*Descending Colon.*
	Rectum (14) (middle third).
Cæcum.	*Vagina* (upper part).
Ascending Colon.	*Bladder* (8) (posterior wall).

Those having no peritoneal investment are the—

Pancreas (10). *Kidneys. Supra-renal Capsules* (glandula[e] suprarenales) (see page 324).

THE STOMACH (VENTRICULUS)

The Stomach, the principal organ of digestion, is a dilated part of th[e] alimentary canal, situated between the termination of the œsophagus an[d] the beginning of the small intestine. It is somewhat pyriform in shap[e] of musculo-membranous structure, about 12 inches long by 4 inches i[n] average diameter, held in position by the lesser omentum, and situate[d] diagonally across the upper abdomen, in the epigastric and left hypochon[driac]

driac regions, above the transverse colon, below the liver and diaphragm
It presents for examination a—

Fundus or Upper End (*c*),—connected to the spleen by the gastro-
   splenic omentum (see under PERITONEUM).

Pyloric or Lower End,—lies in contact with the anterior wall of the abdomen, the under surface of the liver, and the neck of the gall-bladder,
   its position being near the
   end of the cartilage of the
   8th rib.

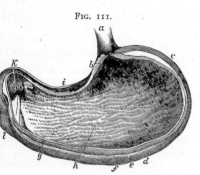

FIG. III.

Greater Curvature (curvatura
   ventriculi major) (*d*),—is
   convex and is connected
   to the colon by the great
   omentum.

Lesser Curvature (curvatura
   ventriculi minor) (*i*),—is
   concave, and connected
   to the liver by the lesser
   omentum, and to the diaphragm by the gastro-
   phrenic ligament.

Œsophageal Orifice (cardia) (*b*),—is situated between the fundus and
   the lesser curvature. It is funnel-shaped, and the highest part of
   the organ.

Pyloric Orifice (pylorus) (*k*),—opens into the duodenum (*l*), and is
   guarded by the circular muscular fibres of the pylorus, which are aggregated into a circular ring, projecting into the cavity, and with its
   covering fold of mucous membrane, forming the *pyloric valve.*

Structure of the Stomach. Its wall consists of 4 coats,—the serous,
muscular, areolar, and mucous; together with vessels and nerves. The—

Serous Coat (tunica serosa),—is derived from the peritoneum, and covers
   the whole external surface, excepting the points where the gastro-
   splenic, great and lesser omenta are attached, and where the stomach
   is in contact with the diaphragm.

Muscular Coat (tunica muscularis) (*f*),—consists of longitudinal (stratum
   longitudinale) external, circular (stratum circulare) middle, and
   oblique (fibræ obliquæ) internal. The *longitudinal* fibres radiate
   from the cardiac orifice, are continuous with the longitudinal fibres
   of the œsophagus and the small intestine, and are the most superficial.
   The *circular* fibres lie deeper, form a layer over the whole organ, and

are aggregated into a circular ring at the pyloric end, which, with its lining mucous fold forms the *pyloric valve*. The *oblique* fibres lie deepest, and are arranged in two sets around the cardiac end.

Areolar or *Sub-mucous Coat* (tela submucosa),—consists of loose areolar tissue, connecting the muscular and mucous coats, and contains the gastric vessels.

Mucous Coat (tunica mucosa) (*g*),—lined with columnar non-ciliated epithelium, covered with polygonal *alveoli*, $\frac{1}{150}$ of an inch in diameter, containing the orifices of the gastric glands. When the stomach is contracted the mucous membrane lies in longitudinal folds or *rugæ* (*h*), one of which aids in forming the valve at the pyloric orifice.

Gastric Glands (glandulæ gastricæ) are of 3 kinds, named *pyloric, cardiac* and *fundus glands*, all tubular in character, and formed by a delicate basement membrane, lined by epithelium. The—

Pyloric Glands,—are most numerous at the pyloric end; each consists of 2 or 3 short, closed tubes, opening into a common duct, the orifice of which is situated at the bottom of an alveolus. They are lined with columnar epithelium throughout.

Cardiac Glands,—situated close to the œsophageal opening (cardia) of the stomach, are tubules lined part way with columnar epithelium, and filled with nucleated cells in their deepest parts.

Fundus Glands,—are most numerous at the fundus and resemble the pyloric glands.

Vessels and Nerves. The *Arteries* of the stomach are—the gastric (a. gastrica sinistra), the pyloric (a. gastrica dextra) and right gastro-epiploic branches of the hepatic, the left gastro-epiploic and vasa brevia from the splenic (a. lienalis). The—

Veins,—terminate either in the splenic (v. lienalis) and superior mesenteric veins, or directly in the portal vein.

Nerves,—are terminal branches of the right and left pneumogastric (nn. vagi), and branches of the semilunar ganglia (ganglia cœliaca) of the sympathetic, forming the *gastric plexus* (see page 241).

THE SMALL INTESTINE

The Small Intestine (intestinum tenue) is a convoluted, tubular digestive organ, about 20 feet in length, extending from the pylorus to the ileo-cæcal valve, where it terminates in the large intestine. It is connected to the spinal column by the mesenteric portion of the peritoneum, and divided into 3 parts, the—

Duodenum (*d*),—about 10 inches long, the first part (pars superior) *ascends* for 2½ inches to the under surface of the liver and the neck of the gall-bladder, the second part (pars descendens) *descends* for 3½ inches in front of the right kidney, and the third part (pars horizontalis inferior) passes transversely for 4 inches to the left, across the spinal column, to the left side of the second lumbar vertebra, where the superior mesenteric artery crosses its junction with the jejunum. The last inch of the duodenum is described as the fourth or ascending portion (pars ascendens). The duodenum has no mesentery, is partially covered with peritoneum, and surrounds the head of the pancreas. Into its descending portion open the ductus communis cholédochus and the pancreatic duct.

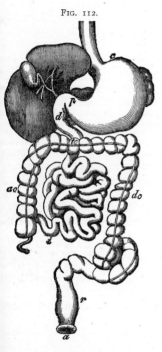

FIG. 112.

Jejunum (intestinum jejunum),—about two-fifths of the rest of the small intestine, its coils lying around the umbilical region. It is named from the fact that it was formerly supposed to be found empty (*jejunus*) after death.

Ileum (intestinum ileum) (*i*),—comprises the remainder of the small intestine; is named from its twisted course, lying below the umbilicus, and terminating in the right iliac fossa, at the *ileo-cæcal valve*, or valve of Bauhin.

Meckel's Diverticulum (diverticulum ilei),—is a blind tube occasionally found connected with the ileum, about 3½ feet above its termination; it represents the remains of the vitelline duct of early fœtal life.

Structure of the Small Intestine, is arranged in 4 coats, like that of the stomach, a serous, muscular, areolar, and mucous coat. The—

Serous Coat (tunica serosa),—is derived from the peritoneum, which partially invests the duodenum, and completely invests the jejunum and ileum, except for a small space along their mesenteric border where the vessels and nerves pass in.

Muscular Coat (tunica muscularis),—consists of external longitudinal (stratum longitudinale) and internal circular (stratum circulare) fibres, the former being thinly distributed along the bowel, the latter forming a thick layer, but not making complete rings.

Areolar Coat (tela submucosa),—contains the vessels of the intestine and connects the muscular and mucous coats together.

Mucous Membrane (tunica mucosa),—is covered with columnar non ciliated epithelium, and thrown into crescentic transverse folds, the *valvulæ conniventes* (plicæ circulares), or valves of Kirkring. It presents also numerous vascular projections or *Villi* (villi intestinales) simple follicles, and three kinds of glands (all described below).

Villi (villi intestinales) (*f*) are minute, vascular processes, which project from the mucous membrane of the small intestine throughout its whole extent, giving to its surface a velvety appearance. They are most numerous in the duodenum and jejunum, and altogether number about 4 millions for the whole length of the intestine. Each villus consists of a lacteal vessel, a plexus of capillary blood-vessels, epithelium, basement membrane, and muscular tissue, supported and held together by retiform lymphoid tissue. The—

FIG. 113.

Lacteal Vessel,—is situated in the axis of the villus, and commences by dilated extremities near its summit.

Blood-vessels,—form a plexus between the lacteal and the basement membrane, enclosing the cells of the villus in their interstices.

Basement Membrane,—surrounds the preceding, and is made up of a stratum of endothelial cells, upon which is a layer of columnar epithelium.

Muscular Tissue,—consists of longitudinal fibres prolonged into the villus from the muscular tissue of the mucosa.

Simple Follicles, or *Crypts of Lieberkühn* (glandulæ intestinales),—are minute, tubular depressions of the mucous membrane, opening between the villi, their orifices appearing as minute dots on the surface of the mucous membrane.

Glands of the Small Intestine. The mucous membrane of the small intestine contains the following glands:—

Duodenal or *Brunner's Glands* (glandulæ duodenales),—are small, compound glands, found only in the duodenum and the first part of the jejunum, being most numerous near the pylorus. In structure they are identical with the racemose glands of the mouth.

Solitary Glands (noduli lymphatici solitarii),—are lymphoid organs, situated throughout the intestine, though most numerous at the lower portion of the ileum. They are agminated into some 20 or 30 oval patches, named—

Peyer's Patches or *Glands* (noduli lymphatici aggregati),—on the surface opposite to the mesenteric attachments, some of which are as much as 4 inches in length. They are most numerous and largest in the ileum, are few and small in the jejunum, and are occasionally seen in the duodenum.

Vessels and Nerves. The *Arteries* of the jejunum and ileum are branches of the superior mesenteric artery, forming an intricate plexus in the areolar tissue, which gives off minute vessels to the glands and villi. The duodenum is supplied by the pyloric (a. gastrica dextra) and pancreatico-duodenal branches of the hepatic, and the inferior pancreatico-duodenal from the superior mesenteric. The—

Veins,—accompany the arteries and have a similar course and arrangement.

Lymphatics,—are in two sets, one for the mucous membrane and one for the muscular coat.

Nerves,—of the duodenum are derived from the solar plexus (plexus cœliacus); those of the rest of the intestine from the sympathetic plexuses around the superior mesenteric artery.

THE LARGE INTESTINE (INTESTINUM CRASSUM)

The Large Intestine (intestinum crassum) extends from the termination of the ileum to the anus. It is about five feet long, of large calibre, and consists of the same coats as the small intestine, the mucous being smooth and without villi, the muscular having its longitudinal fibres collected into 3 narrow bands (tæniæ coli) producing a sacculation (pouching) of its wall. In its course it describes an arch around the convolutions of the small intestine, and is divided into 3 portions, the Cæcum, the Colon, and the Rectum.

The Cæcum (intestinum cæcum) is a large blind pouch, about 2½ inches long and 3 inches broad, situated in the right iliac fossa, immediately behind the abdominal wall, above the outer half of Poupart's ligament (ligamentum inguinale), and below the ileo-cæcal valve, which opens into it.

It lies free in the abdominal cavity, its closed end downward, its open end upward and continuous with the commencement of the colon. It is usually enveloped entirely by peritoneum, and presents for examination the—

Vermiform Appendix (processus vermiformis),—a narrow, worm-like, blind tube, averaging 3 inches in length, directed upward behind the cæcum, or to the left behind the ileum, or downward and inward into the true pelvis. Its canal communicates with the cæcum by an orifice situated below and behind the ileo-cæcal opening. Sometimes the orifice of the vermiform process is partially guarded by a crescentic fold of mucous membrane (valvula processus vermiformis) which is produced on its upper border. Its proximal ⅔ is retained in position by a triangular mesentery, its distal ⅓ is free and completely covered by peritoneum.

Ileo-cæcal Valve, or Valve of Bauhin (valvula coli),—guards the entrance of the small intestine, and is formed by two crescentic folds of the mucous and cellular coats and circular muscular fibres (labium superius et labium inferius) each fold being covered with villi on the side toward the ileum, but smooth on the cæcal side.

The Colon is divided into 4 parts,—the ascending, transverse, and descending colon and the sigmoid flexure. The *Ascending Colon* (colon ascendens) (*ac*) extends from the cæcum upward on the right side of the abdominal cavity, to the under surface of the liver, where it turns to the left, forming the *hepatic flexure* (flexura coli dextra). The *Transverse Colon* (colon transversum) (*tc*) crosses the abdomen from right to left to the lower end of the spleen, where it curves downward, forming the *splenic flexure* (flexura coli sinistra). The *Descending Colon* (colon descendens) (*dc*) passes downward along the outer border of the left kidney, then inward along the outer border of the psoas muscle to the crest of the ilium, where it terminates in the *Sigmoid Flexure* (colon sigmoideum) or pelvic colon. The latter is curved like an *f*, first upward and forward, then downward into a loop, which terminates in the rectum, opposite the left sacro-iliac symphysis. The—

Peritoneum,—covers the transverse colon and the loop of the sigmoid flexure almost completely, forming the transverse mesocolon and the sigmoid mesocolon. It covers the ascending and descending colon and the upper part of the sigmoid flexure on their anterior surface and sides.

Mesocolon,—is the mesentery of the colon, connecting the transverse portion to the posterior abdominal wall in all cases; but exists for the ascending colon in 26 per cent., and for the descending colon in 36 per cent. of the cases. The *sigmoid mesocolon* connects the loop of the sigmoid flexure to the psoas fascia.

Phreno-colic Ligament,—is a fold of peritoneum, connecting the commencement of the descending colon with the diaphragm.

Appendices Epiploicæ,—are small pouches of peritoneum containing fat, and found along the colon and part of the rectum. They are chiefly appended to the transverse colon.

The Rectum (intestinum rectum) (*r*) is the terminal portion of the large intestine, and extends from the sigmoid flexure (colon sigmoideum) or pelvic colon to the anal orifice (*a*). It is about 8 inches long, not sacculated, and, though not straight, is straighter than the rest of the gut. It curves laterally to the middle of the sacrum, and backward about an inch above its termination at the *anus*, where it forms an antero-posterior slit, having its lateral walls in apposition, but capable of considerable distention. The relations of the rectum are as follows:—

First Portion, 4 inches long,—lies on the left pyriformis muscle and the left sacral plexus of nerves; to its left are the left ureter and the branches of the left internal iliac artery.

Second Portion, 3 inches long,—in the male subject lies just behind the trigonum vesicæ and the vesiculæ seminales, and close below the under surface of the prostate gland. In the female it is adherent to the central portion of the posterior wall of the vagina.

Third Portion or *Anal Canal,* 1 to 1½ inch long,—is surrounded by its sphincters and the levator ani muscle, and is separated by the perinæum from the membranous portion and bulb of the urethra in the male, from the vagina in the female.

Peritoneum,—invests the first portion almost completely, forming the *mesorectum,* which connects it to the sacrum; invests the second portion in front and laterally, and is thence reflected to the bladder in the male and to the vagina in the female. The third portion of the rectum has no peritoneal investment.

Sphincters of the Rectum,—are the internal sphincter and the sphincter ani (see page 97).

Valves of Houston (plicæ transversales recti),—are 3 transverse folds of the mucous lining, of semilunar shape, one in the upper part of the rectum on the right side, another about the middle on the left side and the third in front, opposite the base of the bladder.

Glands of the Large Intestine. The *simple follicles* are present throughout its entire length, and are more numerous than in the small intestine. The *solitary glands* (noduli lymphatici solitarii) are most abundant in the cæcum and appendix, but are scattered irregularly over the entire canal. Brunner's glands and villi are absent, the valvulæ conniventes are almost wanting.

Vessels and Nerves. The *Arteries* of the large intestine are the ileo-colic, colica dextra and colica media from the superior mesenteric, to the cæcum, the ascending colon and the transverse colon; the colica sinistra and sigmoid branches of the inferior mesenteric, to the descending colon and the sigmoid flexure; the superior hemorrhoidal from the inferior mesenteric, the middle hemorrhoidal from the internal iliac, and the inferior hemorrhoidal from the pudic (a. pudenda interna), to the rectum.   The—

Veins of the Rectum,—commence in a plexus around the lower end, the hemorrhoidal plexus, which gives off 6 vessels to unite into a trunk, the superior hemorrhoidal vein.   The plexus communicates also with the tributaries of the middle and inferior hemorrhoidal veins, establishing a communication between the systemic and portal circulations.

Lymphatics,—open into the mesenteric, lumbar, sacral and inguinal glands, the latter receiving the vessels from around the anus.

Nerves,—are derived from the sympathetic plexuses around the arteries which are distributed to the large intestine.

THE LIVER (HEPAR)

The Liver is the largest gland in the body, weighing from 3 to 4 pounds, and measuring all the way from 3 to 9 inches in various directions.   It is situated in the right hypochondriac, epigastric and part of the left hypochondriac regions; has 5 fissures, 5 lobes, 5 ligaments, and 5 sets of vessels, and is invested by peritoneum, except for a small space at the attachment of the coronary ligament.   It is also surrounded by a fibrous coat which is continuous at the transverse fissure with the capsule of Glisson.   Its—

Upper Surface (facies superior),—is convex, in relation with the under surface of the diaphragm and lower 6 or 7 ribs, and is divided into two lobes by the falciform ligament.

Under Surface (facies inferior) (Fig. 113),—is concave, covers the stomach, duodenum, hepatic flexure of colon (flexura colidextra), right kidney and supra-renal capsule, and is divided into 5 lobes by 5 fissures.

Posterior Surface (facies posterior),—direct backwards and is in contact with the various structures forming the upper part of the posterior abdominal wall.   It is flat in the vertical axis but is deeply indented by the vertebral column, and deeply grooved by the vena cava.

Anterior Border (margo anterior),—is sharp, and is notched in two places, one at the fundus of the gall-bladder (vesica fellea), the other at the round and falciform ligaments. It corresponds to the lower border of the ribs and costal cartilages, descending a little lower during deep inspiration and in the upright posture.

Posterior Border (margo posterior),—rounded, and deeply grooved (sometimes channeled) for the inferior vena cava (13). The anterior and posterior borders, together form the inferior border (margo inferior).

Fissures of the Liver are 5 in number, situated on the inferior and posterior surfaces, and arranged in the form of the letter H. The left limb of the H is the longitudinal fissure (fossa longitudinalis sinistra), divided into the umbilical fissure (fossa venæ umbilicalis) anteriorly, and

Fig. 114.

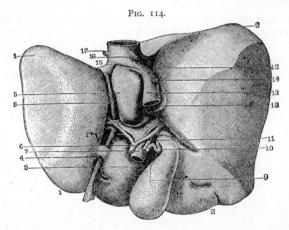

the fissure for the ductus venosus (fossa ductus venosi) (8) posteriorly; the right limb is formed in front by the fissure (fossa vesicæ felleæ) for the gall-bladder (9), behind by the fissure (fossa venæ cavæ) (12) for the vena cava (13). The connecting bar of the H is the transverse fissure (porta hepatis). The—

Longitudinal Fissure (fossa longitudinalis sinistra),—separates the left lobe (lobus hepatis sinister) from the lobus Spigelii (lobus caudatus) and the lobus quadratus. Its anterior portion, in front of the transverse fissure (porta hepatis), is the *umbilical fissure* (fossa venæ umbilicalis), containing the umbilical vein in the fœtus, and its

22

remains, the round ligament, in the adult. It is often bridged over by a process of liver tissue, the *pons hepatis*. The posterior portion is the *fissure of the ductus venosus* (fossa ductus venosi) (8), and lodges the slender cord which, in the adult, represents that fœtal vessel.

Transverse or *Portal Fissure* (porta hepatis),—is about 2 inches long, runs from the longitudinal fissure to the right, and transmits the portal vein (7), hepatic artery (6) and nerves, and the hepatic duct (11) and lymphatics. It separates the quadrate lobe in front from the caudate (processus caudatus) and Spigelian (lobus caudatus) lobes behind.

Fissure for the Gall-bladder (fossa vesicæ felleæ) (9),—on the right of the longitudinal fissure, and nearly parallel with it, extending from the anterior border, backward to near the right end of the transverse fissure.

Fissure for the Vena Cava (fossa venæ cavæ) (12),—extends obliquely upward on the posterior surface, and separates the Spigelian lobe (lobus caudatus) from the right lobe (lobus hepatis dexter). Occasionally this fissure is a complete canal in the substance of the liver.

Lobes of the Liver are 5 in number, but three are mere lobules of the right lobe, formed by the smaller fissures. The—

Right Lobe (lobus hepatis dexter) (2),—is much the largest, and presents the three small fissures and four shallow depressions, one anteriorly for the colon, another posteriorly for the kidney, a third for the duodenum, and a fourth for the supra-renal capsule (glandula suprarenalis).

Left Lobe (lobus hepatis sinister) (1),—is divided from the right lobe by the longitudinal fissure (fossa longitudinalis sinistra), and rests upon the stomach.

Quadrate Lobe (3),—in front of the transverse fissure (porta hepatis) and between the umbilical fissure (fossa venæ umbilicalis) and that (fossa vesicæ felleæ) for the gall-bladder.

Lobus Spigelii (lobus caudatus) (5),—behind the transverse fissure (porta hepatis), and between the fissure (fossa ductus venosi) for the ductus venosus and that (fossæ venæ cavæ) for the vena cava.

Caudate Lobe (processus caudatus) (4),—a connecting ridge from the lobus Spigelii (lobus caudatus) to the right lobe; it separates the fissure for the vena cava (fossa venæ cavæ) from the fissure (fossa vesicæ felleæ) for the gall-bladder, and lies directly above the foramen of Winslow (foramen epiploicum).

Ligaments of the Liver are 5 in number, connecting the organ to the under surface of the diaphragm and the anterior wall of the abdomen. Four are folds of peritoneum; one, the round ligament, is the obliterated umbilical vein of the fœtus. The—

Suspensory or Falciform Ligament (lig. falciforme hepatis), called also the Broad and the Longitudinal Ligament,—is a sickle-shaped double fold reflected over the round ligament (lig. teres hepatis) and is attached to the sheath of the right rectus muscle as low as the umbilicus, and to the diaphragm.

Coronary Ligament (ligamentum coronarium hepatis),—is a double fold, containing firm areolar tissue in its interspace, and extending from the posterior border of the liver to the diaphragm.

Lateral Ligaments 2,—are the triangular extremities of the coronary ligament, and extend from the liver to the diaphragm. They are also known as the lig. triangulare dextrum and the lig. triangulare sinistrum.

Round Ligament (lig. teres hepatis),—ascends in the free margin of the suspensory ligament (lig. falciforme hepatis) from the umbilicus to the longitudinal fissure (fossa longitudinalis sinistra), in which it is continued to the vena cava. It results from the obliteration of the fœtal umbilical vein, and is continued on the posterior surface as the obliterated ductus venosus (8).

STRUCTURE OF THE LIVER

The Liver Substance is composed of numerous *lobules* (lobuli hepatis) held together by fine areolar tissue, and the ramifications of the hepatic artery and veins, portal vein, hepatic ducts, lymphatics and nerves. The whole organ is invested by a fibrous coat, and by a peritoneal coat for the greater part of its surface. The—

Fibrous Coat (capsula fibrosa [Glissoni]),—is formed of connective tissue, and is inflected at the transverse fissure (porta hepatis) along the vessels, forming the so-called capsule of Glisson.

Peritoneal Coat (tunica serosa),—is derived from the gastro-hepatic (lesser) omentum, (ligamentum hepatogastricum) between the layers of which the liver is received, and which forms 4 of its 5 ligaments.

Parts Uninvested by Peritoneum are—on the anterior and superior surfaces, along the line between the two layers which form the suspensory ligament; on the inferior surface, where the gall-bladder is attached, and at the transverse fissure (porta hepatis) where the vessels enter; on the posterior surface of the right lobe, a strip about 3 inches broad, where the liver is in contact with the diaphragm, also a part of the depression for the supra renal capsule (glandula suprarenalis).

The Lobules (lobuli hepatis) (1) are small, granular-looking bodies, of polygonal shape, and about $\frac{1}{20}$ inch in diameter, clustered around the sub lobular branches of the hepatic veins, and connected together by con nective tissue (3), blood-vessels, ducts (2), and lymphatics. Each lobule consists of a mass of *hepatic cells*, surrounded by a dense capillary plexus, and contains the minute beginnings of a bile-duct, the so-called *biliary capillaries;* possessing therefore all the essential constituents of a secreting gland. A lobule contains—

FIG. 115.

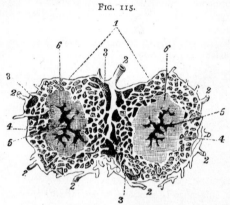

Hepatic Cells,—each about $\frac{1}{1500}$ inch in diameter, having a nucleus and
 nucleolus, yellow coloring matter, glycogen granules, and oil globules.
Lobular Veins (3),—forming a plexus in the lobule.
Intralobular Vein (4),—in the centre of each lobule. } (See Fig. 115)
Plexuses,—of lymphatics, nerves, and bile-ducts.

The Capsule of Glisson (capsula fibrosa) is the fibrous tissue which sur rounds the hepatic *vessels* in the transverse fissure (porta hepatis), and accompanies them in their course throughout the substance of the liver. It is continuous with the fibrous covering of the organ. The *hepatic veins* and their tributaries are not invested by the capsule.

Nerves of the Liver are branches from the *hepatic plexus*, which is formed by branches derived from the cœliac plexus, the left pneumogastric (n. vagus) and the right phrenic nerves.

Vessels of the Liver

Vessels of the Liver are 5 in number, the hepatic artery, portal vein, hepatic veins, hepatic ducts (ductus hepaticus), and lymphatics, all emerging in the transverse fissure except the hepatic veins, which enter the fissure (fossa) for the vena cava. In the transverse fissure (porta hepatis) all the vessels are enveloped in the capsule of Glisson, and the duct, artery and vein are situated from before backward in the order named, represented by the letters DAV. Four of these vessels are described separately below, the—

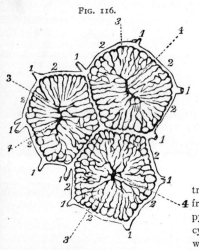

FIG. 116.

Lymphatics,—accompany the blood-vessels in 2 sets, superficial and deep; the latter beginning in lymphatic spaces around the capillaries of the lobules, and accompanying the interlobular vessels. They enter the lumbar glands, the glands of the lesser omentum, those of the œsophagus and of the lesser curvature of the stomach.

The Hepatic Artery is the nutrient vessel of the liver; it arises from the cœliac axis, gives off pyloric, gastro-duodenal and cystic branches, and passes upward in front of the foramen of Winslow to the transverse fissure, where it divides into right and left branches, for the corresponding lobes of the liver. These divide and subdivide, ramifying in the portal canals throughout the organ, and giving off the following branches:—

Vaginal Branches,—to the capsule of Glisson.

Capsular Branches,—to the fibrous covering of the liver.

Interlobular (rami arteriosi interlobulares),—forming an arterial plexus between the lobules.

Lobular,—to the capillary network in the lobules.

The Portal Vein brings blood to the liver from the stomach, intestines, pancreas and spleen; being formed by the union of the superior and inferior mesenteric, splenic and gastric veins, all the main veins of the abdomen except the renal. It is about 4 inches long, enters the transverse fissure of the liver, where it divides into the *right* and *left portal* veins, these dividing into branches, which receive *vaginal* and *capsular* veins, and ramify throughout the liver as *portal canals* (1), in company with the branches of the hepatic artery and duct; finally breaking up into the—

Interlobular Plexus (2),—between the lobules, giving off the—

    Lobular Veins (3),—converge to the centre of the lobule, and end in the—

    Intralobular Vein (4),—vertically in the centre of each lobule, enters the *sublobular* of the hepatic veins below the lobule.

The Hepatic Veins convey blood away from the liver, and are continuations of the intralobular veins of the portal system, beginning as the *sublobular veins* below each lobule, uniting finally into 3 trunks usually, which enter the inferior vena cava in the fissure for that vessel. On section of the liver the hepatic veins gape open, being adherent to the liver substance; the portal veins are closed, being surrounded by the capsule of Glisson.

The Hepatic Ducts carry away bile from the liver. They begin between the cells of the lobules, in minute spaces, the *bile-capillaries*, forming channels which radiate to the circumference of the lobule, and enter an *interlobular plexus* between the lobules; from which plexus ducts pass into the portal canals, are enclosed in the capsule of Glisson with the portal vein and the hepatic artery, and join with other ducts to finally form 2 main trunks, which emerge at the transverse fissure, and by their union form the *Hepatic Duct* (see below).

EXCRETORY APPARATUS OF THE LIVER

The Excretory Apparatus of the liver consists of—the *Hepatic Duct*, formed by the union of the two main trunks above-mentioned; the *Gallbladder*, a reservoir for the bile; the *Cystic Duct*, the duct of the gall-bladder; and the *Ductus Communis Choledochus* or common bile-duct, formed by the junction of the hepatic and cystic ducts. The—

Hepatic Duct,—about $1\frac{1}{2}$ inches long; is formed in the transverse fissure by the union of the two main biliary ducts, from the right and left lobes. It joins the cystic duct from the gall-bladder to form the—

Ductus Communis Choledochus, or Common Bile-duct,—is a fibro-muscular tube, covered by peritoneum and lined with mucous membrane, about 3 inches in length, formed by the junction of the Cystic and Hepatic ducts, and emptying its contents (bile) into the descending part of the duodenum at a point about 3 inches from the pyloric orifice of the stomach, generally in common with the duct of the pancreas.

The Gall-bladder (vesica fellea) is a pear-shaped bag, 3 to 4 inches long, an inch in greatest diameter, holding from 8 to 12 fluid drachms, invested by peritoneum on its under surface and fundus, formed of a fibro-muscular coat and lined by a mucous one, lying in a fissure on the under surface of the liver, close to its anterior border, and directed obliquely downward, forward, and to the right.   Its—

Fundus (fundus vesicæ felleæ),—touches the abdominal wall immediately below the 9th costal cartilage, and is completely invested by peritoneum.

Neck (collum vesicæ felleæ),—is narrow and curves like the letter S; it empties into the—

Cystic Duct (ductus cysticus),—about 1½ inches long, is marked interiorly by spirally arranged crescentic folds of its mucous lining, and joins with the hepatic duct at an acute angle, to form the common bile-duct (see above).

THE PANCREAS

The Pancreas is a compound racemose gland, about 5½ inches long and 1½ inches broad, situated transversely across the posterior wall of the abdomen behind the stomach and in front of the first lumbar vertebra. Its structure resembles that of the salivary glands, being composed of reddish-yellow lobules, vessels and ducts, and ending in closed pouches surrounded by a capillary plexus. It is not enclosed in a capsule, but is surrounded by areolar tissue, which extends into its interior, and connects together the various lobules.   Its—

Fig. 117.

Head or *Right Extremity* (caput pancreatis) (1),— shaped like the head of a hammer, lies in the concave curve of the duodenum, in front of the common bile-duct, the inferior vena cava, the left renal vein, the right crus of the diaphragm, and the aorta.

Neck (2),—about an inch long, lies just below the pylorus, and above the transverse portion of the duodenum.

Body (corpus pancreatis) (3),—is in relation *anteriorly* with the ascending layer of the transverse meso-colon, the posterior wall of the stom-

ach and the transverse colon; *posteriorly* with the aorta, splenic vein
(v. lienalis), origin of the superior mesenteric artery, crura of the
diaphragm, left kidney and supra-renal capsule, and the left quadratus
lumborum muscle.

Tail (cauda pancreatis), *or Left Extremity* (4),—lies above the left kidney
and in contact with the lower part of the inner surface of the spleen.

Pancreatic Duct, or Duct of Wirsung (5),—extends the whole length of
the gland, commencing by the junction of the lobular ducts in the
tail, it receives the ducts of the various lobules, and opens into the
descending portion of the duodenum, about 3 or 4 inches below the
pylorus, usually by an orifice common to it and the common bile-duct,
occasionally by a separate orifice. Sometimes the pancreatic duct is
branched, in which case the upper branch is known as the duct of
Santorini (ductus pancreaticus accessorius).

Arteries, are the—

Pancreatica Magna and Pancreaticæ Parvæ,—from the splenic
(a. lienalis).

Pancreatico-duodenalis,—branch of the hepatic artery.

Inferior Pancreatico-duodenalis,—branch of the sup. mesenteric.

Veins,—open into the splenic and superior mesenteric veins.

Lymphatics, terminate in the lumbar glands.

Nerves,—are filaments from the splenic plexus, which is a subdivision of
the cœliac plexus.

The Lesser Pancreas is a lobe of the head of the pancreas, sometimes
found detached, in which case it opens by a duct into the duodenum about
an inch above the orifice of the pancreatic duct.

DUCTLESS GLANDS

The Ductless Glands are those that discharge their special products
directly into the blood or lymphatic circulation. This is spoken of as
internal secretion, which, however, is not peculiar to this variety of gland,
since many of the other organs such as the liver, pancreas, stomach, intestine, kidney, prostate, testis, uterus, ovary, corpus luteum, and possibly
still other organs, form internal secretions in addition to their obvious
functions. The ductless glands are classified as belonging to the following
systems:

1. Chromaphil system.
2. Cortical system.
3. Ductless glands of ento-dermal origin.
4. Ductless glands associated with the vascular system.

THE CHROMAPHIL (chromaffin or phærochrome) SYSTEM includes those
glands which elaborate *adrenin* (lævo-adrenalin $C_9H_{13}NO_3$ of Aldrich).

They are so named because their cell cytoplasm contains granules which are stained bright yellow to dark brown, by salts of chromium. In this system are included the following:—

1. *Paraganglia* which are small masses of chromaphil tissue associated with the ganglia of the sympathetic nervous system. They may be immediately on the outside, partially within, or entirely within the capsules of the sympathetic ganglia.

2. *Chromaphil Bodies of the Sympathetic Plexuses.* These are associated with the abdominal sympathetic plexuses; those of the aortic plexus are called the *aortic bodies* which are situated close to the origin of the superior mesenteric artery.

3. *Carotid Glands of Bodies* (glomus carotica) are found, one on each side, in or behind the bifurcation of the common carotid artery.

4. The *Large Cells* of the *Anterior* (buccal or glandular) lobe of the *pituitary body* (hypophysis) (see page 186).

5. Medullary portions of the *supra-renal glands* (see page 363).

THE CORTICAL SYSTEM includes several masses of yellow glandular tissue which is rich in *lipoids*, there are of these,—

1. *Cortex of the Supra-renal Glands* (see page 363).

2. *Accessory Cortical Bodies* which are several small masses of cortical tissue found in relation to the testis and ovary.

DUCTLESS GLANDS OF ENTODERMAL ORIGIN include the following,—

1. *Small Cells* of the anterior (buccal or glandular) lobe of the *Pituitary Body* (hypophysis) (see page 186).

2. *Thyreoid Gland* (glandula thyreoidea) is an incapsulated gland surrounding the front and sides of the upper part of the trachea, and the sides of the lower part of the larynx, under cover of the *omo-hyoid*, *sterno-hyoid* and *sterno-thyreoid* muscles.

The *Capsule* consists of a superficial layer and a deep layer. The *superficial layer* of the *capsule* is derived from the deep cervical fascia. It is strongly attached to the trachea and the deep cervical fascia. It is attached loosely by areolar tissue to the deep layer of the capsule. The interval between the two layers is occupied by numerous large blood-vessels, the veins in particular, forming a very large anastomotic plexus.

The thyreoid gland itself usually consists of a *right* and a *left lobe* the lower thirds of which are joined together across the mid-line by the *isthmus*. Often there is an upward production of the upper border of the isthmus forming a *pyramidal lobe* which is usually to the left of the mid-line. Running from the lower border of the hyoid bone to the apex of the pyramidal lobe is the *hyo-thyreoid* ligament which is sometimes muscular (m. levator glandulæ thyreoidea); this, together with the attachments of the *superficial layer of the capsule* to the trachea and deep cervical fascia, holds the gland in place.

Deep Layer of the Capsule (tunica propria glandulæ thyreoidea) is intimately attached to the gland itself into the substance of which it sends many supporting *trabeculæ* and *septa* accompanied by blood-vessels.

Structure,—The gland is made up of many irregular masses called *lobules*, each lobule consists of several closed *vesicles* which do not communicate, each vesicle is lined with a single layer of cuboidal or columnar cells, and filled with a yellowish viscous substance called *colloid*.

Arteries are,—the right and left *superior thyroid* branches of the external carotid arteries, right and left *inferior thyroid* branches of the thyroid axes of the subclavian arteries, and when present, the *thyreoidea ima* branch either of the innominate artery or arch of the aorta.

Veins are,—right and left *superior thyroid* veins which empty into the internal jugular veins, right and left *middle thyroid* veins which, when present, empty into the internal jugular veins, right and left *inferior thyroid* veins which empty into the innominate veins, *thyreoidea ima* vein which when present empties into either the left innominate vein or left inferior thyroid vein.

Lymphatics on the left side empty into the upper loop of the thoracic duct (ductus thoracicus), those of the right side empty into the right lymphatic duct (ductus lymphaticus dexter).

The *nerve* supply is from the middle and inferior cervical ganglia of the sympathetic.

3. *Parathyreoid Glands,*—are small flattened ovoidal masses of a yellow or reddish-brown color, they are slightly lighter in color and of a softer consistency than the thyroid gland itself. Each is surrounded by its own individual capsule to which it is strongly adherent. Each gland possesses a stalk formed by the blood-vessels entering its hilus. The capsule sends many highly vascular supporting trabeculæ and septa into the substance of the gland which is composed of solid masses of polyhedral cells. There may be a considerable variation in both the number and the disposition of these glands. Normally there should be an upper and a lower pair.

Superior parathyreoids,—a right and a left, are usually found, nearer the mid-line than the lower pair, on the upper ends or on the dorsal surface of the upper thirds of the lateral lobes of the thyreoid gland, inside of and strongly adherent to its capsule; or they may be imbedded in the areolar tissue between the two layers of the capsule.

Inferior parathyreoids, a right and a left, usually lie on the dorsal or lateral surface of the lower thirds of the lateral lobes of the thyreoid gland, much further from the mid-line than the upper pair, and more often outside of the capsule. Parathyreoids that have wandered far from the thyreoid gland can hardly be identified except under the microscope.

4. *Thymus Gland* (thymus),—consists of two lateral lobes which are firmly united, each being attached by a ligament to the lower end of the lateral lobe of the thyreoid gland above it. The thymus depends from these *suspensory ligaments* in the lower part of the front of the neck downwards into the superior and anterior mediastina, often reaching the pericardium. In front, it is in relation to the back of the sternum, the sterno-thyreoid and sterno-mastoid muscles. Laterally it is in relation to the pleuræ. Behind it are the great blood-vessels which deeply groove its dorsal surface although actually separated from it by the deep cervico-thoracic fascia. The thymus is subject to much variation both in size and shape, usually it is relatively largest at the age of puberty, becoming progressively smaller thereafter. In color the thymus is reddish gray, tending to become white or yellow as it undergoes involution. It is invested by a thin fibrous capsule which sends numerous septa into the gland substance dividing it up into *lobules* which in turn are divided up into *follicles*. Each follicle consists of a central medulla which is partially surrounded by a cortex which resembles lymphatic gland tissue.

Arteries are numerous, irregular branches of the *internal mammary* and *inferior thyreoid* arteries.

Veins are numerous and irregular, they empty into the *inferior thyreoid*, *internal mammary*, and *left innominate* veins.

Nerves are small branches of the *vagus* which run directly into the gland, and minute branches of the *cervical sympathetic* which are carried in on the arteries.

Lymphatics arise from plexuses around the follicles, pass through the inter-lobular septa and the capsule to the adjacent lymph glands.

DUCTLESS GLANDS ASSOCIATED WITH THE VASCULAR SYSTEM

1. **The Spleen** (lien) is a soft, brittle, highly vascular organ, of dark purplish color, in size about 5 by 3 by 1½ inches, in weight about 7 ounces; situated deeply in the left hypochondrium, between the fundus of the stomach in front and internally, and the diaphragm behind and externally, opposite the 9th, 10th and 11th ribs of the left side. It is connected with the stomach, by the *gastro-splenic omentum* (ligamentum gastrolienale); with the diaphragm, by the *suspensory* or *phreno-splenic ligament;* and with the left kidney, by the *lieno-renal ligament*, all of which are folds of peritoneum. Its—

Fig. 118.

Outer Surface (facies diaphragmatica),—is convex, smooth, and in relation with the under surface of the diaphragm, which separates it from the 9th, 10th and 11th ribs of the left side.

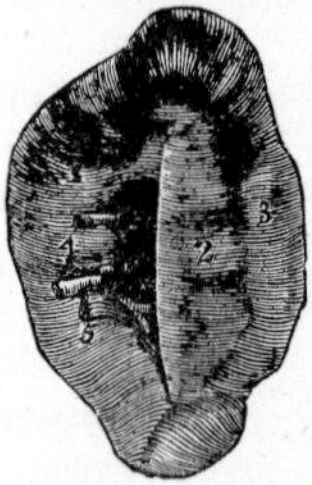

Inner Surface,—is concave, and divisible into two portions, one that is in contact, anteriorly (2) with the posterior wall of the cardiac end of the stomach and the tail of the pancreas (facies gastrica), the other portion being in contact posteriorly (1) with the left kidney (facies renalis).

Hilum (hilus lienis),—a vertical fissure about the middle of the inner surface, pierced by apertures for the vessels and nerves.

Lower End,—is flat and triangular (facies colica or basalis), and rests upon the splenic flexure of the colon and the phreno-colic ligament.

Anterior Border (margo anterior) is between the gastric surface (facies gastrica) and the diaphragmatic surface (facies diaphragmatica), it is always notched.

Posterior Border (margo posterior) is between the diaphragmatic surface (facies diaphragmatica) and renal surface (facies renalis). When it is present, the basal surface (facies colica), at the lower end of the spleen, is separated from the diaphragmatic surface (facies diaphragmatica) by the *inferior border* (margo inferior), from the gastric surface (facies gastrica) by the *anterior intermediate border* (margo intermedius anterior, and from the renal surface (facies renalis) by the *posterior intermediate border* (margo intermedius posterior).

Structure of the Spleen. A fibro-elastic capsule, the *tunica propria*, forms the framework of the spleen. It invests the organ externally, is reflected inward at the hilum along the vessels, and gives off from both parts bands or *trabeculæ lienis*, which traverse the organ in all directions and unite with each other, to form a sponge-like structure, having numerous primary spaces or *areolæ*, in which the pulp is contained. The *splenic pulp* (pulpa lienis) looks like a soft, dark-red mass, resembling grumous blood, but consists of branching connective-tissue corpuscles, the supporting *sustentacular* or *reticular cells*, which form a delicate reticulated tissue, making within the areolæ a number of secondary spaces, in which is blood containing a large proportion of white blood-corpuscles, also red blood-corpuscles in all stages of disintegration. These secondary spaces are continuous with the terminal arterial capillaries and the primary venous radicles, both of which open into them, bringing the blood supply into relation with the pulp elements. The connective-tissue coat of the arteries is converted into a lymphoid tissue in the arterioles, and this tissue presents thickenings of spheroidal shape, the—

Malpighian Bodies (noduli lymphatici lienalis),—vary from $\frac{1}{100}$ to $\frac{1}{25}$ inch in diameter, and are attached to the arterioles of the organ in groups of 6 or 8. Their reticulum is slender and open, densely filled with lymphoid cells (leukocytes and spleen phagocytes), and well supplied with capillaries.

Peritoneal, or Serous Coat (tunica serosa),—covers the whole organ, except at the hilum and the attachments of the suspensory ligament and the gastro-splenic omentum.

Splenic Artery (a. lienalis),—is large and tortuous, and divides at the hilum into 5 or 6 branches (4), each supplying a segment of the organ, and terminating in capillaries which open into the secondary spaces.

Veins,—arise by radicles from the secondary spaces, and anastomose freely, joining to form 6 or more branches (5) which emerge from the hilum and unite into the *splenic vein* (v. lienalis), the largest of the constituents forming the portal vein.

Lymphatics,—are superficial and deep; the two sets joining in the interior of the organ, pass through the lymphatic glands at the hilum, and terminate in the thoracic duct.

Nerves,—are branches of the *splenic plexus* (plexus lienalis), which is formed by branches from the cœliac plexus, the left semilunar ganglion (ganglion cœliacum sinistrum), and the right pneumogastric nerve (n. vagus dexter).

2. **Coccygeal Gland or Body** (glomus coccygeum) is a minute, highly vascular, grayish-red, spherical body capping the terminations of the *middle sacral* blood-vessels which form its stalk. It is situated in the mid-line just beyond the tip of the coccyx, under cover of the coccygeal attachment

of the sphincter ani muscle in the small triangular interval between the
levator ani muscles.   It is invested by a fibrous capsule which sends septa
into its substance dividing it up into follicles or nodules.   The *follicles*
are masses of epithelial cells none of which are susceptible of staining by
chromium salts.   Each follicle is traversed by a blood space or sinus
which affords free intercommunication between the arteries and veins of
the gland.

Nerve supply is by many minute fibres from the *sympathetic*.   It is
not uncommon to find several *accessory coccygeal glands* which in all essentials resemble the principal gland.

3. **Pineal Gland** or **Body** (epiphysis or corpus pineale) while classed
as a ductless gland, is probably not functional in man (see page 194).

4. **Lymphoglandulæ,** the *lymph* glands, *hæmal lymph* glands, and *hæmal*
glands are described under the lymphatic system (see page 172).

ORGANS OF VOICE AND RESPIRATION

THE LARYNX

The Larynx is a musculo-membranous-cartilaginous box, the essential
organ of voice, placed at the upper end of the air-passage, between the
trachea and the base of the tongue, in the upper and fore part of the neck,
where it forms a projection in the middle line.   Its cartilages are 9 in number, 3 single and 3 in pairs, the—

Thyroid Cartilage (cartilago thyreoidea).
Cricoid Cartilage (cartilago cricoidea).
Epiglottis (cartilago epiglottica).
Arytenoid Cartilages 2 (cartilagines arytænoideæ).
Cuneiform Cartilages 2 (cartilagines cuneiformes).
Cornicula Laryngis 2 (cartilagines corniculatæ).

The Thyroid Cartilage (cartilago thyreoidea), or shield-like cartilage,
consists of two *Alæ* or wings (*b*), united in front at an acute angle, the
highest portion of its front being called the *Pomum Adami*, Adam's apple
(prominentia laryngea).   Its—

Outer Surface,—affords attachment to the sterno-thyroid (m. sterno-
thyreoideus) thyro-hyoid (m. thyreo-hyoideus) and inferior constrictor muscles; the first two being attached along its oblique ridge.
Upper Border,—is curved irregularly, has the *thyroid notch* (incisura
thyreoidea superior) (*d*) in front, and gives attachment to the thyro-
hyoid membrane.

Lower Border,—gives attachment to the crico-thyroid membrane in the median line and on each side to the crico-thyroid muscle.

Inner Surface,—gives attachment to the true and false vocal cords, the epiglottis, thyro-arytenoid and thyro-epiglottidean muscles, and the thyro-epiglottidean ligament.

Posterior Border,—of each wing ends above and below in *cornua* (horns), and gives attachment to the stylo- and palato-pharyngeus muscles.

FIG. 119.

Superior Cornu (cornu superius) *(a)*—of each side affords attachment to the thyro-hyoid ligament.

Inferior Cornu (cornu inferius) *(c)*—of each side articulates with the cricoid cartilage by a small oval facet.

The Cricoid Cartilage (cartilago cricoidea), so called from its ring-like shape, is situated below the thyroid, with its narrow part to the front. It has on each side 2 *articular facets,* one on the upper margin posteriorly for the arytenoid cartilage, and one near the lower margin for the inferior cornu of the thyroid cartilage. Its—

Posterior Portion (lamina cartilaginis cricoideæ),—is deep and broad, gives attachment in the middle line to the longitudinal fibres of the œsophagus, and on each side to the crico-arytenoideus posticus muscle (m. crico-ary-
tænoideus posterior).

FIG. 120.

Anterior Portion (arcus cartilaginis cricoideæ),—is narrow and convex, and affords attachment to the crico-thyroid muscles and part of the inferior constrictor.

Upper Border,—affords attachment to the crico-thyroid membrane and the crico-arytenoidei laterales muscles (mm. crico-arytænoidei laterales), and articulates with the arytenoid cartilages.

Lower Border,—is connected to the upper ring of the trachea by fibrous membrane.

The Arytenoid Cartilages (cartilagines arytænoideæ), or pitcher-like cartilages, are 2 in number, pyramidal-shaped, and situated on the upper margin of the cricoid cartilage posteriorly, closing in the back of the larynx. Each cartilage has 3 surfaces, 2 angles, a base and an apex. The—

Anterior Surface,—gives attachment to the *plica ventricularis* or false vocal cord, and the thyro-arytenoideus muscle (m. thyreo-arytænoideus).

Anterior Angle,—gives attachment to the *plicæ vocales* or true vocal cord and the thyro-arytenoideus muscle (m. thyreo-arytænoideus).

Posterior Surface,—has attached to it the arytænoideus (m. arytæ-noideus).

Posterior Angle,—gives attachment to the crico-arytenoideus lateralis and posticus muscles (mm. crico-arytænoidei laterales et posterior).

Internal Surfaces of each—look toward each other.

Base,—has a facet for articulation with the cricoid.

Apex,—articulates with the corniculum laryngis.

Fig. 121.

The **Cornicula Laryngis** (cartilagines corniculatæ) are 2 small cartilaginous nodules attached to the apices of the arytenoid cartilages, and are also called the *Cartilages of Santorini.* To them are attached the aryteno-epiglottidean folds (plicæ arytæno-epiglotticæ).

The **Cuneiform Cartilages,** or *Cartilages of Wrisberg* (cartilagines cunei-formes), are 2 rods of yellow elastic cartilage contained in the free borders of the aryteno-epiglottidean folds (plicæ arytæno-epiglotticæ) one on each side, just in front of the arytenoid cartilages.

The **Epiglottis** (cartilago epiglottica) is a cartilaginous lid for the larynx. It is leaf-shaped, situated behind the base of the tongue, and attached by its *apex* to the posterior surface of the thyroid cartilage, just below the median notch. Its—

Fig. 122.

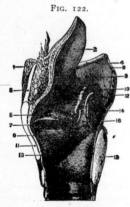

Base,—is free, and curves over the base of the tongue.

Apex, (petiolus epiglottidis),—is connected to the receding angle of the thyroid cartilage by the thyro-epiglottic ligament.

Anterior Surface,—is attached to the hyoid bone by the hyo-epiglottic ligament, and to the tongue by 3 glosso-epiglottidean folds (plicæ glosso-epiglotticæ).

Posterior Surface,—covers the superior aperture of the larynx when food passes through the pharynx.

Lateral Margins,—are connected to the arytenoid cartilages by the aryteno-epiglottidean folds (plicæ arytæno-epiglotticæ).

Ligaments of the Larynx are 20 in number,—8 Extrinsic Ligaments, connecting the larynx to the hyoid bone (1), the tongue, and the trachea (15); and 12 Intrinsic Ligaments, binding its several cartilages together. The Extrinsic Ligaments 8 are the—

Hyo-epiglottic Ligament,—connecting the hyoid bone (1) with the epiglottis (2).

Glosso-epiglottic Folds three (plicæ glosso-epiglotticæ),—from the tongue to the epiglottis.

Thyro-hyoid Membrane (membrana hyo-thyreoidea) (3),—connecting the thyroid cartilage (11) with the hyoid bone (1), and bounded laterally by the two—

Lateral Thyro-hyoid Ligaments (ligamenta hyo-thyreoidea laterales) (6)—each containing a nodule of cartilage, the *cartilago triticea*.

Crico-tracheal Ligament,—from the cricoid cartilage (18) to the trachea. Intrinsic Ligaments 12, are the—

Thyro-epiglottic Ligament (ligamentum thyreo-epiglotticum),—connecting the thyroid cartilage (11) with the epiglottis (2).

Crico-thyroid Membrane (conus elasticus) (13),—connecting the cricoid (18) and thyroid (11) cartilages.

Crico-thyroid Capsular Ligaments 2,—enclosing those articulations.

Crico-arytenoid Ligaments (ligamenta cricoarytænoidea) 2,—connect the cricoid and arytenoid cartilages together.

Crico-arytenoid Capsular Ligaments 2,—enclosing those articulations.

Superior Thyro-arytenoid or *Thyreo-arytenoid Ligaments* 2,—in the false vocal cords (plicæ ventriculares) (5).

Inferior Thyro-arytenoid or *Thyreo-arytænoid Ligaments* 2,—in the true vocal cords (plicæ vocales) (9).

Interior of the Larynx presents a cavity which is divided into two parts by the inward projection of the true vocal cords. The superior part, sometimes called the *vestibule*, is broad and triangular in shape; the inferior part of the cavity is at first elliptical and lower down is circular, becoming continuous with the tube of the trachea. The—

Glottis or *Rima Glottidis*,—is a narrow chink or interval between the inferior vocal cords, formed by the projection into the cavity of the larynx of these cords and the thyro-arytenoidei muscles. Its greatest length is less than an inch, its greatest breadth about half an inch. Its form is a narrow fissure of varying width.

Superior or False Vocal Cords (plicæ ventriculares) (5),—contain the superior thyro-arytenoid ligaments, extend from the angle of the thyroid cartilage around to the anterior surfaces of the arytenoids, and consist of two folds of mucous membrane, each having a free crescentic margin.

Inferior or True Vocal Cords (plicæ vocales) (9),—contain the inferior thyro-arytenoid ligaments, extend from the angle of the thyroid cartilage around to the anterior angles of the bases of the arytenoids, and consist of two thin layers of mucous membrane covering the ligaments

23

named, each having the thyro-arytenoideus muscle external and parallel to it.

Ventricle of the Larynx (ventriculus laryngis) (7),—is an oblong fossa on each side of the larynx, between the true and false vocal cords, leading up to the sacculus laryngis by a narrow opening.

Sacculus Laryngis (appendix ventriculæ) or Laryngeal Pouch,—is a membranous sac, placed between the superior vocal cord and the thyroid cartilage. It is of conical shape, and contains 60 or 70 small mucous glands which secrete a fluid for the lubrication of the true vocal cord. The sacculus is covered in by the aryteno-epiglottideus inferior muscle internally, and by the thyro-epiglottideus externally, both muscles compressing it to discharge its contents. The Sacculus Laryngis is also called the *Sinus of Morgagni*, and the lower part of the ventricle is sometimes named the *Sac of Hilton*.

Epithelium,—is stratified *squamous* epithelium over the true vocal cords, the upper part of the aryteno-epiglottidean folds, and the upper half of the posterior surface of the epiglottis; over all the rest of the larynx, the lining mucous membrane is covered by columnar *ciliated* cells.

Muscles of the Larynx are 8 in number, 5 of which are the muscles of the vocal cords and rima glottidis, and 3 are connected with the epiglottis. The former are the—

> *Crico-thyroid* (m. crico-thyreoideus).
> *Crico-arytenoideus Posticus* (m. crico-arytænoideus posterior).
> *Crico-arytenoideus Lateralis* (m. crico-arytænoideus lateralis).
> *Arytenoideus* (m. arytænoideus).
> *Thyro-arytenoideus* (m. thyreo-arytænoideus).

Muscles of the Epiglottis are the—

> *Thyro-epiglottideus* (m. thyreo-epiglottideus).
> *Aryteno-epiglottideus* (arytæno-epiglottideus) *Superior* and *Inferior*.

These muscles are described at page 85.

Vessels of the Larynx. The *Arteries* are the Superior Laryngeal and Crico-thyroid branches of the superior thyroid (a. thyreoidea Superior) from the external carotid: and the Inferior Laryngeal Branch of the inferior thyroid (a. thyreoidea inferior) from the thyroid axis (truncus thyreocervicalis). The—

Veins,—open into the internal jugular and the innominate vein.

Lymphatics,—open into glands near the bifurcation of the common carotid artery, and others in front of the crico-thyroid membrane.

Nerves of the Larynx are the Superior and Recurrent (inferior) Laryngeal branches of the pneumogastric (n. vagus), joined by filaments from the spinal accessory (n. accessorius) and the sympathetic. The—

Superior Laryngeal,—is the nerve of sensation. It enters the larynx by a hole in the thyro-hyoid membrane, and supplies the mucous membrane, and the crico-thyroid and arytenoideus muscles. It has the following branches, namely—

External Laryngeal. Internal Laryngeal.

Recurrent Laryngeal (n. laryngeus inferior),—is the motor nerve. It winds from before backwards, around the subclavian artery on the right side, around the arch of the aorta on the left side, and is distributed to all the laryngeal muscles except the crico-thyroid and arytenoideus giving off, in its course, cardiac, œsophageal, tracheal, and pharyngeal filaments, and finally anastomosing with the superior laryngeal nerve.

THE TRACHEA AND BRONCHI

The Trachea is a membrano-cartilaginous, cylindrical tube, about 4½ inches long, and ¾ to 1 inch in diameter, beginning at the lower border of the larynx, opposite the 6th cervical vertebra, and ending opposite the upper border of the 5th thoracic, by its bifurcation into the two bronchi. It is composed of a fibro-elastic membrane containing 16 to 20 imperfect cartilaginous rings, connected by muscular fibres. It is lined with mucous membrane covered with ciliated columnar epithelium, and furnished with racemose glands, the *tracheal glands*.

Anteriorly,—it is convex, and is covered from above downward by the—

Isthmus of the Thyreoid Gland. Thymus Gland.
Inferior Thyreoid Veins. Arch of the Aorta.
Sterno-hyoid Muscle. Left Innominate Vein.
Sterno-Thyreoid Muscle. Innominate Artery.
Cervical Fascia. Left Carotid Artery.
Manubrium of the Sternum. Deep Cardiac Plexus.

Posteriorly,—it is flat, and in relation with the œsophagus.
Laterally,—it is in relation with the—

Common Carotid Arteries. Recurrent or Inferior Laryngeal Nerves.
Thyreoid Gland, lateral lobes. Pleuræ.
Inferior Thyreoid Arteries. Pneumogastric or Vagus Nerves.

The Bronchi are two tubes similar in formation to the trachea, extending from its bifurcation into the lungs, where they divide and subdivide into bronchial tubes (rami bronchiales), losing their rings at the 2d or 3d subdivision, whence plates of cartilage extend in their walls to their minuter ramifications. The—

Right Bronchus (bronchus dexter),—the wider, and the more horizontal, is about 1 inch long, has 6 to 8 rings, and divides into 2 main divisions, the *eparterial branch*, to the upper lobe, given off above the pulmonary artery, and the *hyparterial branch*, passing under the artery to be divided into two branches, for the middle and lower lobes. The right bronchus lies behind the vena cava superior and the right auricle of the heart having the right pulmonary artery at first below, then anterior to it, and the vena azygos major arching over it from behind forward.

Left Bronchus,—the narrower and more oblique, is nearly 2 inches long, has 9 to 12 rings, and divides into 3 main divisions (though its lung has but 2 lobes). It passes beneath the arch of the aorta and in front of its descending portion, also in front of the œsophagus and the thoracic duct, having the left pulmonary artery above and in front of it.

Vessels and Nerves. The *Arteries* are the Tracheal, branches of the inferior thyreoid, from the thyreoid axis (truncus thyreocervicalis); and the Bronchial, from the thoracic aorta. The—

Veins,—open into the thyreoid plexus and the bronchial veins.

Lymphatics,—terminate in the mediastinal glands.

Nerves,—are derived from the pneumogastric (n. vagus) and its recurrent or inferior laryngeal branch, also from the sympathetic.

THE PLEURÆ

The Pleuræ are two delicate serous sacs, one surrounding each lung, and reflected over the pericardium, the diaphragm, and the inner surface of the thorax. The right sac is shorter, wider, and reaches higher into the neck than the left. The two sacs meet for a short space behind the middle of the sternum, at the approximation of the anterior borders of the lungs. The—

Pleura Pulmonalis, or Visceral Layer,—covers the lung, and invests that organ as far as its root.

Pleura Costalis, or Parietal Layer,—lines the inner surface of the parietes of the chest.

Cavity of the Pleura,—is the space between the two layers.

Ligamentum Latum Pulmonis, or Broad Ligament of the Lung,—is a triangular fold or reflection of pleura, which descends from the root of the lung posteriorly to the upper surface of the diaphragm.

The Mediastinum is the space between the two pleuræ in the median line of the thorax, extending from the sternum to the vertebral column, and containing all the thoracic viscera except the lungs. The—

Superior Mediastinum,—lies above the upper level of the pericardium and contains the—

Origins of the Sterno-hyoid and Sterno-thyroid Muscles.

Longus Colli Muscles, their lower ends.	Pneumogastric Nerve (n. vagus).
	Cardiac and Phrenic Nerves.
Arch of the Aorta.	Left Recurrent or Inferior Laryn-
Innominate Artery.	geal Nerve.
Left Carotid Artery, in part.	Trachea.
Left Subclavian Artery, in part.	Œsophagus.
Superior Vena Cava, upper half.	Thoracic Duct.
Innominate Veins.	Thymus Gland.
Left Superior Intercostal Vein.	Lymphatic Glands.

Anterior Mediastinum,—between the sternum and the pericardium, contains—

Areolar Tissue.	Branches of Internal Mammary Artery.
Triangularis Sterni Muscle.	Lymphatic Vessels and Glands.

Middle Mediastinum,—contains the—

Heart and Pericardium.	Bifurcation of the Trachea.
Ascending Aorta.	Pulmonary Arteries and Veins.

Superior Vena Cava, lower half. Phrenic Nerves. Lymphatic Glands.

Posterior Mediastinum,—contains the—

Descending Aorta.	Œsophagus.
Azygos Veins.	Thoracic Duct.
Pneumogastric (nn. vagi) and Splanchnic Nerves.	Lymphatic Glands.

THE LUNGS (PULMONES)

The Lungs are the two essential organs of respiration contained in the cavity of the thorax, where they are separated from each other by the heart (1) and the other contents of the mediastinum. They are covered by the pleuræ, and are characterized by lightness (sp. gr. 0.345 to 0.746), sponginess, elasticity, and crepitation when pressed. They weigh together about 42 ounces, the right lung being the heavier by about 2 ounces. At birth their color is a pinkish-white, becoming mottled as age advances by slate-colored patches, from the deposit of carbonaceous granules in the areolar tissue of the organ. *The Right Lung* is the larger and has 3 lobes; the *Left Lung* has 2 lobes. Each lung presents for examination an—

Apex (apex pulmonis),—situated in the neck, behind the interval between the two heads of the sterno-mastoid muscle, and rising about

an inch above the clavicle.   It is in relation with the subclavian arter
and the scaleni muscles.

Base (basis pulmonis),—is broad, concave, and directed obliquely down
ward and backward, resting on the upper convex surface of the dia
phragm.

External Surface (facies costalis),—is convex, smooth, marked by th
fissures, and corresponds in form to that of the thorax.

Inner Surface (facies mediastinalis),—is concave, presents in front
depression for the heart and behind a deep fissure, the *hilum*, whic
gives attachment to the root of the lung.

FIG. 123.

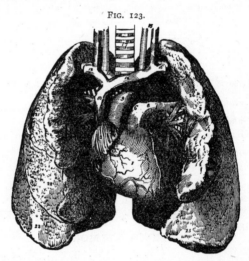

Root (radix pulmonis),—is where the bronchus (18), vessels (20), an
nerves enter the lung, bound together by areolar tissue.   In front
the root is the phrenic nerve, behind it the pneumogastric nerve (
vagus).   Its chief structures are arranged in the following manner:-

$$\text{From before backward....} \left\{ \begin{array}{l} \text{Pulmonary veins.} \\ \text{Pulmonary artery.} \\ \text{Bronchus, etc.} \end{array} \right\} \text{V. A. B.}$$

$$\begin{array}{l} \text{From above downward, on} \\ \text{right side of body,} \end{array} \left\{ \begin{array}{l} \text{Bronchus (18), etc.} \\ \text{Pulmonary artery.} \\ \text{Pulmonary veins (20).} \end{array} \right\} \text{B. A. V.}$$

From above downward, on left side of body, $\left\{\begin{array}{l}\text{Pulmonary artery (7).}\\ \text{Bronchus (19), etc.}\\ \text{Pulmonary veins (20).}\end{array}\right\}$ A. B. V.

Structure of the Lung. The lung has a serous coat (the pleura); a sub-serous, elastic areolar tissue, investing the entire organ, and extending inward between the lobules; and the parenchyma, or true lung-tissue, composed of—

Fig. 124.

Lobules,—each consisting of several air-cells or compartments, arranged around the termination of a bronchiole, and surrounded by 6 plexuses of pulmonary and bronchial arteries and veins, lymphatics and nerves. Each lobule is a miniature lung, pyramidal in form, with base outward, and about $\frac{1}{12}$ inch in diameter. Fig. 123 shows 2 lobules.

Alveoli, or *Air-cells,*—are separated from each other by thin septa, are lined with pavement epithelium on a basement membrane, and vary in diameter from $\frac{1}{200}$ to $\frac{1}{70}$ inch.

Vessels and Nerves of the Lungs. The lungs are nourished by the bronchial arteries, and supplied with blood for oxygenation by the pulmonary arteries.

Bronchial Arteries,—are derived from the thoracic aorta.

Bronchial Veins,—open on the right side into the vena azygos major, on the left side into the superior intercostal vein.

Pulmonary Arteries (5, 6, 7),—are derived from the right heart. Their terminal (lobular) branches do not anastomose with each other.

Pulmonary Veins (20),—open by 4 large orifices into the left auricle of the heart, carrying oxygenated blood from the lungs to the left heart. The veins anastomose freely.

Lymphatics,—terminate in the bronchial glands, at the root of the lung.

Nerves,—are branches from the vagus and the sympathetic forming the anterior and posterior *pulmonary plexuses,* from which filaments are distributed to each lobule.

THE URINARY ORGANS

THE KIDNEYS (RENES)

The Kidneys (renes) are two organs, situated in the back part of the abdominal cavity, one on each side of the vertebral column, behind the peritoneum, extending from the 11th and 12th ribs to within 2 inches of the crest of the ileum, the right kidney being a little lower than the left one. Each kidney is about 4 inches by 2 by 1, in the male adult weighs from 4½ to 6 oz.; and presents on its inner concave border the—

Hilum,—a fissure leading into the sinus or cavity of the organ, and permitting the passage of the vessels, nerves, and ureter, arranged in the following order, from before backward, the renal vein, renal artery ureter, VAU.

Relations of the Kidneys. They are partially covered by peritoneum on their anterior surface, but not at all posteriorly. They are surrounded by a mass of fat and areolar tissue, and have the following relations:—

Anterior Surface (facies renis anterior) *of the Right Kidney*,—is in relation with the supra-renal gland, the right lobe of the liver, the descending duodenum, and the ascending colon.

Anterior Surface of the Left Kidney,—with the supra-renal gland, the stomach, the tail of the pancreas, the descending colon, the jejunum and part of the spleen.

Posterior Surface (facies renis posterior),—with the crus of the diaphragm, 12th rib and the transverse processes of the upper three lumbar vertebræ, psoas magnus, quadratus lumborum, and the aponeurosis of the transversalis muscle.

Upper Extremity (extremitas superior),—is capped by the supra-renal capsule (1).

Lower Extremity (extremitas inferior),—extends to within 2 inches of the crest of the ilium.

General Structure of the Kidney. A vertical section from its convex to its concave border, shows it to consist of a central cavity or *sinus*, surrounded except on one side by the kidney substance proper (parenchyma). The latter is divided into a *cortical portion* externally, and a *medullary portion* internally, the medullary being arranged in pyramidal masses whose apices project into the central cavity. A dense, fibrous *capsule* (tunica fibrosa) invests the organ, and is reflected inward at the hilum lining the sinus and forming sheaths for the vessels. It gives off an interstitial *stroma* of connective tissue, which binds the vessels and tubes firmly together throughout the substance of the kidney. The—

Cortical Portion,—consists of uriniferous tubules (tubuli renales). Malpighian bodies (glomerula or renal corpuscles), blood-vessels, nerves, lymphatics, connective tissue, and a granular matrix. It is of a red

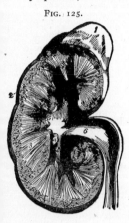

FIG. 125.

color, and is prolonged down between the pyramids, to the sinus; the prolongations being named *columns of Bertin* (columnæ renales) and the portions over the bases of the pyramids are the *cortical arches.*

Medullary Substance (3),—contains chiefly the straight, collecting portion of the uriniferous tubules, arranged in pyramidal masses, the *pyramids of Malpighi* (pyramides renales), the apices of which project into the sinus.

Sinus,—receives the pelvis (6) of the ureter (7), and is divided into 3 *infundibula* (5), and they into 7 to 13 *calices,* into which open the orifices of the uriniferous tubules, 1000 on each *papilla* or apex of a pyramid.

Minute Structure of the Kidney commences in the cortical substance of the organ as the *Malpighian bodies* (corpuscula renis), small round masses of deep-red color, averaging about $\frac{1}{120}$ inch in diameter, and each consisting of a central glomerulus of vessels and a membranous envelope (capsula glomeruli) or Bowman's capsule, the latter being the commencement of a uriniferous tubule. The—

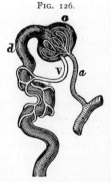

FIG. 126.

Malpighian Tuft,—or vascular glomerulus, is a network of convoluted capillary blood-vessels, beginning by the *afferent vessel* and ending in the *efferent vessel,* which are the respective radicles of some of the branches of the renal artery (*a*) and the renal vein (*v*). The afferent vessels are usually the larger.

Bowman's Capsule (capsula glomeruli) (*c*),—surrounding the glomerulus, is the dilated extremity of a uriniferous tubule (*d*), and is lined on its inner surface by a layer of squamous epithelial cells, on a delicate supporting membrane, closely surrounding the convolutions of the glomerulus and dipping in between them.

The Tubuli Renales, or *Uriniferous Tubules,* begin at the capsule of Bowman in the Malpighian bodies, and open into the sinus of the kidney by orifices on the surface of the papillæ. During their course they leave the cortical portion, enter the medullary portion, return to the cortical and again to the medullary, in which they continue to their termination. In their course they become first convoluted, then spiral, then looped, again spiral and convoluted, curved and finally straight; and have received the following names:—

Proximal Convoluted Tube,—the first portion, below the *neck* at Bowman's capsule, in the cortical zone. Epithelium lining the tube is polyhedral and of striated appearance.

Spiral Tube of Schachowa,—in the cortical zone. Epithelium polyhedral and striated.

Henle's Loop,—in the medullary zone, consists of a descending limb, a loop, and an ascending limb, the latter becoming spiral as it ascends into the cortical zone. Epithelium flat in the descending limb, polyhedral and striated in the ascending one.

Irregular Tubule,—in the cortical zone. Epithelium angular and striated.

Distal Convoluted Tubule,—in the cortical zone. Epithelium polyhedral.

Curved Tube,—in the cortical zone. Epithelium varied, angular, spindle-shaped, polyhedral.

Straight or *Collecting Tube,*—partly in the cortical zone, descends through the medullary portion and joins with others, forming the *pyramids of Ferrein* (apices outward) in the cortical zone, and the *pyramids of Malpighi* (apices inward) in the medullary substance. Epithelium more or less columnar.

Connective Tissue or *Stroma,*—binds the tubules firmly together.

Arteries of the Kidney arise from the renal artery, a large branch of the abdominal aorta. It divides into 4 or 5 branches, which enter the kidney at the hilum (hilus renis), giving off small branches to the suprarenal capsules, the ureter, etc. These again divide and end in the—

Arteriæ Propriæ Renales,—the renal arteries proper, which enter the kidney substance in the columns of Bertin (see page 360), form arterial arches over the bases of the pyramids, and divide into ascending and descending branches. The—

Ascending or *Interlobular Branches,*—pass to the capsule and end in the capillary network of that part of the cortex, giving off in their course the *afferent vessels* to the Malpighian tufts (see page 360).

Descending or *Arteriolæ Rectæ,*—supply the medullary pyramids and end at their apices in the venous plexuses there situated.

Veins of the Kidney arise from 3 sources,—the stellate veins beneath the capsule of the organ, the venous radicles in the Malpighian tufts, and the venous plexuses at the apices of the pyramids of Malpighi. Those from the stellate plexuses on the surface of the kidney join together, forming the—

Interlobular Veins,—which pass inward between the pyramids of Ferrein, receive branches from the plexuses on the convoluted uriniferous tubes, and join with the *venæ rectæ* from the apices of the pyramids of Malpighi, to form the—

Venæ Propiæ Renales,—the renal veins proper, accompany the arteries of the same name, receive the *efferent vessels* from the Malpighian bodies adjacent, and join with corresponding veins in the sinus to form the—

Renal Vein,—emerges at the hilum and opens into the inferior vena cava; the left vein being longer than the right, having to cross in front of the abdominal aorta.

Nerves of the Kidney are derived from the *renal plexus,* which is formed by branches from the solar plexus (plexus cœliacum), the aortic plexus, the semilunar ganglion, and the lesser and smallest splanchnic nerves. They have small ganglia upon them, and communicate with the spermatic plexus.

Lymphatics consist of a superficial and a deep set, and terminate in the lumbar glands.

THE URETERS

The Ureter, the excretory duct of the kidney, is a musculo-membranous tube, which conducts the urine from the kidney to the bladder. It commences within the sinus of the kidney by 7 to 13 short tubes or *calices,* which encircle the apices of the pyramids of Malpighi, and converge into 2 or 3 tubular divisions or *infundibula,* these by their junction forming the *pelvis* or upper dilated extremity of the duct. The—

Ureter Proper,—begins at the lower end of its pelvis, is about 16 inches long, and of the diameter of a small goose-quill. It descends, through the lumbar region of the abdomen and the pelvic cavity, to the base of the bladder, and opens into the cavity of that organ about 2 inches from its fellow.

Course of the Ureter. In its course the ureter passes obliquely downward and inward through the lumbar region, and downward, inward and forward through the pelvic cavity, enters the posterior false ligament of the bladder, passes obliquely between the muscular and mucous coats of that organ for nearly an inch, and ends by a constricted orifice at one of the posterior angles of the trigone at the base of the bladder.

Relations of the Ureter. The junction of the renal pelvis and the ureter proper is opposite the spinous process of the first lumbar vertebra, about 2 inches from the middle line of the back. The ureter lies upon the psoas muscle and behind the peritoneum; behind the ileum on the right side and the sigmoid flexure of the colon on the left side. It crosses the common or the external iliac artery; and is crossed by the spermatic vessels, and the branches of the mesenteric arteries, also by the vas deferens in the male. The right ureter lies close to the outer side of the inferior vena cava. In the female the ureters pass along the sides of the neck of the uterus and the upper part of the vagina, and beneath the root of the broad ligament.

Structure of the Ureter. It is composed of 3 coats,—fibrous, muscular, and mucous. The *fibrous coat* (tunica adventitia) is continuous with the capsule of the kidney and with the fibrous structure of the bladder. The—

Muscular Coat (tunica muscularis),—consists of longitudinal fibres externally (stratum externum), and circular fibres internally (stratum medium). A third layer (stratum internum), consisting of longitudinal fibres, is found internal to the circular layer, in the neighborhood of the bladder.

Mucous Coat,—is prolonged over the papillæ of the kidney, and is continuous with the mucous lining of the bladder. Its epithelium resembles that of the bladder, and is known as *transitional epithelium*, consisting of 3 layers of cells, the innermost of which are quadrilateral in shape.

Vessels and Nerves. The *Arteries* of the ureter are branches from the renal, spermatic, internal iliac, and inferior vesical. The *Nerves* are derived from the inferior mesenteric, spermatic, and pelvic plexuses.

THE SUPRA-RENAL GLANDS OR CAPSULES (GLANDULÆ SUPRARENALES)

The **Supra-renal Glands** are properly classed with the ductless glands of the *chromaphil* and *cortical* systems (see page 344). They are two small, yellowish bodies, situated one above each kidney, behind the peritoneum, and in the posterior portion of the abdomen. They vary in size in different individuals, but are usually $1\frac{1}{2}$ inches long and wide, and from 2 to 3 lines in thickness. Each capsule has a small furrow, the *hilum*, on its anterior surface, in which the vessels enter the organ, and in structure consists of a—

Fibrous Capsule,—which is very thin, closely adherent, and sends numerous septa inward.

Cortical Substance,—composed of columnar masses of polyhedral cells, held together in layers by a fibrous stroma.

Medullary Substance,—is darker than the cortical portion, and pulpy. It consists of granular cells, supported by a delicate stroma, and believed by some anatomists to be prolonged into the nerve fibres of a very intricate plexus.

Relations of the Supra-renal Glands. Their surface is surrounded by areolar tissue containing much fat; their bases rest on the upper front parts of the kidneys, their posterior surfaces on the crura of the diaphragm, about the level of the 10th thoracic vertebra. The—

Anterior Surface,—of the right gland is covered by the liver; that of the left one by the spleen and pancreas.

Superior Surface,—of each is in relation internally with the great splanchnic nerve and semilunar ganglion.

Vessels and Nerves. The *Arteries* are the Supra-renal branches of the aorta, renal, and phrenic arteries, forming a dense capillary plexus in the cortical portion of the organ.

Veins,—of each open into a single trunk, the *Supra-renal Vein,* which on the right side of the body empties into the inferior vena cava, on the left side into the left renal vein.

Lymphatics,—open into the lumbar glands.

Nerves,—are derived from the solar (cœliac) and renal plexuses, with some filaments from the phrenic and vagus nerves, forming a complicated network in the medullary substance of the organ, and having numerous small ganglia developed upon them.

THE BLADDER (VESICA URINARIA)

The Bladder, the reservoir for the urine, is a musculo-membranous sac, situated in the anterior portion of the pelvis, behind the pubes, and in front of the rectum in the male, in front of the cervix uteri and vagina in the female. When empty and contracted, or when slightly distended, it is contained in the pelvic cavity; when greatly distended it is ovoid in shape, and rises into the abdominal cavity, often extending nearly as high as the umbilicus. When moderately distended it measures about 5 by 3 inches, and holds about a pint. The—

Summit,—is connected to the umbilicus by the *urachus* (ligamentum umbilicale medium) and the obliterated hypogastric arteries (ligamenta umbilicales laterales) of the fœtus, forming three fibrous cords, the Superior Ligament of the bladder.

Superior or *Abdominal Surface,*—is free, and is covered by peritoneum.

Anterior or *Pubic Surface,*—is partly covered by peritoneum above, and is in relation below with the internal obturator muscles, the recto-vesical fascia, and the anterior true ligaments of the bladder.

Posterior Surface,—is covered by peritoneum, and is in relation with the rectum in the male, with the uterus and upper part of the vagina in the female.

Lateral Surfaces,—are partly covered by peritoneum behind and above; each is crossed obliquely by the obliterated hypogastric artery and the vas deferens (*c*), the first passing from below forward, the latter from below backward.

Fundus or *Base,*—is partly covered by peritoneum, and rests on the second portion of the rectum in the male, on the lower part of the cervix uteri and adherent to the anterior wall of the vagina in the female.

Cervix or Neck,—is constricted and continuous with the urethra (*i*). It is surrounded in the male by the prostate gland (*h*), and is directed downward and forward.

Fig. 127.

Ligaments of the Bladder are 10 in number, of which 5 are true ligaments, and 5 are false ligaments, being formed by folds of peritoneum. The true ligaments are the—

Anterior or *Pubo-prostatic*, 2,—are formed by the recto-vesical fascia, and extend from the neck of the bladder, over the prostate gland, to the back of the pubic bone.

Lateral, 2,—also formed by the recto-vesical fascia, are attached to the sides of the base of the bladder, and the prostate gland.

Urachus,—the superior ligament (ligamentum umbilicale medium), connects the summit of the bladder with the umbilicus. It is the obliterated remains of a canal, which in the embryo connects the bladder with the allantois and is situated between the two obliterated hypogastric arteries (ligamenta umbilicales laterales).

False Ligaments, folds of peritoneum, are the—

Posterior False Ligaments (plicæ vesico-uterinæ) female, (plicæ recto-vesicalis) male, 2,—pass from the postero-lateral parts of the bladder, to the sides of the rectum in the male, to the sides of the uterus in the female.

Lateral False Ligaments (plicæ umbilicales laterales), 2,—from the iliac fossæ and lateral walls of the pelvis to the sides of the bladder.

Superior, or *Suspensory Ligament* (plica umbilicalis media),—from the summit of the bladder to the umbilicus, being peritoneum carried off from the bladder by the urachus and the obliterated hypogastric arteries.

Interior of the Bladder is lined by mucous membrane, which forms folds or *rugæ* when the viscus is empty, being loosely connected to the muscular coat, except at the trigone and the uvula, where it is closely adherent. The floor of the bladder presents the—

Trigonum Vesicæ, or Vesical Trigone (1, Fig. 127),—a pale-colored, triangular space, extending from the urethral opening in front to a line connecting the orifices of the ureters behind; and characterized by its smooth surface and the intimate adhesion between its mucous and muscular coats.

Uvula Vesicæ (3, Fig. 127),—is a small elevation of mucous membrane projecting from the floor of the bladder into the urethral orifice. It is said to be lifted by the anterior fibres of the levator ani muscle.

Orifices of the Ureters (2, Fig. 127),—about 2 inches apart, at the base of the trigone, and 1½ inches from the urethral opening.

Structure of the Bladder. The bladder has 4 coats,—serous or peritoneal, muscular, sub-mucous, and mucous. The peritoneal coat is a partial one, investing only the superior and posterior surfaces, and the upper portion of the lateral surfaces. The—

Muscular Coat,—consists of unstriped muscular fibres, arranged in 3 layers; an external layer, chiefly longitudinal, the so-called *detrusor urinæ* muscle; a middle layer, mostly circular, and forming a *sphincter vesicæ* around the neck; and an internal layer, chiefly longitudinal.

Muscles of the Ureters,—are two bands of oblique fibres, extending from behind the orifices of the ureters to the middle lobe of the prostate gland.

Sub-mucous Coat,—is a layer of areolar tissue, connecting the muscular with the mucous coat.

Mucous Coat,—is thin, smooth, of a pale rose color, and is continuous with the lining membrane of the ureters and the urethra. Its epithelium is of the transitional variety, consisting of an inner layer of polyhedral, flattened, nucleated cells; beneath which are two layers of club-shaped and spindle-shaped cells, wedged together. It contains no mucous glands.

Vessels and Nerves. The *Arteries* of the bladder are the superior middle, and inferior Vesical in the male, with additional branches from the uterine and vaginal in the female; all from the anterior trunk of the internal iliac. The—

Veins,—form a plexus around the neck, sides, and base of the bladder, and terminate in the internal iliac vein.

Lymphatics,—terminate in the internal iliac glands.

Nerves,—are derived from the pelvic plexus to the upper part of the organ, from the 3d and 4th sacral nerves to its base and neck.

THE MALE URETHRA

The Urethra is the urinary canal from the neck of the bladder to the meatus urinarius; in the male it is chiefly within the penis, is from 8 to 9 inches in length, and is divided into three parts,—the *prostatic, membranous,* and *spongy portions* of the urethra.

The Prostatic Portion (pars prostatica) of the Urethra is that part of the canal which pierces the prostate gland (4), is about 1¼ inches in length, of spindle shape, and the widest and most dilatable part of the urethra. Its floor presents the—

Verumontanum, or *Caput Gallinaginis* (colliculus seminalis) (6),—an elevation of the mucous membrane (crista urethralis) and its adjacent tissue, ¾ inch long, and supposed to contain muscular and erectile tissue.

Prostatic Sinus (7),—one on each side of the verumontanum, containing the orifices of the prostatic ducts.

Sinus Pocularis, or *Uterus Masculinus* (utriculus prostaticus) (5),—is a small cul-de-sac situated at the front part of the verumontanum. It extends for ¼ inch upward and backward into the prostate gland beneath its middle lobe.

Orifices of the Ejaculatory Ducts (8),—open on the margins of the sinus pocularis.

The Membranous Portion (pars membranacea) (9) is ¾ inch long above, and ½ inch along its floor, being that part of the canal lying between the superior and inferior layers of the triangular ligament of the perinæum. Its walls are very thin, and almost destitute of erectile tissue. It is surrounded by the deep transversus perinei or compressor urethræ muscle, and except the orifice, is the narrowest part of the urethral canal. On its sides are the—

Ducts of Cowper's Bulbo-urethral Glands (11),—on their way to open into the bulb of the urethra.

The Cavernous or Spongy Portion (pars cavernosa) (16) is about 6 inches long, and has two dilatations, one at each end, named respectively the Bulb and the Fossa Navicularis. The—

Bulb of the Urethra (13),—is the upper end of the cavernous portion, projects backward for ¼ inch, and contains the orifices (15) of the ducts of the bulbo-urethral or Cowper's glands.

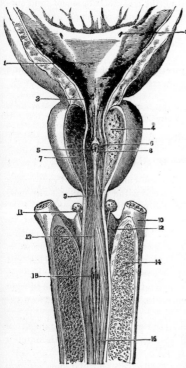

FIG. 128.

Fossa Navicularis,—is the lower dilatation of the urethra, and is situated within the glans penis.

Lacuna Magna (lacuna urethralis of Morgagni),—the largest of several orifices of mucous follicles, situated on the roof of the fossa navicularis.

Glands of Littré (glandulæ urethrales),—are numerous mucous glands and follicles, opening into the urethral canal, their orifices being directed forwards.

Meatus Urinarius,—the external orifice; is the most contracted portion of the urethra, and presents a vertical slit, about 3 lines long, bounded laterally by two small labia.

Structure of the Urethra.—It is composed of a continuous mucous membrane, continuous with the mucous lining of the bladder, ureters, and kidneys, and prolonged into the ducts opening into the urethra. The mucous membrane is supported by a submucous tissue, which connects it with the various structures through which it passes. The—

Submucous Tissue,—consists of a vascular erectile layer, outside which is a circular layer of unstriped muscular fibres.

Voluntary Muscles of the Urethra,—are the deep transversus perinei or

24

compressor urethræ and the bulbo-cavernosus or accelerator urinæ, described on page 98.

Epithelium,—is of the columnar variety, except near the meatus where it is squamous.

THE FEMALE URETHRA

The Urethra in the female is only about $1\frac{1}{2}$ inches long, imbedded in the anterior wall of the vagina, perforating the triangular ligament, and surrounded by fibres of the deep transversus perinei or compressor urethræ muscle. Its diameter is about $\frac{1}{4}$ inch, but it is capable of considerable dilatation, being surrounded by softer structures than are those around the male urethra. The—

Meatus Urinarius,—is situated directly in front of the vaginal opening and about an inch behind the glans clitoridis.

ORGANS OF GENERATION

THE MALE ORGANS OF GENERATION

THE URETHRAL GLANDS

The Prostate Gland (prostata) is a musculo-glandular organ, which surrounds the neck of the male bladder and the beginning of the male urethra. It is situated in the pelvic cavity, behind the lower part of the symphysis pubis, and above the deep layer of the triangular ligament, its posterior surface resting on the rectum. It is perforated by the urethra and the common seminal ducts, but its own ducts open into the prostatic portion of the urethra. It measures about $1\frac{1}{2}$ inches by $1\frac{1}{4}$ inches by 1 inch, weighs about $\frac{3}{4}$ oz., resembles a horse-chestnut in size and shape, and consists of three lobes, two being lateral and of equal size, the third or middle lobe being a small prominence situated in the notch between the lateral lobes. Its—

Position,—is maintained by the anterior or pubo-prostatic ligaments of the bladder, the deep layer of the triangular ligament, and the anterior portions of the levator ani muscles.

Structure,—is glandular substance arranged in follicular pouches, and dense muscular tissue, the whole being invested by a firm fibrous capsule, which gives off thin trabeculæ into the substance of the gland.

Ducts,—are 12 to 20 in number, lined by columnar epithelium, and open on the floor of the prostatic portion of the urethra.

Arteries,—are derived from the internal pudic, vesical and hæmorrhoidal arteries.

Veins,—terminate in the internal iliac vein.

Nerves,—are branches from the pelvic or hypo-gastric plexus.

Cowper's Glands (glandulæ bulbo-urethrales) are two small, rounded bodies, about the size of peas, situated between the two layers of the triangular ligament, one on each side of the membranous portion of the urethra, close above the bulb, and enclosed by the transverse fibres of the compressor urethræ muscle. The—

Excretory Duct,—of each gland opens by a minute orifice on the floor of the bulbous part of the cavernous portion of the urethra, after traversing the wall of the urethra for about 1 inch, beneath its mucous coat.

THE PENIS

The Penis is composed of a mass of erectile tissue enclosed in three cylindrical compartments, each surrounded by a fibrous sheath which is prolonged inward, forming numerous bands or trabeculæ, which divide the compartments into a number of spaces. The compartments are the two *corpora cavernosa* and the *corpus spongiosum* (corpus cavernosum urethræ) (6), the latter lying between and beneath the former, like the ramrod of a double-barreled gun. The—

Erectile Tissue,—is lodged in the interspaces between the trabeculæ of the fibrous structure, and consists of an intricate venous plexus, supplied by afferent arteries and emptied by efferent veins.

The Corpora Cavernosa lie side by side, forming the upper and lateral parts of the penis. They are joined together along their anterior three-fourths, their posterior one-fourth forming the

FIG. 129.

Crura, which arise from the tuberosities of the ischia and their rami, and meet beneath the symphysis pubis, forming two grooves, one above for the dorsal vessels (1), and nerves (3), the inferior one for the corpus spongiosum (6).

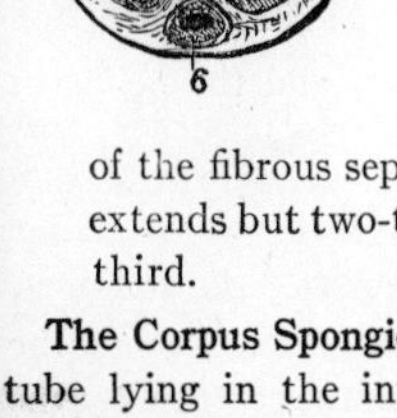

Suspensory Ligament (lig. suspensorium penis), —a fibrous membrane which connects the root of the organ to the symphysis pubis.

Septum Pectiniforme (5),—is the front portion of the fibrous septum between the corpora cavernosa. This septum extends but two-thirds along the penis, and is wanting for its anterior third.

The Corpus Spongiosum (corpus cavernosum urethræ) (6) is an erectile tube lying in the inferior groove between the two corpora cavernosa, having within it the urethra, and expanded at both ends to form the glans penis and the bulb. It is composed of trabecular (band-like) structure, derived from a fibrous sheath, and containing erectile tissue. The—

Bulb of the Corpus Spongiosum (bulbus urethræ),—receives the urethra and is surrounded by the (bulbo-cavernosus) or accelerator urinæ muscle.

Glans Penis,—is the external expansion of the corpus spongiosum (corpus cavernosum urethræ) and covers by its base the ends of the two corpora cavernosa. Its base presents a rounded border, called the *corona glandis,* behind which is a deep sulcus, the *cervix* (collum glandis).

Glands of Tyson,—small lenticular sebaceous glands opening on the corona and cervix of the glans, and secreting an odorous sebaceous matter, the *smegma.*

Meatus Urinarius,—the external orifice of the urethra, is situated at the summit of the glans penis.

Prepuce (præputium),—a prolongation of the integument of the penis, covering or partly covering the glans penis.

Frœnum Prœputii (frænulum præputii),—a fold of mucous membrane lying along the raphé of the glans penis, and connecting the prepuce with the glans.

Vessels and Nerves. The *Arteries* are branches of the internal pudic, named as follows: the artery of the bulb, to the bulb of the corpus spongiosum; the arteries of the corpora cavernosa, to that structure; and the dorsal artery of the penis, to the integument and fibrous sheath of the corpora cavernosa, the glans and prepuce. The—

Helicine Arteries,—are vine-like branches, which project into the cavernous spaces, and are most abundant in the back part of the corpora cavernosa.

Veins,—empty into the dorsal vein of the penis and the prostatic venous plexus. They form intricate and well-developed plexuses in the erectile tissue.

Lymphatics,—the superficial terminate in the inguinal glands; the deep join the deep lymphatics of the pelvis.

Nerves,—are derived from the internal pudic nerve, and the pelvic or hypogastric plexus of the sympathetic.

THE TESTES

The Testes or *Testicles* are the glandular organs which secrete the seminal fluid,—two oval bodies suspended obliquely in the scrotum by the spermatic cords, each measuring about an inch in diameter, and weighing

¾ oz. to an ounce. Their coverings, from without inward, are 6 in number, as follows:—

Skin (4),—of the scrotum. } Scrotum (see Fig. 131).
Dartos (5),—the vascular tunic. }

Intercolumnar Fascia,—the external spermatic fascia (6, Fig. 131).

Cremasteric Fascia (7, Fig. 131),—muscular fibres, the *cremaster* muscle, derived from the lower border of the internal oblique muscle.

Infundibuliform Fascia (9, Fig. 131),—internal spermatic fascia, or fascia propria; a continuation downward of the transversalis fascia.

Tunica Vaginalis,—the serous covering, originally a process of the peritoneum (see below).

The Scrotum is a cutaneous pouch, consisting of 2 layers—the integument and the *Dartos;* the latter being a contractile vascular tunic, continuous with the superficial fascia of the thighs and perinæum, and forming a septum in the scrotum between the two cavities for the testes.

FIG. 130.

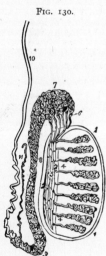

The Epididymis is an appendix to the testicle, lying along its posterior border, and consists of a single duct about 20 feet in length when unraveled, but which is wound upon itself so as to occupy a very small space. The—

Head or *Globus Major* (7),—is formed by the coni vasculosi, or efferent ducts (6) of the testis, which therein open into the single duct which forms the epididymis.

Body (8),—is formed by the convolutions of the tube, held together by fine connective tissue.

Tail or *Globus Minor* (9),—the lower expanded portion, similarly formed, and connected to the testis by cellular tissue.

Vas or *Ductus Aberrans* (11),—a narrow tube, sometimes found opening into the canal of the epididymis near its lower end, and ending in a blind extremity.

Hydatids of Morgagni (appendices testis),—small pedunculated bodies, found attached to the epididymis or to the upper end of the testicle. One of them is believed to be the remains of the duct of Müller.

Tunics of the Testis are 3 in number,—the *tunica vaginalis,* or serous covering, externally; the *tunica albuginea,* or fibrous covering, in the middle; and the *tunica vasculosa,* or pia mater testis, internally. The—

Tunica Vaginalis, the serous covering,—has a visceral layer (11) (tunica vaginalis propria) and a parietal layer (8) (tunica vaginalis reflexa). Originally a part of the peritoneum, its upper end becomes obliterated, and the lower end remains as a closed sac, the space between the layers being the cavity (10) of the tunica vaginalis. It forms a pouch, the *digital fossa* (13), between the epididymis and the testicle.

Tunica Albuginea (12), the fibrous covering,—consists of white fibrous tissue, and forms an incomplete vertical septum within the gland, the corpus *Highmorianum* or *mediastinum testis* (2), from which fibrous bands (trabeculæ) cross the gland, dividing its interior into spaces for the lobules of the organ.

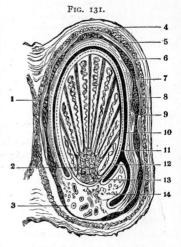

FIG. 131.

Tunica Vasculosa, the vascular covering,—lies beneath the preceding, and lines the septa in the interior of the gland. It consists of a plexus of blood-vessels, held together by a delicate areolar tissue.

Structure of the Testis. The glandular structure consists of 250 to 400 *olbules*, which are each contained in one of the spaces formed by the trabeculæ, and formed of 1 to 3 or more minute, convoluted tubes, the *tubuli seminiferi*. The latter consist of a basement membrane, lined by several layers of cells, from which the spermatozoa are developed. In the apices of the lobules the tubuli become straight, and join to form 20 or 30 ducts, the—

Vasa Recta (4, Fig. 130),—are each about $\frac{1}{50}$ inch in diameter; then enter the mediastinum, passing upward and backward, and forming the—

Rete Testis (5),—a network of anastomosing tubes or channels in the fibrous stroma of the mediastinum; they end in the—

Vasa Efferentia (6),—12 to 20 ducts, which perforate the tunica albuginea of the testis, and form a number of conical masses, the *coni vasculosi* which together constitute the *globus major* (7) of the Epididymis (see Fig. 130).

Descent of the Testis. In early fœtal life the testes are situated in the abdominal cavity, just below the kidneys, and are connected to the dartos of the scrotum and the tissues about the inguinal canal by a cord named the *gubernaculum testis*, which prevents the testicle rising with the growth of the fœtus, and the testicle is drawn first into the inguinal canal and eventually into the scrotum, the cord itself becoming shortened as development proceeds. The descent begins about the commencement of the 5th month; during the 7th month the testicle enters the inguinal canal, and ordinarily arrives in the scrotum by the end of the 8th month. A process of peritoneum is carried down in front of the testis; which process, by obliteration of the canal, becomes a separate structure, the *tunica vaginalis*. The structures of the inguinal canal are also brought down with the testicle, and constitute some of its coverings.

Vessels and Nerves. The *Arteries* are the Spermatic, from the aorta to the testicle itself; its coverings are supplied by the superficial and deep External Pudic from the femoral, the superficial Perineal branch of the Internal Pudic from the internal iliac, and the Cremasteric branch of the epigastric from the external iliac.

Veins.—The spermatic veins emerge at the back of the testis, receive branches from the epididymis, and unite into the convoluted *pampiniform plexus*, which forms the chief mass of the spermatic cord. From this plexus 3 or 4 veins arise, they unite into 2, and these join into a single trunk, which on the right side empties into the inferior vena cava, on the left side into the left renal vein.

Lymphatics,—of the testis terminate in the lumbar glands; those of its coverings in the inguinal glands.

Nerves,—of the testes are derived from the spermatic plexus, joined by filaments from the pelvic plexus; those of their coverings are the ilio-inguinal branch of the lumbar plexus, the superficial perineal branches of the internal pudic, the inferior pudendal branch of the small sciatic, and the genital branch of the genito-crural.

APPENDAGES OF THE TESTES

The Vas Deferens (ductus deferens) is the continuation of the epididymis, and the excretory duct of the testicle. Beginning at the globus minor it ascends along the back of the spermatic cord to the inguinal canal, and enters the abdominal cavity through the internal abdominal ring. It curves around the outer side of the epigastric artery, crosses the external iliac vessels, and descends into the pelvis at the side of the bladder, crossing to the inner side of the ureter and the inner border of the vesicula seminalis. At the base of the prostate gland it joins the duct of the seminal vesicle to form the ejaculatory duct. The vas deferens is about 2 feet long, and has a canal of only half a line in diameter. Its walls are very dense, making it feel like a piece of wire or whip-cord when grasped between the fingers. In structure it consists of three coats, the—

> *Areolar Coat,*—externally, beneath which is the—
>
> *Muscular Coat,*—in 2 layers of unstriped fibre, the outer longitudinal, and the inner circular; but a third longitudinal layer is found at the commencement of the vas, internal to the circular layer.
>
> *Mucous Coat,*—internally, is pale and in longitudinal folds; its epithelium is columnar.
>
> *Artery of the Vas or Ductus Deferens,*—a branch of the superior vesical, ramifies on its coats and anastomoses with the spermatic artery.

The Spermatic Cord (funiculus spermaticus) extends from the internal abdominal ring to the globus minor of the epididymis, and is about 4 inches long. At the external abdominal ring it rests upon the inguinal or Poupart's ligament, having the aponeurosis of the external oblique muscle in front, and the conjoined tendon behind it. It is composed of arteries, veins, lymphatics, nerves, and the vas deferens, bound together by areolar tissue, and invested by the layers brought down by the descent of the testicle. The structures, composing the spermatic cord, are 12 in number, and are named as follows: the—

> *Vas or Ductus Deferens.*   *Spermatic Plexus of Nerves.*
> *Spermatic Artery.*   *Branch of the Ileo-inguinal nerve.*
> *Cremasteric Artery.*   *Branch of the Genito-crural* (genito-
> *Artery of the Vas Deferens.*   femoral) *Nerve.*
> *Deferential Veins.*   *Obliterated Processus Vaginalis* of the
> *Spermatic Veins.*   peritoneum (ligament of Cloquet).
> *Internal Cremaster Muscle.*   *Lymphatics.*

Coverings of the Cord, from within outward, are the—
> *Infundibuliform Fascia,* from the transversalis fascia.
> *Cremasteric Fascia,* from the internal oblique muscle.
> *Intercolumnar Fascia,* the external spermatic fascia.
> *Superficial Fascia,* and the *Skin,* of the scrotum.

The Vesiculæ Seminales (*d*, Fig. 127) are two lobulated membranous pouches, which serve as reservoirs for the semen, and secrete a fluid to be added to the secretion of the testicles. They are about 2½ inches long, and are situated externally to the lower ends of the vasa or ductus deferentia, between the base of the bladder and the rectum. They are composed of 3 coats,—an external areolar, a middle muscular, and an internal mucous coat, lined with columnar epithelium. Their anterior extremities converge toward the base of the prostate gland, where a duct from each joins with the corresponding vas or ductus deferens to form—

Ejaculatory Ducts (ductus ejaculatorii),—one on each side, are formed by the junction of the vasa or ductus deferentia with the ducts of the vesiculæ seminales. They are about ¾ inch in length, and terminate in the prostatic portion of the urethra, by orifices on the sides of the verumontanum (colliculus seminalis).

Arteries,—are derived from the middle and inferior vesical, and the middle hæmorrhoidal; they are accompanied by veins and lymphatics.

Nerves,—are branches from the pelvic or hypogastric plexus.

THE FEMALE ORGANS OF GENERATION
(Organa Genitalia Muliebria)

THE VULVA

The Vulva, or *Pudendum Muliebre,* are the external genital organs of the female, viz.,—the mons Veneris, the labia majora and minora, the clitoris, and the orifice of the vagina. The—

Mons Veneris (commissura labiorum anterior),—is the rounded eminence in front of the pubic symphysis, formed of fatty tissue beneath the skin, and covered with hair after puberty.

The Labia Majora Pudendi (1) are two prominent longitudinal folds extending from the mons Veneris to the perinæum. They are formed of hairy integument externally and modified skin internally, between which are areolar and dartoid tissues, fat, vessels, nerves, and glands. They meet in front, forming the *anterior commissure* (10), and nearly meet behind in the *posterior commissure* at the anterior boundary of the perinæum. They correspond to the scrotum of the male. The—

Fourchette (commissura labiorum posterior) (2),—is the curved anterior edge of the perinæum, and between it and the hymen (8) there is a depression, the *fossa navicularis.*

Nerves,—the superficial perineal from the pudic, and the inferior pudendal from the small sciatic.

The Labia Minora Pudendi (3), or *Nymphæ,* are two small folds, situated internally to the labia majora, and extending from the prepuce of the clitoris (præputium clitoridis) (4) obliquely backward for 1½ inches on each side of the vaginal orifice, where they are lost on the inner surface of the labia majora. They are composed of modified skin, and have sebaceous follicles (glandulæ vestibulares minores) on their internal surface.

Clitoris,—is situated beneath the anterior commissure, its *glans* (4) only appearing externally as a small rounded tubercle between the anterior extremities of the labia minora. It is a diminutive penis, in all but the corpus spongiosum and urethra; having two corpora cavernosa, two crura, a glans, prepuce, suspensory ligament and muscles, the erectores clitoridis (ischio-cavernosi).

Vestibule (vestibulum vaginæ) (6),— is a triangular depression in front of the vaginal orifice, bounded laterally by the labia minora.

Meatus Urinarius (orificium urethræ externum) (5),—situated in the vestibule, about an inch below the clitoris, and close to the vaginal orifice.

Bulbi Vestibuli,—are two oblong erectile bodies, situated one on either side of the vestibule, and consisting of a venous plexus surrounded by a fibrous membrane. They are the analogues of the bulb of the corpus spongiosum in the male.

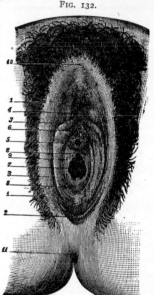

FIG. 132.

Pars Intermedia,—is a small venous plexus situated between the glans clitoridis and the bulbi vestibuli. It is the analogue of the corpus spongiosum.

Orifice of the Vagina (7),—is surrounded by the sphincter vaginæ muscle, and in the virgin is sometimes partly closed by the hymen.

Hymen (8),—a fold of mucous membrane situated across the lower part of the vaginal orifice, of various shapes, usually a ring, but often semilunar, the concavity upward. It is frequently absent in virgins. Its cicatrization after rupture gives rise to small eminences along the margin of the vaginal orifice, named the *carunculæ myrtiformes* (carunculæ hymenales).

Glands of Bartholin (glandulæ vestibulares majores),—one on each side of the vaginal orifice, their ducts opening (9) near the inner sides of

the labia minora. They are the analogues of Cowper's glands
(glandulæ bulbo-urethrales) in the male.

Nerves,—to the labia minora as to the labia majora; the bulbi vestibuli
and other erectile structures are supplied by filaments from the dorsal
nerve of the clitoris, superficial perineal, and hypogastric plexus.

THE VAGINA

The Vagina is a curved canal extending from the vulva to the uterus,
placed between the bladder in front and the rectum behind. Its length
is about $2\frac{1}{2}$ inches along the anterior wall (paries anterior), $3\frac{1}{2}$ inches
along the posterior wall (paries posterior), and its walls are usually in contact with each other. It is very dilatable, especially near its upper end,
which surrounds the vaginal portion of the cervix uteri, its attachment
extending higher up on the posterior wall of the uterus than on the anterior
wall. Its relations are—

Anteriorly,—the urethra and the base of the bladder.

Posteriorly,—the anterior wall of the rectum, and the recto-vaginal fold
of peritoneum which forms *Douglas' pouch* (excavatio recto-uterina)
behind its upper fourth.

Laterally,—are attached the levatores ani muscles, and the recto-vesical
portion of the *pelvic* fascia.

Structure of the Vagina. The vaginal wall consists of a muscular coat
(tunica muscularis) externally, a layer of erectile tissue, and a mucous
lining (tunica mucosa) covered with squamous epithelium, and furnished
with mucous crypts and follicles, but has no glands. The vagina is partially covered laterally by the *recto-vesical* portion of the pelvic fascia.

Columns of the Vagina (columnæ rugarum anterior et posterior),—
are two longitudinal raphés situated along its inner surface, one
anteriorly, the other posteriorly, which are connected by numerous
transverse ridges or *rugæ vaginales.*

Sphincter Vaginæ Muscle,—surrounds the lower end of the vagina; it is
described on page 99.

Vessels and Nerves. The *Arteries* of the vagina are the Vaginal
branches of the internal iliac, and branches of the uterine artery, which
form in front and behind a longitudinal vessel, the *azygos arteries of the
vagina.* The—

Veins,—are disposed similarly to the arteries, form a rich plexus in the
muscular and mucous coats, and terminate in the vaginal and uterine
trunks.

Lymphatics,—terminate in the pelvic and inguinal glands.

Nerves,—are derived from the hypogastric plexus, the fourth sacral nerve, and the pudic nerve (n. pudendus), forming a vaginal plexus.

THE UTERUS

The Uterus is a hollow, pear-shaped, muscular organ, measuring about 3 inches long, 2 inches broad, and 1 inch thick, flattened from before backward, placed base upward, forming an angle with the vagina, which partially receives its cervix, and situated in the pelvic cavity, between the bladder in front and the rectum behind. Its—

Fundus uteri (A),—is broad, convex, having walls ⅝ inch thick, and is covered by peritoneum.

Body (corpus uteri),—is about 1⅝ inches long, walls ½ inch thick, flat anteriorly, convex posteriorly, concave laterally, and joined to the bladder by its lower anterior fourth. It is invested by peritoneum **posteriorly**, and in front for its upper three-fourths.

FIG. 133.

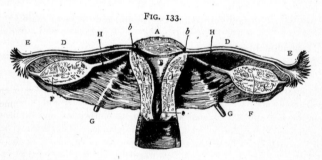

Cervix Uteri or *Neck,*—is the lower constricted portion, about 1⅜ inches long, walls ¼ inch in thickness, and is embraced for ½ to ¾ inch by the upper extremity of the vagina.

Cavity of the Body (cavum uteri) (B),—is small and triangular, flattened from before backward, about 1⅛ inches in length, and has two lateral *cornua* above, and a constricted orifice, the *os internum* (orificium internum uteri), at its lower angle, opening into the cavity of the cervix.

Cavity of the Cervix (canalis cervicis uteri),—is spindle-shaped, about 1⅜ inches long, and presents on its inner surface transverse folds of mucous membrane proceeding from a longitudinal fold, giving an appearance named the *arbor vitæ* (plicæ palmatæ) (*o*).

Os Uteri (orificium externum uteri),—is a transverse orifice at the lower end of the cervical cavity, opening into the vagina, and having an anterior (labium anterius) and a posterior lip (labium posterius).

Ligaments of the Uterus are 8 in number,—1 anterior, 1 posterior, 2 lateral or broad ligaments, 2 sacro-uterine, and 2 round ligaments, all except the last-named being formed of peritoneum. The—

Anterior Ligament, utero-vesical,—is reflected from the front of the uterus on to the bladder. It forms the floor of the *utero-vesical pouch* (excavatio vesico-uterina).

Posterior Ligament, recto-vaginal,—passes from the posterior wall of the uterus over the upper fourth of the vagina, and thence on to the rectum and sacrum, forming *Douglas' pouch* (excavatio recto-uterina) behind the upper portion of the vagina.

Lateral or *Broad Ligaments* (ligamenta lata uteri) 2,—pass from the sides of the uterus to the lateral walls of the pelvis, and form a septum across the pelvic cavity. They contain, between the two folds of peritoneum of which they are composed, the Fallopian tubes (tubæ uterinæ) the round ligaments, the ovaries, the parovaria or organs of Rosenmüller, connective tissue, unstriped muscular fibre, blood-vessels, and nerves.

Sacro-uterine Ligaments (plicæ recto-uterinæ) 2,—pass from the sides of the uterus to the sides of the rectum, and thence to the sacrum.

Round Ligaments (ligamenta teres uteri) 2 (G),—are two cords, about 4 or 5 inches long, composed of muscular tissue prolonged from the uterus, also areolar and fibrous tissue, vessels and nerves, extending one on each side, from the lateral aspects of the fundus uteri, through the inguinal canals, to the labia majora, where they are lost. Each ligament lies, for a part of its course, between the two layers of the broad ligament, and is covered by a process of peritoneum. The—

Canal of Nuck,—is the extension of the above-mentioned process of peritoneum into the inguinal canal. It exists in the fœtus, but is usually obliterated in the adult.

Structure of the Uterus. The wall of the uterus is composed of 3 coats, an external serous, a middle muscular, and an internal mucous coat. The *muscular coat* (tunica muscularis) forms the chief bulk of the organ, and consists of bundles of unstriped muscular fibres, disposed in 3 layers interlaced together; circular fibres predominating in the cervix, longitudinal fibres in the body of the uterus. The—

Peritoneal or *Serous Coat* (tunica serosa),—invests the body of the organ, except its lower anterior fourth.

Mucous Coat (tunica mucosa),—is very thick, $\frac{1}{12}$ to $\frac{1}{8}$ inch, and closely adherent to the muscular tissue, having no basement layer of connective tissue. It is covered with ciliated columnar epithelium, and studded with mucous follicles and tubular glands (glandulæ uterinæ), which are most numerous in the cervix.

Vessels and Nerves. The *Arteries* of the uterus are the Uterine from the internal iliac, and the Ovarian from the aorta; the two meeting on the side of the body and forming an anastomotic trunk, from which lateral branches are given off to the uterus. They are remarkably tortuous and anastomose freely. The—

Veins,—accompany the arteries, and in the impregnated state become sinuses. They end in the uterine plexuses.

Lymphatics,—those of the cervix end in the pelvic glands, those of the body in the lumbar glands.

Nerves,—are derived from the inferior hypogastric and ovarian plexuses, and from the 3d and 4th sacral nerves.

Appendages of the Uterus

The Fallopian Tubes, or *Oviducts* (tubæ uterinæ) (D), are two tubes, each about 4 inches in length, and $1\frac{1}{16}$ inch in calibre, situated in the free margin of the broad ligament, and extending from the superior angles of the uterus (*b*) outward, to terminate in free, trumpet-shaped ends. They open by one end into the uterus at its cornua, by the other end into the peritoneal cavity. Their structure is similar to that of the uterus, the mucous lining being continuous with the uterine mucous membrane and with the peritoneum, and lined with ciliated columnar epithelium. Their—

Isthmus Tubæ Uterinæ,—is the inner constricted third of the tube.

Ampulla Tubæ Uterinæ,—is the outer dilated portion, curving over the ovary.

Infundibulum Tubæ Uterinæ,—the trumpet-shaped outer end, with its open mouth, the *ostium abdominale tubæ uterinæ*, surrounded by—

Fimbriæ Tubæ Uterinæ (E),—fringe-like processes, one of which, the *fimbria ovarica*, is attached to the ovary.

Hydatids of Morgagni (appendices vesiculosi) (see page 372),—one or more small vesicles floating on a long stalk of peritoneum, are frequently found in connection with or near the fimbriæ.

Vessels and Nerves,—The vessels are those of the ovaries; the nerves are branches from one of the uterine nerves.

The Ovaries (ovaria) (F) are two oval bodies, of grayish-pink color, situated in the broad ligament, behind and below the Fallopian tubes, (tubæ uterinæ,) one on each side of the uterus, to which they are attached by the ligament of the ovary. They each measure about 1½ inches by ¾ by ⅓, and are invested by peritoneum, except posteriorly. They are composed of a vascular stroma containing the *Graafian vesicles* (folliculi oöphori vesiculosi) in various stages of development, and are surrounded by the *tunica albuginea*, a condensed layer of the stroma.

The Graafian Vesicles (folliculi oöphori vesiculosi) are the ovisacs containing the ova, are very numerous (about 70,000 in each ovary), vary in diameter from $\frac{1}{100}$ to $\frac{1}{60}$ inch, but after puberty a few are found of from $\frac{1}{20}$ to $\frac{1}{6}$ inch or more. Each vesicle has an external fibro-vascular coat, and an internal coat (tunica externa) or *ovicapsule*, (theca folliculi) which is lined by the *membrana granulosa* (stratum granulosum) and contains a transparent fluid of albuminous character, containing the immature ovum. The—

Membrana Granulosa (stratum granulosum),—is a layer of nucleated cells, lining the ovicapsule; at one point the cells are heaped up in a mass, the *discus proligerus* (cumulus oöphorus), in which the ovum is embedded.

Corpus Luteum,—is a puckered yellow spot in the substance of the ovary, produced as a result of the rupture of a Graafian vesicle and the discharge of an ovum, probably by the organization of the extravasated blood, forming *lutein cells*. In old age the corpus luteum undergoes involution, loses its yellow color, and is then called the *corpus albicans*.

Vessels and Nerves. The *Arteries* are the Ovarian, from the aorta, which also supply the Fallopian tubes, and anastomose with the uterine arteries. The—

Veins,—accompany the arteries, and form a plexus, the *pampiniform plexus*, near the ovary.

Nerves,—are derived from the inferior hypogastric or pelvic plexus, and from the ovarian plexus.

The Parovarium, or *Organ of Rosenmüller*, is a group of tubules, situated in the broad ligament, between the ovary and the Fallopian tube, and converging to a large duct, the *duct of Gärtner*, which ramifies in the broad ligament, descends along the side of the uterus, and terminates in a bulbous enlargement. It is the atrophied remains of the Wolffian Body of foetal life.

THE MAMMÆ

The Mammæ, or *Breasts*, are two hemispherical eminences, situated one on each antero-lateral aspect of the chest, extending from the sternum to the axilla, and from the 3d rib to the 7th. Each breast contains the

Mammary Gland (corpus mammæ) and is surmounted by the *nipple* (papilla mammæ), around the base of which is a zone of colored cutaneous tissue, the *areola mammæ*, pink in virgins, darker in women who have borne children. In the male the mammæ are rudimentary organs, but capable of development under special circumstances.

FIG. 134.

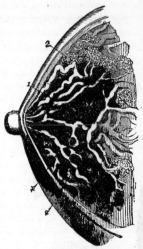

Structure of the Mammary Gland. Is composed of 15 or 20 lobes (lobi mammæ) and their ducts (1), with a packing of areolar and adipose tissue (subcutaneous tela), enveloped by a thin fibrous capsule or stroma which forms septa between the lobes. Each lobe is made up of lobules (2), and these again are formed by the aggregation of *alveoli*, terminal vesicles by which the milk is secreted. The—

Tubuli Lactiferi (ductus lactiferi) (1),
—are the excretory ducts of the lobes, one for each. They are formed by the junction of the ducts from each lobule, and converge towards the areola, beneath which they form *ampullæ* or dilatations, and thence, piercing the nipple, open on its summit by separate orifices.

Vessels and Nerves. The *Arteries* are derived from the thoracic branches of the axillary, the intercostals, and the internal mammary arteries.

Veins,—form the *circulus venosus*, an anastomotic venous circle around the base of the nipple, from which larger veins run outward, and terminate in the axillary and internal mammary veins.

Lymphatics,—terminate in the axillary glands; a few going to the anterior mediastinal glands.

Nerves,—are derived from the lateral cutaneous branches of the 4th, 5th, and 6th intercostal nerves and from the thoracic portion of the sympathetic cord.

HERNIA

A Hernia is a protrusion of any viscus from its natural cavity. The term, when unqualified as to the viscus, is understood to mean a protrusion of the intestines or mesentery, or both, from the abdominal cavity. Anatomically the most important herniæ are—

Oblique Inguinal Hernia,—in which the protrusion follows the spermatic cord through the inguinal canal; passing to the outer side of the epigastric artery, and through both the internal and external abdominal rings.

Direct Inguinal Hernia,—occurs at Hesselbach's triangle, escaping to the inner side of the epigastric artery, and through the subcutaneous inguinal or external abdominal ring only.

Femoral Hernia,—in which the protrusion descends through the femoral or crural canal.

INGUINAL HERNIA

The Inguinal Canal is a passage in the abdominal wall, parallel to the *inguinal* or Poupart's ligament, and just above it. It commences at the *abdominal inguinal* or internal abdominal ring and ends at the *subcutaneous inguinal* or external abdominal ring (1), being about 1½ inches in length. It serves for the passage of the spermatic cord in the male, and the round ligament of the uterus in the female; is directed downward and inward, and is bounded as follows:—

Anteriorly,—the skin, superficial fascia, (camper's) external oblique muscle for its entire length, and the internal oblique (the part attached to the inguinal ligament) for the outer third of the canal.

Posteriorly,—the conjoined tendon of the internal *oblique* and *transversalis,* transversalis fascia, triangular fascia (5) for the medial two-thirds, sub-peritoneal tissue, transversalis fascia, and peritoneum for its entire length.

Above,—the arched fibres of the internal oblique and transversalis muscles.

Below,—the union of the transversalis fascia (5) with Poupart's (inguinal) ligament (10).

The Internal or **Deep Abdominal Ring** (annulus inguinalis abdominis),—is an oval opening in the transversalis fascia, formed by the prolongation of this fascia around the cord, as the infundibuliform fascia. It lies ½ inch above Poupart's (inguinal) ligament (10) and midway between the anterior superior spine of the ilium and the spine of the pubes (8). It is bounded above and externally by the arched fibres of the transversalis muscle; below and internally by the epigastric vessels. The—

Deep Epigastric Artery,—lies between the transversalis fascia and the peritoneum, passing obliquely upward and inward along the lower and inner margins of the internal ring.

Infundibuliform Fascia,—or infundibuliform process of the transversalis fascia, is a thin, funnel-shaped membrane, arises from the circum-

25

ference of the internal ring, and is continued (internal spermatic fascia) around the cord and testis, enclosing them in a distinct pouch.

The External or Superficial Abdominal Ring (annulus inguinalis subcutaneous) (1),—is a somewhat triangular opening in the aponeurosis of the external oblique muscle, situated just above and external to the crest of the pubes. It is about 1 inch long, and ½ inch wide, and is bounded laterally by its own margins, called the *external* (crus inferius) (2) *and internal* (crus superius) (3) *pillars* of the ring. It may be easily felt in

FIG. 135.

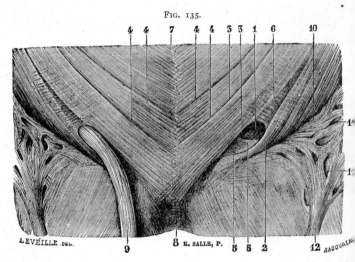

L. LEVÉILLE DEL.   E. SALLE, P.   BADOUREAU

the living male, by invaginating the skin of the scrotum with the finger, and feeling up along the spermatic cord (9). It is much larger in men than in women. The—

Intercolumnar or *External Spermatic Fascia* (fibræ intercrurales) (6),—is formed by tendinous fibres which arch across the lower part of the aponeurosis of the external oblique, between the pillars of the external ring, and are connected together by delicate fibrous tissue. It is continued downward as a tubular prolongation around the cord and testis, enclosing them in a distinct sheath.

Cremasteric Fascia (fascia cremasterica),—passes through the external ring, and consists of a series of muscular loops, united by areolar tissue, forming a thin covering over the spermatic cord and testis.

The muscular fibres (Cremaster muscle) are supposed to have been originally part of the internal oblique muscle, carried down by the testicle in its descent to the scrotum. It does not exist in the female.

Poupart's Ligament (ligamentum inguinale), or the *Crural Arch*, is that portion of the aponeurosis of the external oblique muscle which

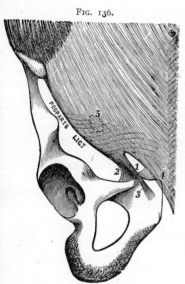

FIG. 136.

extends from the anterior superior spine of the ilium to the spine of the pubes. Its lower portion (3) forms the external pillar of the external abdominal ring, and its reflection along the pectineal line is called *Gimbernat's ligament* (ligamentum lacunare) (2). Other fibres, reflected behind the internal pillar of the ring (4), upward to the linea alba, are termed the *triangular fascia* (ligamentum inguinale reflexum) (1).

Gimbernat's Ligament (ligamentum lacunare) (2),—is that portion of the aponeurosis of the external oblique which is reflected upward and outward from the spine of the os pubis to be inserted into the pectineal line. Its anterior margin is continuous with Poupart's (inguinal) ligament.

Triangular Fascia (ligamentum inguinale reflexum) (1),—is a triangular band, attached by its apex to the pectineal line, where it is continuous with Gimbernat's (lacunar) ligament; passes inward beneath the spermatic cord, behind the internal pillar (crus superius) of the external or subcutaneous inguinal ring, and in front of the conjoined tendon, to interlace with its fellow of the opposite side at the linea alba (see 5, Fig. 134). It is often undeveloped or wanting.

Hesselbach's Triangle is a small triangular space on the lower abdominal wall, bounded externally by the deep epigastric artery, internally by the margin of the rectus muscle, below by Poupart's (inguinal) ligament.   Its inner $\frac{2}{3}$ is crossed by the conjoined tendon.   Through this space a direct inguinal hernia forces its way.   The—

> *Inguinal Peritoneal Fossæ*,—are 3 depressions of peritoneum in the inguinal region above Poupart's (inguinal) ligament.   The internal (fovea supravesicalis) and middle (fovea inguinalis medialis) ones lie in Hesselbach's triangle, the external fossa (fovea inguinalis lateralis) usually corresponds to the internal abdominal or abdominal inguinal ring.

Coverings of Inguinal Hernia depend, in the oblique form, upon the extent to which the hernia descends in or through the inguinal canal. When it has escaped from the external abdominal or subcutaneous inguinal ring, and is therefore complete, its coverings, from without inward, are 7 in number, as follows:—

> 1. *Skin.*
> 2. *Superficial Fascia,*—2 layers.
> 3. *Intercolumnar Fascia,*—from the external abdominal ring.
> 4. *Cremasteric Fascia,*—from the inguinal canal.
> 5. *Infundibuliform Fascia,*—from the internal abdominal ring.
> 6. *Subserous Areolar Tissue,*—almost inappreciable.
> 7. *Peritoneum,*—the hernial sac proper.

Direct Inguinal Hernia has the same coverings, except that the *Conjoined Tendon* is substituted for the cremasteric fascia, and the *Transversalis Fascia* for the infundibuliform.

FEMORAL HERNIA

The Femoral or **Crural Canal** is a narrow interval, $\frac{1}{4}$ to $\frac{1}{2}$ inch long, between the femoral vein (4) and the inner wall of the femoral sheath (fascia cruris), extending from Gimbernat's (lacunar) ligament to the *saphenous opening* (fossa ovalis).   It exists as a distinct canal only when the sheath has been separated from the vein by the pressure of a hernia or tumor, or by dissection.   It lies beneath Poupart's (inguinal) ligament (1), is closed above by the *septum crurale* of Cloquet (septum femorale), below by the *cribriform fascia* (fascia cribrosa), and is bounded as follows:—

> *Anteriorly,*—by a continuation downward, under Poupart's (inguinal) ligament, of the transversalis fascia, covered by the falciform process (margo falciformis) of the fascia lata.
>
> *Posteriorly,*—by a downward continuation of the iliac fascia, covering the pubic portion of the fascia lata.
>
> *Externally,*—by the fibrous septum separating it from the inner side of the femoral vein.

Internally,—by the outer edge of Gimbernat's (lacunar) ligament, and the junction of the processes of the transversalis fascia and the iliac fascia, which form the inner side of the femoral sheath.

The Femoral or **Crural Ring** (annulus femoralis), the upper opening of the femoral canal, is an oval-shaped opening, about ½ inch in diameter

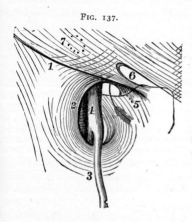

FIG. 137.

(larger in the female), situated below the internal abdominal or subcutaneous inguinal ring (7) and Poupart's (inguinal) ligament (1), and between the inner side of the femoral vein and the margin of Gimbernat's (lacunar) ligament (5). It is closed by the *septum crurale* (septum femorale) and a small lymphatic gland. The arrow in the figure points into the femoral ring. The—

Femoral Vein (4),—lies next on its outer side.

Deep Epigastric Artery (a. epigastrica inferior),—crosses its upper and outer angle.

Obturator Artery,—when arising from a common trunk with the epigastric, as it does once in 3½ subjects, may lie close along its internal and superior margins.

Communicating Branch,—between the deep epigastric and obturator arteries, lies in front of the ring.

Spermatic Cord (funiculus spermaticus),—in the male, lies directly above its anterior margin, replaced by the round ligament in the female.

Septum Crurale, or Fascia of Cloquet (septum femorale),—is a layer of condensed areolar tissue, supporting a lymphatic gland, and perforated for the passage of lymphatic vessels. It lies across the femoral ring, and forms one of the coverings to any hernia escaping thereby.

The Saphenous Opening (fossa ovalis), the lower orifice of the femoral canal, is an oval-shaped aperture, 1½ by ½ inch in diameter, formed by a reflection of the fascia lata inward, around and under the end of the internal saphenous vein (3). It is situated below the inner third of Poupart's (inguinal) ligament, and is covered by the *cribriform fascia* (fascia cribrosa). Its inner margin curves upward behind the saphenous vein and under the outer margin, and is blended with the pubic portion of the fascia lata over the pectineus muscle. Its outer margin curves over the inner to the spine of the pubes, as a—

Falciform Process, or Superior Cornu (margo falciformis),—is thin but strong, sharply defined, and lies on a plane anterior to the inner margin. It ascends in front of the femoral vessels, and curving inward is attached to Poupart's (inguinal) ligament, the spine of the os pubis, and the pectineal line, where it is continuous with the pubic portion. It is sometimes named the ligament of Burns, its pubic end is called the ligament of Hey.

Cribriform Fascia (fascia cribrosa) (11, Fig. 134),—is the portion of the deep layer (Scarpa's) of the superficial fascia which covers the saphenous opening (fossa ovalis). It is perforated by the internal saphenous vein and by numerous blood-vessels and lymphatics.

The Femoral or **Crural Sheath**, the investing sheath of the femoral vessels, is a funnel-shaped prolongation of the lining fasciæ of the abdomen, the transversalis fascia in front, and the iliac fascia behind. The sheath is divided by two septa into 3 compartments, the external of which contains the *femoral artery*, the middle one the *femoral vein*, the internal one being the *femoral canal*. The sheath is perforated anteriorly by the genito-crural nerve, internally by the internal saphenous vein, and forms one of the coverings of a femoral hernia. The—

Deep Crural Arch,—is the thickened border of the transversalis fascia, which arches across the front of the crural sheath, and is intimately connected to it. Externally it is attached to the centre of Poupart's (inguinal) ligament, internally it is inserted into the pectineal line behind the conjoined tendon.

Coverings of Femoral Hernia depend upon whether the hernia has or has not escaped from the saphenous opening (fossa ovalis), and is therefore complete or incomplete. In the latter case, the covering, from without inward would be—skin, superficial fascia, cribriform fascia, femoral sheath, septum crurale, subserous areolar tissue (fascia propria of Sir Astley Cooper), and peritoneum. The coverings of a complete femoral hernia are as follows:—

1. *Skin.*
2. *Superficial Fascia,*—its superficial layer (subcutaneous tela).
3. *Cribriform Fascia,*—from the saphenous opening.
4. *Femoral Sheath,*—from the transversalis fascia.
5. *Septum Crurale,*—from the femoral ring.
6. *Subserous Areolar Tissue,*—the fascia propria of Cooper.
7. *Peritoneum,*—the proper hernial sac.

THE PERINÆUM, PROPER

The Perinæum is a triangular space containing the structures which close the inferior outlet of the pelvic cavity anterior to a line drawn between the tuberosities of the ischia. Posteriorly to this line the corresponding space is named the *Ischio-rectal Region*. The Perinæum is bounded laterally by the rami of the pubes and ischia, anteriorly by the symphysis pubis, and posteriorly by the line above mentioned, which averages about 2¾ inches in length.

For the Muscles of the Perinæum, see page 98.

THE PELVIC CAVITY

The Pelvic Cavity is that portion of the abdominal cavity which lies below the level of the ilio-pectineal line and the promontory of the sacrum. The osseous pelvis is described on page 9. The boundaries of the pelvic cavity are as follows:—

Anteriorly and Laterally,—the pubes and ischia, covered by the obturator muscles.

Posteriorly,—the sacrum and coccyx, the pyriformis muscles, and the great sacro-sciatic ligaments (lig. sacro-tuberosa).

Floor,—is formed by the recto-vesical fascia, covering the levator ani and coccygeus muscles of each side, and the triangular ligament (diaphragma-urogenitale) of the urethra.

Contents of the Pelvic Cavity are the bladder, rectum, some convolutions of the small intestine, and some of the organs of generation. They are partially covered by peritoneum, and supplied with vessels and nerves.

THE PELVIC FASCIA

The Pelvic Fascia lines the pelvic cavity and is continuous with the iliac and transversalis fascia above. At the level of a line drawn from the back of the symphysis pubis to the spine of the ischium, it is thickened into a *white line* or band (arcus tendineus), where it gives origin to the levator ani muscle, and divides into 2 layers, the *recto-vesical fascia* or visceral layer, and the *obturator fascia* or parietal layer. The—

Recto-vesical Fascia, visceral layer of the pelvic fascia,—descends from the white line (arcus tendineus) over the upper or pelvic surface of the levator ani muscle, and is prolonged over the prostate gland, rectum, vesiculæ seminales, and the bladder, forming the lateral true ligaments of the latter organ.

Obturator Fascia, the parietal layer of the pelvic fascia,—descends from the white line along the wall of the pelvis, and covers the obturator

internus muscle, near the lower border of which it forms a canal between its layers, *Alcock's canal*, for the pudic vessels and nerve.
Above this canal it gives off a thin membrane, the *ischio-rectal* or *anal
fascia* over the lower or perineal surface of the levator ani muscle; also
a process, which with its fellow of the opposite side forms the deep
(superior) layer of the triangular ligament (diaphragma urogenitale).

Illustration of the Pelvic Fascia. The capital letter K, having a horizontal arm added to it, thus **⊢**, will illustrate the pelvic fascia of the right
side, seen from the front in vertical section. The vertical line of the K
represents the pelvic fascia above, the obturator fascia below. The upper
arm represents the lateral ligament of the bladder, the horizontal arm the
recto-vesical fascia, and the lower arm the ischio-rectal fascia. The space
between the lower arm and the vertical line represents the ischio-rectal
fossa.

THE MALE PERINÆUM

The Male Perinæum, in the adult, varies in breadth on the base line,
from 2 to $3\frac{1}{2}$ inches, the average
being $2\frac{3}{4}$ inches. Its middle line
is convex, corresponds to the bulb
of the urethra, and presents a
prominent *raphé*, which is continuous in front with the raphé
of the scrotum. Its muscles are
described on page 98.

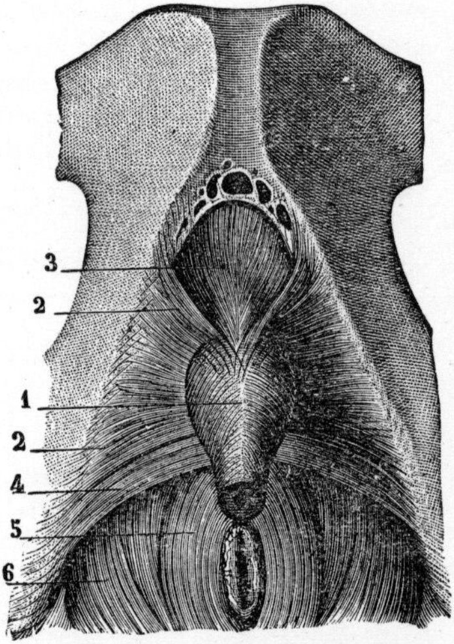

Fasciæ of the Perinæum are
superficial and deep, each consisting of two layers; the deep
fascia being usually called the
triangular ligament of the urethra.
The—

FIG. 138.

*Superficial Layer of the Super-
    ficial Fascia* (subcutaneous
    tela),—is thick, loaded with
    fat, and continuous with the
    subcutaneous fascia of the
    thighs.

Deep Layer of the Superficial Fascia, Colles' Fascia,—is thin but strong,
    continuous in front with the dartos of the scrotum, and attached on
    each side to the rami of the pubes and ischium; posteriorly it joins the
    deep perinæal fascia under the superficial transversus perinæi muscle.

Superficial Layer of the Deep Perinæal Fascia (fascia diaphragmatis urogenitalis inferior),—is triangular in shape, and extends from the sides of the pubic arch and the sub-pubic ligament, laterally to the rami of the pubes and ischia, and posteriorly to the central tendinous portion of the perinæum, where it becomes blended with Colle's fascia and the deep layer of the deep fascia. It embraces the anterior part of the membranous portion of the urethra.

Deep Layer of the Deep Perinæal Fascia (fascia diaphragmatis urogenitalis superior),—has the same attachments as the superficial layer above described, in its course it embraces the posterior part of the membranous portion of the urethra, and is in connection with the apex of the prostate gland.

Buck's Fascia is a continuation of the deep layer of the superficial fascia of the perinæum, extending forward upon the penis, which it invests completely as far as the glans. It is continuous above with the suspensory ligament of the penis, and is held by some anatomists to prove that the deep layer aforesaid is not continuous in front with the dartos of the scrotum. This fascia was named from Dr. Buck, an American surgeon, who, in 1846, first insisted on the importance of this structure. It modifies the direction of urinary infiltration of the perinæum, until perforated.

The Superficial Perinæal Interspace or *Fossa* is the interval between the deep layer of the superficial fascia (Colles' fascia) and the triangular ligament or urogenital diaphragm. It contains the following structures:—

Crura of the Penis (4).

Corpus Spongiosum (corpus cavernosum urethræ).

Bulb of the Urethra.

Bulbo-cavernosus or *Accelerator Urinæ Muscle* (8).

Ischio-cavernosus or Erector Penis Muscle (10).

Superficial Transversus Perinæi Muscle (14).

Superficial Transversus Perinæi Artery.

Superficial Perinæal Vessels and Nerves (5).

The Deep Perinæal Interspace or *Fossa* is the interval between the two layers of the triangular ligament or urogenital diaphragm. It contains the following structures:—

Membranous Urethra.

Deep Transversus Perinæi or *Compressor Urethræ Muscle.*

Pudic Vessels and Nerve (11).

Cowper's Glands (glandulæ bulbo-urethrales) *and Ducts.*

Dorsal Vein of the Penis.

Artery of the Bulb.

Nerve of the Bulb.

Plexus of Veins.

Central Tendinous Point is a fibrous point in the middle line of the perinæum, internal to the deep layer of the superficial fascia and about ½ inch in front of the anus. It corresponds to the centre of the posterior margin or base of the triangular ligament or urogenital diaphragm (12), and is the point of attachment for 4 converging muscles, the— external sphincter (16), bulbo-cavernosus or accelerator urinæ (8), and two superficial transverse perinæal (14).

ISCHIO-RECTAL REGION

The Ischio-rectal Space is the horse-shoe-shaped space behind and above the perinæum. It is somewhat triangular in cross-section. It extends posteriorly to the tip of the coccyx, laterally to the tuberosities and rami of the ischia and anteriorly, on each side, it presents an *Anterior Extension* which extends forwards as far as the body of the pubis. In fat subjects this extension is distended with fat, in which case it is triangular

Fig. 139.

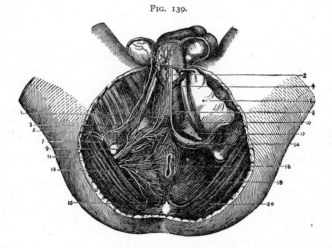

in cross-section, the floor being formed by the deep layer of the triangular ligament (uro-genital diaphragm), outer wall by obturator fascia and muscle, and the inner wall by the levator ani muscle and its fascia. In the middle line it presents the *anal orifice*, and deeply on each side, the *Ischio-rectal Fossa*, which contains the lower part of the rectum, areolar tissue and fat. The fossa is about 1 inch broad at its base and about 2 inches deep; its apex, directed upward, corresponds to the junction of the obturator fascia and the ischio-rectal fascia. It contains the—

Superficial Fascia (subcutaneous tela),—is thick, areolar in texture, with much fat in its meshes, also branches of the perforating cutaneous nerve. It is a single layer.

Muscles,—the corrugator cutis ani, external and internal sphincters (16), and the levator ani (18).

Rectum,—surrounded by areolar tissue and fat.

Internal Pudic (pudendal) Artery (11),—with its veins and the two divisions of the nerve, about ½ inch above the margin of the tuberosity of the ischium.

Inferior Hemorrhoidal Vessels and Nerves (13),—cross the space transversely.

Superficial Perinæal Vessels (5) *and Nerves* (3),—in the front part of the space for a short distance.

Branch of the 4th Sacral Nerve,—at the back of the space, near the coccyx.

Ischio-rectal or Anal Fascia,—a thin membrane given off from the obturator fascia over the levator ani muscle, at the apex of the fossa (see pages 390–391).

Obturator Fascia,—covering the obturator internus muscle, at the outer side of the fossa (see page 390).

Recto-vesical Fascia,—invests the internal surface of the levator ani muscle, near the base of the fossa; also the rectum at the inner side of the fossa (see page 390).

THE FEMALE PERINÆUM

The Female Perinæum performs the special function of supporting the posterior wall of the vagina, and thereby aiding materially in the support of the whole vagina, the uterus and the bladder. The—

Perinæal Body,—is the pyramidal-shaped prolongation of the female perinæum upward between the vagina and the rectum. It measures about 1¼ inches antero-posteriorly, and extends laterally from one ischial tuberosity to the other. In it are situated the muscles of the external organs of generation.

Differences between the Female and Male Perinæa are chiefly due to the perforation of the structures in the median line of the female perinæum by the vulvo-vaginal passage. The—

Superficial Fascia,—is incomplete, by reason of its perforation by the orifice of the vulva, but consists of two layers, subcutaneous tela and Colles' fascia, as in the male.

Deep Perinœal Fascia (urogenital diaphragm),—being also perforated by the vagina is less apparent than in the male, though presenting two layers, with the urethra perforating them, as in the other sex.

Bulbi Vestibuli and *Partes Intermediales,*—represent the corpus spongiosum of the male, divided into two lateral segments.

Prostate Gland,—is absent in the female, but its place is occupied by a number of minute glands disposed around the neck of the bladder.

Muscles,—The Sphincter Vaginæ in the female, takes the place of the bulbo-cavernosus or accelerator urinæ in the male; the Superficial Transversus Perinæi is similar in both sexes; the Erector Clitoridis is smaller than the erector penis, but differs in no other respect; both are called *ischio-cavernosus;* the Deep Transversi Perinæi or Compressores Urethræ are separate and attenuated in the female, their anterior fibres passing in front of the urethra, the middle fibres to the sides of the vagina, the posterior fibres to the central tendinous point of the perinæum.

Structures Divided in Lithotomy. In the Lateral Operation the knife is inserted deeply 1½ inches in front of the anus, a little to the left of the median line, and the incision is carried obliquely backward and outward, becoming more superficial as it is extended, to a point midway between the anus and the tuberosity of the left ischium, dividing the—

Skin and Superficial Fascia (first layer of the latter).

Inferior Hemorrhoidal Vessels and Nerves (13).

Deep Layer of the Superficial Fascia (6).

Superficial Perinæal Vessels (5) *and Nerves* (3).

Bulbo-cavernosus (Accelerator Urinæ) *Muscle* (8) (posterior fibres).

Superficial Transversus Perinæi Muscle (14) *and Artery.*

Inferior Layer of the Triangular Ligament (12).

Deep Transversus Perinæal (Compressor Urethræ) Muscle (a few fibres).

Levator Ani Muscle (18) (anterior fibres).

Membranous and Prostatic Portions of the Urethra (2).

Superior Layer of the Triangular Ligament (Urogenital diaphragm) (12).

Prostate Gland (part of the left lobe).

Neck of the Bladder (in part).

In Median Lithotomy, the incision, 1½ inches long, is made transversely through the central tendinous point and raphé, dividing the—

Skin and Superficial Fascia.

Sphincter Ani Muscle (16) (some of its anterior fibres).

Branches of the Transverse Perinæal Vessels and Nerves.

Base of the Triangular Ligament (Urogenital diaphragm) (12).

Membranous Portion of the Urethra (2).

Bulbo-Cavernosus (*Compressor Urethræ*) *Muscle.*

Structures to be Avoided in Lithotomy. In the Lateral Operation the structures to be remembered and avoided in making the incision are the—

Bulb, its Artery, and the *Rectum,*—inwardly and in front; avoided by not making the primary incision too near the middle line nor too far forward.

Pudic Artery (11),—externally; avoided by not carrying the incision too far outwardly.

Prostrate Gland and *Veins,*—behind; avoided by not carrying the deep incision too far backward, so as to cut through the entire lobe of the prostate gland, permitting the urine to infiltrate into the loose areolar tissue around the rectum, instead of escaping externally.

INDEX

26

Arthralogy

Syndesmology —

Diagnostic Methods

CHEMICAL, BACTERIOLOGICAL AND MICROSCOPICAL

6th Edition, Revised and Enlarged. 207 Illustrations, including 37 Colored Plates. 883 Pages. 88 More Pages than Previous Edition. Cloth $9.00 Postpaid.

By RALPH W. WEBSTER, M.D., Ph.D.

Asst. Prof. Pharmacologic Therapeutics, Instructor in Medicine, Rush Medical College, (University of Chicago.)

For all who think in the problems of present-day medicine, there is hardly another book that can be so useful, both to the general practitioner and to the man who is devoting his time to laboratory work. The various sections are divided so as to present the problems to be met, details of methods available, and the practical significance of positive and negative findings in the chosen method. It points out beforehand likely objects that may interfere with results. Simple tests as well as the more complicated are carefully detailed so that anyone following directions can obtain good results.

Medical Diagnosis

4th Edition, Revised and Enlarged. 548 Text Illustrations, 14 Colored Plates. 8vo. xix + 1302 pages. Cloth $13.00 Postpaid. Contains 577 more Pages and 307 more Illustrations than previous edition.

By CHARLES LYMAN GREENE, M.D.

Formerly Professor of Medicine and Chief of the Department of Medicine and Medical Clinic, College of Medicine, University of Minnesota.

"It consists of a dictionary of diagnosis, a textbook of medicine and a treatise on clinical methods rolled into one. . . . There is a vast amount of information in the volume and it is readily accessible by means of a good index."—*British Medical Journal.*

"Includes both physical diagnostic methods and laboratory procedures. Considerable space is given to practical advice on case taking, relative values of various observations, and other points culled by the author from his experience of many years."—*Jour. Am. Med. Assoc.*

5-8-22 2½M

WILCOX. MATERIA MEDICA AND THERAPEUTICS: INCLUDING PHARMACY AND PHARMACOLOGY. By REYNOLD WEBB WILCOX, M.D., LL.D., Professor of Medicine (Retired) at the New York Post-Graduate Medical School and Hospital. This work is divided into two distinct parts: Materia Medica and Pharmacy; and Pharmacology and Therapeutics. It offers a very complete presentation of the subjects treated with its natural separation and in logical order. Tenth Edition Revised in accordance with the U. S. P. IX. xii + 860 pages.

Cloth, $4.75

STEWART. A MANUAL OF SURGERY. For Students and Physicians. By FRANCIS T. STEWART, M.D., late Professor of Clinical Surgery, Jefferson Medical College. 580 Illustrations, 21 printed in colors. Fifth Edition. Thoroughly Revised and Enlarged. Octavo.

Cloth, $10.00

LANG. GERMAN-ENGLISH MEDICAL DICTIONARY. By the late DR. HUGO LANG, B.A. (Munich). Second Edition, Edited and Revised by MILTON K. MEYERS, M.D., Neurologist to the Jewish Hospital Dispensary and to St. Agnes Hospital Dispensary, Philadelphia, etc. Octavo. 668 pages.

Cloth, $6.00

McGUIGAN. AN INTRODUCTION TO CHEMICAL PHARMACOLOGY. Pharmacodynamics. In Relation to Chemistry. 8vo; xii+418 pp. By HUGH McGUIGAN, PH.D., M.D., Professor of Pharmacology, University of Illinois, College of Medicine.

Cloth, $4.00

MacNEAL. PATHOGENIC MICROORGANISMS. 2d Edition, Revised. 221 Illustrations. 12mo; xx+488 pp. By WARD J. MacNEAL, M.D., Professor of Pathology and Bacteriology, New York Post-Graduate Medical School.

Cloth, $4.00

BRUBAKER. A TEXT-BOOK OF HUMAN PHYSIOLOGY. By ALBERT P. BRUBAKER, A.M., M.D., Professor of Physiology and Hygiene, Jefferson Medical College. Colored Plate and 359 Illustrations. Octavo. Sixth Edition. xii + 794 pages.

Cloth, $4.75

DAVIS. PLASTIC SURGERY. ITS PRINCIPLES AND PRACTICE. By JOHN STAIGE DAVIS, PH.B., M.D., F.A.C.S., formerly Captain U. S. Army Medical Corps, Instructor in Clinical Surgery, Johns Hopkins University. 864 Illustrations, containing 1637 figures. 8vo.

Cloth, $12.00

POTTER. THERAPEUTICS, MATERIA MEDICA, AND PHARMACY. By SAMUEL O. L. POTTER, M.A., M.D., M.R.C.P., (Lond.) Including the Physiological Action of Drugs, Special Therapeutics of Diseases and Symptoms. The Modern Materia Medica, Official and Practical Pharmacy, Minute Directions for Prescription Writing, Incompatibility, etc. Also Antidotal and Antagonistic Treatment of Poisoning and over 650 Prescriptions and Formulæ. Thirteenth Edition. Revised by ELMER H. FUNCK, M.D., Associate in Medicine, Jefferson Medical College, Philadelphia. In accordance with the Ninth Revision U. S. Pharmacopœia. 8vo. xvi + 960 pages. Thumb Index in Each Copy.

Cloth, $8.50